COMPUTING METHODS IN OPTIMIZATION PROBLEMS

COMPUTING METHODS IN OPTIMIZATION PROBLEMS

EDITED BY

A. V. Balakrishnan

UNIVERSITY OF CALIFORNIA
LOS ANGELES

Lucien W. Neustadt

AEROSPACE CORPORATION AND
UNIVERSITY OF MICHIGAN

Proceedings of a conference held at
University of California, Los Angeles
January 30-31, 1964

1964

ACADEMIC PRESS New York and London

ACADEMIC PRESS INC.
111 Fifth Avenue, New York, New York 10003

United Kingdom Edition published by
ACADEMIC PRESS INC. (LONDON) LTD.
Berkeley Square House, London W.1

LIBRARY OF CONGRESS CATALOG CARD NUMBER: 64-22381

PRINTED IN THE UNITED STATES OF AMERICA.

PREFACE

The impact of high-speed computers on optimization problems has been well recognized and indeed the phrase 'computer revolution' is now a cliche. That the need is not so much for existence theory as for efficient computing algorithms is no longer disputed. Nevertheless our knowledge of specific computing methods for such problems is still sparse. Much extant theory on direct methods for instance is still based on experience with hand-computers. The conference on Computing Methods on Optimization Problems was organized to provide a forum for the dissemination of recent research progress in the area and in particular to share computing experience gained in specific large-scale problems.

This book is based on the papers presented at the Conference. Owing to the press of time in trying to meet an early publication date it has not been possible to include the Discussion contributions. It was also found that it would be inefficient to rearrange the papers further by subtopics. The lone exception is the group of the final three papers on 'hybrid computing methods' which is separable as a unit under this heading. We have therefore merely followed the conference sequence.

It is our pleasant duty to acknowledge the active cooperation and help of the UCLA Department of Engineering and Chairman Duke in the preparation of the book. We would also like to thank Academic Press for its invaluable assistance throughout.

A. V. Balakrishnan and
L. W. Neustadt

LIST OF CONTRIBUTORS

Page

Bekey, George A., Electrical Engineering Department, University of Southern California 305

Bellman, R., The RAND Corporation 135

Brunner, Walter, Electronic Associates, Inc 285

Fadden, Edward J., Instrumentation Engineering Program, The University of Michigan 167

Faulkner, Frank D., Department of Mathematics and Mechanics, U. S. Naval Postgraduate School 147

Gilbert, Elmer G., Instrumentation Engineering Program, The University of Michigan 167, 261

Goldstein, A. A., The University of Texas. 159

Halbert, Peter, Electronic Associates, Inc 285

Halkin, Hubert, Bell Telephone Laboratories 211

Hestenes, Magnus R., Department of Mathematics, University of California, Los Angeles 1

Hillsley, R. H., International Business Machines Corporation, Federal Systems Division, Space Guidance Center 107

Hsieh, H. C., Department of Electrical Engineering, Northwestern University 193

Kalaba, R., The RAND Corporation 135

Kopp, R. E., Research Department, Grumman Aircraft Engineering Corporation 65

McGhee, Robert B., Electrical Engineering Department, University of Southern California 305

McGill, R., Research Department, Grumman Aircraft Engineering Corporation 65

Page

Moyer, H. Gardner, Research Department, Grumman Aircraft Engineering Corporation 91

Paiewonsky, Bernard, Aeronautical Research Associates of Princeton, Inc 285

Perret, R., Faculté des Sciences, Grenoble, France. 241

Pinkham, Gordon, Research Department, Grumman Aircraft Engineering Corporation 91

Robbins, H. M., International Business Machines Corporation, Federal Systems Division, Space Guidance Center 107

Rosenbrock, H. H., Cambridge University* 23

Rouxel, R., Batelle Memorial Institute 241

Storey, C., I.C.I. Central Instrument Laboratory. 23

Woodrow, Peter, Aeronautical Research Associates of Princeton, Inc 285

* Present address - Massachusetts Institute of Technology

CONTENTS

PREFACE v

LIST OF CONTRIBUTORS vii

Variational Theory and Optimal Control Theory 1
Magnus R. Hestenes

On the Computation of the Optimal Temperature Profile in a Tubular Reaction Vessel 23
C. Storey and H. H. Rosenbrock

Several Trajectory Optimization Techniques
Part I, Discussion 65
R. E. Kopp and R. McGill
Part II, Application 91
H. Gardner Moyer and Gordon Pinkham

A Steepest Ascent Trajectory Optimization Method Which Reduces Memory Requirements 107
R. H. Hillsley and H. M. Robbins

Dynamic Programming, Invariant Imbedding and Quasi-Linearization: Comparisons and Interconnections 135
R. Bellman and R. Kalaba

A Comparison Between Some Methods for Computing Optimum Paths in the Problem of Bolza 147
Frank D. Faulkner

Minimizing Functionals on Hilbert Space 159
A. A. Goldstein

Computational Aspects of the Time-Optimal Control Problem 167
Edward J. Fadden and Elmer G. Gilbert

An On-Line Identification Scheme for Multivariable Non-linear Systems 193
H. C. Hsieh

Method of Convex Ascent 211
Hubert Halkin

Study of an Algorithm for Dynamic Optimization 241
R. Perret and R. Rouxel

The Application of Hybrid Computers to the Iterative Solution of Optimal Control Problems 261
Elmer G. Gilbert

Synthesis of Optimal Controllers Using Hybrid Analog-Digital Computers 285
B. Paiewonsky, P. Woodrow, W. Brunner, and P. Halbert

Gradient Methods for the Optimization of Dynamic System Parameters by Hybrid Computation. 305
George A. Bekey and Robert B. McGhee

VARIATIONAL THEORY AND OPTIMAL CONTROL THEORY*

by Magnus R. Hestenes

University of California
Department of Mathematics
Los Angeles, California

1. Introduction. The problem to be considered is that of minimizing a function of the form

$$I = g(w) + \int_{t^0}^{t^1} f(t,x(t),u(t),w)\,dt$$

in a class of functions and parameters

$$x^i(t), \quad u^k(t), \quad w^\sigma$$

$$(t^0 \leqq t \leqq t^1;\ i=1, \ldots, n;\ k=1, \ldots, q;\ \sigma=1, \ldots, r)$$

satisfying the differential equations and auxiliary conditions

$$\dot{x}^i = f^i(t,x,u,w) \tag{1:1a}$$

$$t^s = T^s(w), \quad x^i(t_s) = X^{is}(w) \quad (s=0,1). \tag{1:1b}$$

$$\varphi_\alpha(t,x,u,w) \leqq 0 \ (1 \leqq \alpha \leqq m'), \quad \varphi_\alpha(t,x,u,w) = 0 \ (m' < \alpha \leqq m) \tag{1:1c}$$

$$I_\gamma \leqq 0 \ (1 \leqq \gamma \leqq p'), \ I_\gamma = 0 \ (p' < \gamma \leqq p)$$

where

$$I_\gamma = g_\gamma(w) + \int_{t^0}^{t^1} f_\gamma(t,x(t),u(t),w)\,dt \tag{1:2}$$

In addition one may have constraints of the form

$$\psi_\beta(t,x,w) \leqq 0 \quad (1 \leqq \beta \leqq h) \tag{1:3}$$

---

*The preparation of this paper was sponsored by the Office of Naval Research and the U. S. Army Research Office (Durham). Reproduction in whole or in part is permitted for any purpose of the United States Government.

We have omitted conditions of the form

$$\psi_\beta(t,x,w) = 0$$

in (1:3) since these can be replaced by the conditions

$$\varphi_{m+\beta}(t,x,u,w) = \psi_{\beta t} + \psi_{\beta x^i} f^i = 0$$

$$I_{p+\beta} = \psi_\beta \left[T^0(w),\ X^{i0}(w),w\right] = 0$$

which are of the form (1:1c) and (1:1d). It should be observed that there is no generality of including w^σ in f, f_γ, φ_α, since the parameters w^σ in these functions may be replaced by new variables $x^{n+\sigma}$ subject to the conditions

$$\dot{x}^{n+\sigma} = 0\,,\quad x^{n+\sigma}(t^0) = x^{n+\sigma}(t^1) = w^\sigma .$$

We have included w^σ in these functions in order to indicate how they enter into the multiplier rule.

The inequality constraints

$$\varphi_\alpha(t,x,u,w) \leqq 0 \qquad I_\gamma \leqq 0$$

can be replaced by the constraints

$$\varphi_\alpha + (u^{q+\alpha})^2 = 0 \qquad I_\gamma + (w^{r+\gamma})^2 = 0$$

in which $u^{q+\alpha}$ are additional functions and $w^{r+\gamma}$ are additional variables. This method is due to Valentine (1). We shall not make this replacement, since it is unnecessary to do so in deriving first-order necessary conditions. It is, however, convenient to use this device in the derivation of second-order conditions.

We shall not discuss the case in which constraints of the form (1:3) are present. Problems of this type have been discussed by Berkowitz (2), Gamkrelidze (3), and more recently by Guinn (4). In the development of this theory one uses unilateral variations. Elementary cases have been treated by Bliss and Underhill (5) and others.

The problem formulated above is a very general problem in the calculus of variations and is equivalent to the problem of Bolza, as we shall see presently. It contains as special cases a large class of optimal control problems arising in applications. We shall accordingly refer to this problem as the optimal control problem in variational theory. The variables u^k will be called control variables, the parameters w^σ will be called control parameters, and the variables x^i will be called state variables. The first general formulation of problems of this type known to the author was that given by the author (6) in a Rand report concerned with paths of least time. This report was not published in a journal. In this report constraints of the form (1:1d) and (1:3) were not considered. The technique employed would admit constraints of the form (1:1d) but would have to be modified to include those of the form (1:3).

The general problem of Bolza referred to above is that of minimizing a function of the form

$$I = g(w) + \int_{t^0}^{t^1} f(t,x(t),\dot{x}(t),w)\,dt$$

in a class of arcs and parameters

$$x^i(t), \qquad w^\sigma, \qquad (t^0 \leqq t \leqq t^1;\ i=1,\ldots,n;\ \sigma=1,\ldots,r)$$

satisfying the relations

$$\varphi_\alpha(t,x,\dot{x},w) \leqq 0\ (1 \leqq \alpha \leqq m'),\quad \varphi_\alpha(t,x,\dot{x},w) = 0\ (m' < \alpha \leqq m) \tag{1:4a}$$

$$t^s = T^s(w),\quad x^i(t^s) = X^{is}(w)\quad (s = 0,1). \tag{1:4b}$$

These arcs may be subject to constraints

$$I_\gamma \leqq 0\ (1 \leqq \gamma \leqq p'),\quad I_\gamma = 0\ (p' < \gamma \leqq p)\ , \tag{1:4c}$$

where

$$I_\gamma = g_\gamma(w) + \int_{t^0}^{t^1} f_\gamma(t,x(t),\dot{x}(t),w)\,dt.$$

In addition one may have constraints of the form (1:3). This problem with inequality constraints excluded is equivalent to one studied by Bliss (7) in his book on the calculus of variations. The case in which inequality constraints occur in (1:1) can be reduced to the case in which no inequality constraints occur. This can be done by the method of Valentine described above. To account for conditions of the form (1:3) one can use the theory of unilateral variations.

The problem of Bolza as formulated above reduces to an optimal control problem by considering

$$\dot{x}^i = u^i$$

to be the control variables. Conversely, the optimal control problem can be reduced to one of Bolza type by introducing new variables x^{n+k}, w^{r+k} connected by the relations

$$x^{n+k}(t) = \int_{t^0}^{t} u^k(s)\, ds, \quad x^{n+k}(t^1) = w^{r+k}$$

and eliminating u^k by the substitution

$$u^k = \dot{x}^{n+k} .$$

It follows that the two problems are equivalent and that the theory for one can be deduced from the theory for the other. The author prefers the optimal control formulation to that given by Bliss because it appears to be more convenient for applications and because it leads to an approach to variational theory that is both novel and instructive. The present paper is concerned with this approach.

In 1936 Bliss (8) wrote a paper entitled "The Development of Problems in the Calculus of Variations." In this paper he traced the development of the Problem of Bolza from the time of Euler and Lagrange. He pointed out that both Euler and Lagrange studied variational problems of generality comparable to the one here considered. He made a strong case for the study of the problem of Bolza as a standard problem in variational theory. However, in his evaluation he did not consider the optimal control problem here formulated.

Professor Bliss was the leader of the Chicago School in Variational Theory. L. M. Graves, W. T. Reid, E. J. McShane, and the author, together with their students, were active members of this school. This group together with Marston Morse developed the theory for the Problem of Bolza to a state of completion comparable with those of simple problems. Most of the known results for the optimal control problem are readily deducible from known results for the Problem of Bolza.

At the time that I formulated the general control problem here considered and obtained the corresponding multiplier rule there was very little interest in the problem. Several years later it became evident that this problem was of great importance in control theory. Consequently it has been studied intensely both here and abroad. Two principles have evolved that have become popular, namely the maximum principle of Pontryagin (9) and the principle of optimality of Bellman (10).

In each case they represent the first-order necessary conditions for an optimal solution. By first-order conditions are meant those derivable by the use of first derivatives, namely the Euler-Lagrange equations, the transversality condition and the Weierstrass condition or their equivalents. The maximum principle of Pontryagin can be derived under weaker hypotheses than have been used heretofore. The optimality principle of Bellman can be looked upon as an extension of Hamilton Jacobi theory, and reduces to this theory when applied to classical variational problems.

The technique used by Pontryagin is a modification of one used by McShane (11). They obtained the first-order necessary conditions by finding a hyperplane of support to a suitably chosen convex cone. McShane used both strong and weak variations to construct the cone. Pontryagin used only strong variations. The modification of Pontryagin is significant because it enables one to weaken the hypotheses made. Moreover, inequality constraints can be treated more readily. There is a further modification of these methods which will simplify the arguments, particularly when inequality constraints are involved. It is our purpose to give an outline of this modified approach to the establishment of the first-order conditions. The details of the program described below were given in a seminar on variational theory at the University of California, Los Angeles.

2. First-order necessary conditions for a local minimum.

Let

$$x_0: \qquad x_0^{\,i}(t), \qquad u_0^{\,k}(t), \qquad w^\sigma \qquad (t^0 \leqq t \leqq t^1)$$

be a solution to the optimal control problem in which the constraints (1:1) hold. As remarked above, we shall omit the discussion of the case when constraints of the form (1:3) are present. We shall assume that the control functions $u_0^{\,k}(t)$ are piecewise continuous for the purposes of our discussion. In addition we shall assume that the $m \times (q+m)$ dimensional matrix

$$\begin{pmatrix} \dfrac{\partial\varphi_\alpha}{\partial u^k} & \delta_{\alpha\beta}\varphi_\beta \end{pmatrix} \qquad (\beta \text{ not summed})$$

has rank m. Here $\delta_{\alpha\alpha} = 1$, $\delta_{\alpha\beta} = 0$ $(\alpha \neq \beta)$. Under these assumptions, together with the usual continuity and differentiability assumptions, one can prove the following theorem. In this theorem the functions

$$H(t,x,u,p,\mu) = p_i f^i - \lambda_0 f - \lambda_\gamma f_\gamma - \mu_\alpha \varphi_\alpha \qquad (2:1)$$

$$G(w) = \lambda_0 g + \lambda_\gamma g_\gamma$$

are introduced. Here and elsewhere a repeated index denotes summation with respect to that index unless otherwise specified or implied.

THEOREM 2:1. MULTIPLIER RULE. IF x_0 IS A SOLUTION TO THE OPTIMAL CONTROL PROBLEM, THERE EXIST MULTIPLIERS $\lambda_0 \geqq 0, \lambda_\gamma$, $p_i(t)$, $\mu_\alpha(t)$ SUCH THAT

1) λ_0, λ_γ, $p_i(t)$ DO NOT VANISH SIMULTANEOUSLY;

2) $\lambda_\gamma \geqq 0$ $(\gamma \leqq p')$, THE EQUALITY HOLDING IF $I_\gamma < 0$ ON x_0;

3) $\mu_\alpha(t)$ IS PIECEWISE CONTINUOUS AND IS CONTINUOUS AT EACH POINT OF CONTINUITY OF $u_0(t)$. $\mu_\alpha(t) \geqq 0$ $(\alpha \leqq m')$, THE EQUALITY HOLDING WHENEVER $\varphi_\alpha(t,x_0(t),u_0(t)) < 0$;

4) THE MULTIPLIERS $p_i(t)$ ARE CONTINUOUS AND THE RELATIONS

$$\dot{x}^i = H_{p^i}, \quad \dot{p}_i = -H_{x^i}, \quad H_{u^k} = 0 \qquad (2:2a)$$

HOLD ALONG x_0. IN ADDITION, H IS CONTINUOUS ALONG x_0 AND

$$\frac{d}{dt} H = H_t \qquad (2:2b)$$

ALONG x_0. MOREOVER, ON x_0 WE HAVE

$$dG + \left[-H\, dT^s + p_i\, dX^{is}\right]_{s=0}^{s=1} - \int_{T^0}^{T^1} \frac{\partial H}{\partial w^\sigma}\, dw^\sigma\, dt = 0 \qquad (2:3)$$

FOR ALL dw^σ.

5) THE INEQUALITY

$$H(t,x_0(t),u,p(t),0) \leqq H(t,x_0(t),u_0(t),p(t),0) \qquad (2:4a)$$

HOLDS, SUBJECT TO THE CONDITIONS

$$\varphi_\alpha(t,x_0(t),u,w_0) \leq 0 \ (\alpha \leq m'), \qquad (2:4b)$$

$$\varphi_\alpha(t,x_0(t),u,w_0) = 0 \ (m' < \alpha \leq m) .$$

If this result holds with $\lambda_0 = 0$, the arc x_0 is abnormal and the multiplier rule is independent of the function I to be minimized. The multiplier rule is of real significance only in case one can choose $\lambda_0 > 0$. In this event one can choose $\lambda_0 = 1$.

The equations (2:2) are the Euler-Lagrange equations and (2:3) is called the transversality condition. The condition (2:4) is the Weierstrass condition. The multiplier rule is one form of the maximum principle of Pontryagin.

3. Further remarks relative to constraints. Let $\mathcal{R}$ represent the collection of points (t,x,u,w) satisfying the constraints

$$\varphi_\alpha(t,x,u,w) \leq 0 \quad (\alpha \leq m'), \quad \varphi_\alpha(t,x,u,w) = 0 \quad (m' < \alpha \leq m). \ (3:1)$$

and let x_0 be defined by

$$x_0: \qquad x_0^{\ i}(t), \qquad u_0^{\ k}(t), \qquad w_0^{\ \sigma} \qquad (t^0 \leq t \leq t^1).$$

The assumption that the matrix

$$\left(\frac{\partial \varphi_\alpha}{\partial u^k} \quad \delta_{\alpha\beta}\varphi_\beta \right) \qquad (3:2)$$

has rank m on $\mathcal{R}$ was made in order to insure that $\mathcal{R}$ has the following two properties

1) There exist functions $U_0^{\ k}(t,x,w)$ such that $U_0^{\ k}(t,x_0(t),w_0) = u_0^{\ k}(t)$ and such that $(t,x,U_0(t,x,w),w)$ is in $\mathcal{R}$ for all (t,x,w) is a neighborhood of those on x_0 and such that $\dfrac{\partial U_0^{\ k}}{\partial x^i}$, $\dfrac{\partial U_0^{\ k}}{\partial w^\sigma}$ exist and have suitable continuity properties.

2) Given an element $(\bar{t},x_0(\bar{t}),\bar{u},w_0)$ in $\mathcal{R}$, there is a continuous function $U^k(t,x,w)$ defined over a neighborhood $\mathcal{N}$ of $(\bar{t},x(\bar{t}),w)$ such that

$$U^k(\bar{t},x_0(\bar{t}),w_0)=\bar{u}^k$$

and that $(t,x,U(t,x,w),w)$ is in $\mathcal{R}$ when (t,u,w) is in $\mathcal{N}$ and such that $\frac{\partial U^k}{\partial x^i}$, $\frac{\partial U^k}{\partial w^\sigma}$ are continuous on $\mathcal{N}$.

These two properties of $\mathcal{R}$ are used in the proof of the multiplier rule. It follows that in place of (3:1) we may assume the existence of a region $\mathcal{R}$ with these properties or make some equivalent assumption.

If the conditions (3:1) are of the form

$$\varphi_\alpha(u) \leqq 0 \qquad (\alpha \leqq m'), \qquad \varphi_\alpha(u) = 0 \qquad (m' < \alpha \leqq m)$$

the properties (1) and (2) hold on $\mathcal{R}$ with $U_0{}^k = u_0{}^k(t)$ and $U^k = \bar{u}^k$. In this event one need not assume that the matrix (3:2) has rank m.

If the conditions (3:1) are of the form

$$\varphi_\alpha(t,u) \leqq 0 \ (\alpha \leqq m'), \ \varphi_\alpha(t,u) = 0 \ (m'<\alpha\leqq m) \tag{3:3}$$

then the choice $U_0{}^k = u_0{}^k(t)$ can be made in (1). Moreover, one can select $U^k(t,x,w)$ to be of the form $U^k = u^k(t)$ in condition (2), provided the matrix (3:2) has rank m.

In Sections 5, 6, 7 we shall assume that the constraints are of the form (3:3) or that the elements (t,u,w) are restricted to lie on a set $\mathcal{R}$ with the property that if $(\bar{t},\bar{u},\bar{w})$ is in $\mathcal{R}$, there is a continuous function $u(t)$ such that $u(\bar{t}) = \bar{u}$ and $(t,u(t),w)$ is in $\mathcal{R}$ if (t,w) lie in a neighborhood of $(\bar{t},\bar{w})$. For purposes of reference such elements (t,u,w) will be called admissible. Observe that there is no restriction on the state variables x^i.

4. A basic lemma. Necessary conditions for maxima and minima are obtained by reducing the problem to one of a finite number of variables. The basic lemma to be used in this connection will be described in this section.

Consider now a class $\mathscr{C}$ of elements x and let J_0, $J_1, \ldots, J_p$ be real valued functions defined on $\mathscr{C}$. Let x_0 be a point in $\mathscr{C}$. A class K of vectors $k = (k_0, \ldots, k_p)$ will be called a <u>derived cone</u> for $J_0, \ldots, J_p$ at x_0 if K is a convex cone and if for every finite set of vectors $k^\sigma (\sigma = 1, \ldots, q)$ in K there exists q-parameter family

$$x(b_1, \ldots, b_q) \qquad 0 \leqq b_j \leqq \epsilon$$

of elements in $\mathscr{C}$ such that $x(0) = x_0$ and such that for each ρ the function

$$f_\rho(b) = J_\rho(x(b)) \qquad (\rho = 0, 1, \ldots, p)$$

is continuous and has

$$df_\rho = k_\rho{}^j \, db_j$$

as its differential at $b = 0$. Hence $k_\rho{}^j$ is the derivative of $J_\rho(x(b))$ with respect to b_j at $b = 0$. With this concept in mind one can establish the following.

LEMMA 4:1. LET K BE A DERIVED CONE FOR J_ρ AT x_0 AND SUPPOSE THAT x_0 MINIMIZES $J_0(x)$ SUBJECT TO THE RELATIONS

$$J_\gamma(x) \leqq 0 \quad (1 \leqq \gamma \leqq p'), \qquad J_\gamma(x) = 0 \quad (p' < \gamma \leqq p).$$

THERE EXIST MULTIPLIERS $\lambda_0 \geqq 0, \lambda_1, \ldots, \lambda_p$, NOT ALL ZERO, SUCH THAT

1) $\lambda_\gamma \geqq 0 \ (1 \leqq \gamma \leqq p')$, THE EQUALITY HOLDING IF $J_\gamma(x_0) < 0$.

2) THE INEQUALITY

$$L(k) = \lambda_\rho k_\rho \geqq 0 \qquad (4:1)$$

FOR ALL VECTORS k IN THE DERIVED CONE K.

The proof of this lemma consists of showing that the cone K is separated by a hyperplane $L(k) = 0$ from a convex cone K^- consisting of all vectors k such that $k_0 < 0$, $k_\gamma < 0 \ (1 \leqq \gamma \leqq p')$ if $J_\gamma(x_0) = 0$, $k_\gamma = 0 \ (p' < \gamma \leqq p)$.
The cone K^- consists of vectors which under normal circum-

stances could not be in K if x_0 is to be a solution to this problem. Having obtained a hyperplane

$$L(k) = \lambda_\rho k_\rho = 0$$

such that $L(k) \geqq 0$ on K and $L(k) \leqq 0$ on K^-, we obtain the signs of the multipliers as follows. The vector $\bar{k} = (-1, 0, \ldots, 0)$ is in the closure of K^-. Hence $L(\bar{k}) = -\lambda_0 \leqq 0$. If $1 \leqq \gamma \leqq p'$ and $J_\gamma(x_0) = 0$, the vector k' with $k'_\gamma = -1$ and $k'_\rho = 0$ $(\rho \neq \gamma)$ is also in the closure K^-. Hence $L(k') = -\lambda_\gamma \leqq 0$. If $1 \leqq \gamma \leqq p'$ and $J_\gamma(x_0) < 0$, the vector k'' with $k''_\gamma = \pm 1$ and $k''_\rho = 0$ $(\rho \neq \gamma)$ is in the closure of K^-. Consequently $L(k'') = \pm \lambda_\gamma \leqq 0$, that is, $\lambda_\gamma = 0$. The multipliers λ_ρ therefore are the signs described in the lemma.

The proof that the cones K and K^- are separated is obtained by the use of an implicit function theorem together with certain elementary properties of the convex cones K and K^-.

5. Control problems without state variables. It is instructive to consider the special case in which no state variables occur. Consider, therefore, the problem of minimizing

$$J_0 = G_0(w) + \int_{T^0(w)}^{T^1(w)} f_0(t,u(t),w)\, dt$$

in a class of control variables and parameters

$$u^k(t), \quad w^\sigma \quad (T^0(w) \leqq t \leqq T^1(w))$$

subject to constraints of the form

$$J_\gamma \leqq 0 \quad (1 \leqq \gamma \leqq p'), \qquad J_\rho = 0 \quad (p' < \gamma \leqq p)$$

where

$$J_\gamma = G_\gamma(w) + \int_{T^0(w)}^{T^1(w)} F_\gamma(t,u(t),w)\, dt\,.$$

The variables (t,u,w) are restricted to lie in a set $\mathcal{R}$ with the property that if $(\bar{t},\bar{u},\bar{w})$ is in $\mathcal{R}$ there is a continuous function $u(t)$ $\bar{t} \leqq t \leqq \bar{t}+\epsilon$ such that $(t,u(t),w)$ is in $\mathcal{R}$ if $\bar{t} \leqq t \leqq \bar{t}+\epsilon$ and $|w^\sigma - \bar{w}^\sigma| < \epsilon$. Elements (t,u,w)

will be called admissible if they are in $\mathcal{R}$.

Suppose that

$$u_0: \qquad u_0^k(t), \qquad w_0^\sigma \qquad (T^0 \leq t \leq T^1)$$

is a solution to the problem. Let K' be all vectors k of the form

$$k_\rho = F_\rho(t,u,w_0) - F_\rho(t,u_0(t),w_0) \tag{5:1}$$

or of the form

$$k_\rho = dG_\rho + \left[F_\rho^s\, dT^s\right]_{s=0}^{s=1} + \int_{T^0}^{T^1} \frac{\partial F_\rho}{\partial w^\sigma}(t,u_0(t),w_0)\, dw_\sigma\, dt \tag{5:2}$$

where F^s is the value of F on u_0 at $t = T^s(w_0)$. Let K be the convex hull of K'; that is, all vectors obtained form K' by taking finite linear combinations of vectors with non-negative coefficients. It is not difficult to show that K is a derived cone for $J_0, \ldots, J_p$ at u_0. Hence by Lemma 4:1 there exist multipliers λ_ρ having the properties described in this lemma. If we set

$$F = \lambda_\rho F_\rho, \qquad G = \lambda_\rho G_\rho; \tag{5:3}$$

then by (4:1) and (5:1) we have

$$F(t,u,w_0) \geq F(t,u_0(t),w_0) \qquad (t,u,w) \text{ in } \mathcal{R}. \tag{5:4a}$$

Using (4:1) and (5:2), we see that

$$dG + \left[F^s\, dT^s\right]_{s=0}^{s=1} + \int_{T^0}^{T^1} \frac{\partial F}{\partial w^\sigma}\, dw^\sigma\, dt = 0 \tag{5:4b}$$

holds on u_0 for all dw^σ. In obtaining the equality in (5:4b) we used the fact that if k is given by (5:2) then k and -k are in K.

THEOREM 5:1. IF u_0 AFFORDS A MINIMUM TO THE PROBLEM HERE DESCRIBED, THEN THERE EXIST MULTIPLIERS λ_ρ SUCH THAT (5:4) HOLDS ON u_0, WHERE F AND G ARE GIVEN BY (5:3). WE HAVE $\lambda_0 \geq 0$ AND $\lambda_\gamma \geq 0$ $(1 \leq \gamma \leq p')$, THE EQUALITY HOLDING IF $J_\gamma < 0$ ON u_0. THE FUNCTION $F(t,u_0(t),w_0)$ IS CONTINUOUS ON $T^0 \leq t \leq T^1$.

The region $\mathcal{R}$ may be defined by inequalities of the form

$$\varphi_\alpha(t,u) \leqq 0 \quad (1 \leqq \alpha \leqq m'), \qquad \varphi_\alpha(t,u) = 0 \quad (m' < \alpha \leqq m) \tag{5:5}$$

if the matrix

$$\left(\frac{\partial \varphi_\alpha}{\partial u^k} \qquad \delta_{\alpha\beta}\,\varphi_\beta \right)$$

has rank m on $\mathcal{R}$. In this event, by the use of Lemma 4:1, it can be shown that there exist multipliers $\mu_\alpha(t)$ such that

$$\frac{\partial F}{\partial u^k} + \mu_\alpha(t)\,\frac{\partial \varphi_\alpha}{\partial u^k} = 0$$

holds on u_0. The multipliers $\mu_\alpha(t) \geqq 0$ $(\alpha \leqq m')$, the equality holding whenever $\varphi_\alpha < 0$ on u_0. The functions $\mu_\alpha(t)$ are continuous whenever $u_0(t)$ is continuous. It can be shown further that $\overline{F} = F + \mu_\alpha(t)\,\varphi_\alpha$ is continuous along u_0 and that

$$\frac{d}{dt}\,\overline{F} = \overline{F}_t$$

along u_0. The function $-\overline{F}$ is the function H described in Theorem 2:1.

It is of interest to observe that the following problem is reducible to one of the type just discussed. Suppose the state variable $x^i(t)$ is determined by the system

$$\begin{aligned} &\ddot{x}^i = f^i(t,u) \qquad\qquad (i = 1, \ldots, n) \\ &x^i(0) = 0, \dot{x}^i(0) = 0, \quad x^i(T) = b^i, \quad \dot{x}^i(T) = c^i. \end{aligned} \tag{5:6}$$

The problem is to choose $u(t)$ $(0 \leqq t \leqq T)$ such that (5:6) has a solution and such that

$$J_0 = G_0(T) + \int_0^T F_0(t,u(t))\,dt$$

has a least value. The variable T plays the role of a control parameter. It is assumed that the elements (t, u, T) are restricted to lie in a set $\mathcal{R}$ of admissibility.

Using the identities

$$\dot{x}^i(0) - \dot{x}^i(T) + \int_0^T \ddot{x}^i(t)\,dt = 0$$

$$x(T) - T\dot{x}(T) - x(0) + \int_0^T t\,\ddot{x}(t)\,dt = 0$$

one finds by (5:6) that the problem is equivalent to minimizing J_0 subject to the conditions

$$J_i = -c^i + \int_0^T f^i(t,u)\,dt = 0$$

$$J_{n+i} = b^i - Tc^i + \int_0^T tf^i(t,u)\,dt = 0.$$

The new problem is independent of $x^i(t)$ and is of the type described at the beginning of this section.

6. Control problems linear in the state variables. In this section we consider the case in which

$$f^i = A_j{}^i(t)\,x^j + \bar{f}^i(t,u,w), \quad f_\beta = B_{\beta i}(t)\,x^j + \bar{f}_\beta(t,u,w) \qquad (6:1)$$

and

$$I_\beta = g_\beta(w) + \int_{t^0}^{t^1} f_\beta\,dt \qquad (\beta = 0, 1, \ldots, p). \qquad (6:2)$$

The problem at hand is to minimize I_0 in a class of state and control functions

$$x^i(t), \qquad u^k(t), \qquad w^\sigma \qquad (t^0 \leqq t \leqq t^1)$$

subject to the conditions

$$\dot{x}^i = f^i(t,x,u,w), \qquad (6:3a)$$

$$t^s = T^s(w), \quad x^i(t^s) = X^{is}(w), \qquad (6:3b)$$

$$I_\gamma \leqq 0 \quad (1 \leqq \gamma \leqq p'), \quad I_\gamma = 0 \quad (p' < \gamma \leqq p). \qquad (6:3c)$$

In addition, the elements (t,u,w) are restricted to lie in an admissible set $\mathcal{R}$ having the properties described in the last section.

We shall show that this problem is equivalent to one of the type described in the last section. To this end let $q_{\beta j}(t)$, $P_{ij}(t)$ be solutions of the system

$$\dot{q}_{\beta j} = -q_{\beta h}\,A_j{}^h + B_{\beta j}, \quad \dot{P}_{ij} = -P_{ih}\,A_j{}^h, \quad \det\ (P_{ij}) \neq 0. \qquad (6:4a)$$

Set

$$F_\beta = \bar{f}_\beta - q_{\beta j}\,\bar{f}_\beta{}^j, \quad G_\beta = g_\beta + \Big[q_{\beta j}\,(T^s)\,X^{js}\Big]_{s=0}^{s=1}$$

$$F_{p+i} = -\,P_{ij}\,\bar{f}^j, \quad G_{p+i} = \Big[P_{ij}(T^s)\,X^{js}\Big]_{s=0}^{s=1} \tag{6:4b}$$

$$J_\rho = G_\rho + \int_{T^0}^{T^1} F_\rho\,dt \qquad (\rho = 0, 1, \ldots, p+n).$$

With these notations in mind we can prove the following

LEMMA 6:1. THE CONTROL PROBLEM DESCRIBED ABOVE IS EQUIVALENT TO THAT OF MINIMIZING J_0 IN THE CLASS OF CONTROL VARIABLES

$$u^k(t), \qquad w^\sigma \qquad (T^0(w) \leqq t \leqq T^1(w))$$

WITH (t,u,w) IN $\mathcal{R}$ AND

$$J_\rho \leqq 0 \quad (1 \leqq \rho \leqq p'), \qquad J_\rho = 0 \qquad (p' \leqq \rho \leqq p+n).$$

This lemma follows because if $x^i(t)$ is a solution of the system

$$\dot{x}^i = f^i(t,x,u(t),w), \quad x^i(T^0) = X^{i0}(w),$$

then by virtue of (6:4) we have

$$J_{p+i} = G_{p+i} - \int_{T^0}^{T^1} \frac{d}{dt}\,(P_{ij}x^j)\,dt = P_{ij}(T^1)\,\big[X^{i1} - x^i(T^1)\big]$$

$$J_\beta = G_\beta + \int_{T^0}^{T^1} \Big\{f_\rho - \frac{d}{dt}\,(q_{\beta j}x^j)\Big\}\,dt = \underline{I}_\beta + q_{\beta j}\big[X^{i1} - x^i(T^1)\big].$$

Hence $J_{p+i} = 0$ if and only if $x^i(T^s) = X^{is}$. Moreover, if $J_{p+i} = 0$ we have $J_\beta = I_\beta$. This proves the equivalence of the two problems. Hence control of problems linear in state variables can be reduced to one in which state variables do not appear.

Applying the results described in Theorem 5:1, we see that there exist multipliers $\lambda_0, \ldots, \lambda_{p+n}$ not all zero, such that if we set

$$F = \lambda_\rho\,F_\rho, \quad G = \lambda_\rho\,G_\rho$$

such that (5:4) holds and $\lambda_0 \geq 0$, $\lambda_\gamma \geq 0$ $(1 \leq \gamma \leq p')$, the equality holding if $J_\gamma < 0$. Setting

$$p_j = \lambda_\beta q_{\beta j} - \lambda_{p+i} P_{ij} \tag{6:5}$$

we see by (6:4) that

$$\dot{p}_i = - p_j A_i^{\ j} + \lambda_\beta B_{\beta j} \tag{6:6}$$

and that

$$F = \lambda_\beta \bar{f}_\beta - p_j(t)\bar{f}^j , \quad G = \lambda_\beta g_\beta + \Big[p_i(T^s) X^{is} \Big]_{s=0}^{s=1}$$

If we set

$$H(t,x,u,w,p) = p_i f^i - \lambda_\beta f_\beta , \quad g = \lambda_\beta g_\beta \tag{6:7}$$

we see, by (6:1) and (6:6), that

$$- H(t,x,u,w,p(t)) = F + \dot{p}_i x^i \tag{6:8}$$

and that on x_0

$$dG + \Big[F\, dT^s \Big]_{s=0}^{s=1} = dg + \Big[- H\, dT^s + p_i(T^s) dX^{is} \Big]_{s=0}^{s=1} . \tag{6:9}$$

Moreover, the equations (6:6), (6:1) and $\dot{x}^i = f^i$ yield the relations

$$\dot{p}_i = - H_{x^i} , \quad \dot{x}^i = H_{p^i} , \tag{6:10}$$

which hold along x_0. Using these results with (5:4), we obtain

THEOREM 6:1. IF x_0 IS A SOLUTION TO THE PROBLEM HERE CONSIDERED, THERE EXIST FUNCTIONS H, g GIVEN BY (6:7) WITH MULTIPLIERS λ_β, $p_i(t)$, NOT ALL ZERO, SUCH THAT

$$\dot{p}_i = - H_{x^i} , \quad \dot{x}^i = H_{p_i}$$

$$dG + \Big[- H\, dT^s + p_i(T^s)\, dX^{is} \Big]_{s=0}^{s=1} - \int_{T^0}^{T^1} \frac{\partial H}{\partial w^\sigma} dw^\sigma\, dt = 0 \tag{6:11}$$

HOLD ON x_0. MOREOVER, IF (t,u,w_0) IS IN $\mathscr{R}$, THEN

$$H(t,x_0(t),u,w_0,p(t)) \leq H(t,x_0(t),u_0(t),w_0,p(t)) . \tag{6:12}$$

IN ADDITION $\lambda_0 \geq 0$ AND $\lambda_\gamma \geq 0$ $(1 \leq \gamma \leq p')$, THE EQUALITY HOLDING IN CASE $I_\gamma < 0$ ON x_0. THE FUNCTION H IS CONTINUOUS ALONG x_0.

The function H differs from the one given in Theorem 2:1 in that we have not adjusted H to account for the constraints defining the region $\mathcal{R}$. If the constraints are of the form (5:5) one can select multipliers $\mu_\alpha(t)$ such that

$$H_{u^k} = \mu_\alpha \varphi_{\alpha u^k}$$

with $\mu_\alpha(t) \geqq 0$ $(\alpha \leqq m')$, and $\mu_\beta \varphi_\beta = 0$ on x_0 for each β. The new function $\overline{H} = H - \mu_\alpha \varphi_\alpha$ has the properties described in Theorem 2:1.

7. <u>Control problem nonlinear in the state variables.</u> In this section we shall consider the optimal control problem described in Section 1 with the constraints (1:1c) replaced by by the condition that the elements (t,u,w) lie on an admissible set $\mathcal{R}$ having the properties described in the last paragraph of Section 3. This region $\mathcal{R}$ also appeared in Sections 5 and 6. The technique used in the last section can be used to reformulate the problem so that first-order necessary condition can be obtained by a simple extension of the proof used to establish Theorem 5:1.

Let

$$x_0: \qquad x_0{}^i(t), \qquad u_0{}^k(t), \qquad w_0{}^\sigma \qquad (t^0 \leqq t \leqq t^1)$$

be a solution to the problem. Set

$$A_j{}^i(t) = \frac{\partial f^i}{\partial x^j}, \qquad B_{\beta j}(t) = \frac{\partial f_\beta}{\partial x^j} \tag{7:1}$$

where the right members are evaluated along x_0. If we define

$$\overline{f}^i(t,x,u,w) \neq f^i - A_j{}^i x^j, \quad \overline{f}_\beta(t,x,u,w) = f_\beta - B_{\beta j} x^j \tag{7:2}$$

then $\overline{f}^i$, $\overline{f}_\beta$ have the property that

$$\frac{\partial \overline{f}^i}{\partial x^j} = 0, \quad \frac{\partial \overline{f}_\beta}{\partial x^j} = 0 \quad \text{along} \quad x_0. \tag{7:3}$$

It is this property that is useful in the proof of first-order conditions. Let $q_{\beta i}$, P_{ij} be defined by (6:4a) and (7:1), and let F_ρ, G_ρ, J_ρ be given by (6:4b) and (7:2). In view of (7:3) we have

$$\frac{\partial F_\rho}{\partial x^j} = 0 \quad \underline{\text{along}} \quad x_0. \tag{7:4}$$

By the argument used in the proof of Lemma 6:1 we obtain the following

LEMMA 7:1. LET $\mathscr{C}$ BE THE CLASS OF SOLUTIONS

$$x: \quad x^i(t), \quad u^k(t) \quad w^\sigma \quad (T^0(w) \leq t \leq T^1(w))$$

OF THE SYSTEM

$$\dot{x}^i = f^i(t,x,u,w), \quad x^i(T^0(w)) = X^{i0}(w) \tag{7:5}$$

WHOSE ELEMENTS (t,u,w) ARE IN THE ADMISSIBLE SET $\mathscr{R}$. THEN x_0 IS A LOCAL SOLUTION TO THE PROBLEM HERE CONSIDERED IF AND ONLY IF x_0 MINIMIZES J_0 (LOCALLY) ON $\mathscr{C}$ SUBJECT TO THE CONSTRAINTS

$$J_\rho \leq 0 \quad (1 \leq \rho \leq p'), \quad J_\rho = 0 \quad (p' < \rho \leq p+n). \tag{7:6}$$

In view of this lemma our problem is reduced to a problem of the type considered in Lemma 4:1.

We now proceed as in the proof of Theorem 5:1 and let K' be the class of all vectors of the form

$$k_\rho = F_\rho(t,x_0(t),u,w_0) - F_\rho(t,x_0(t),u_0(t),w_0) \tag{7:7a}$$

and of the form

$$k_\rho = dG_\rho + \Big[F_\rho \, dT^s\Big]_{s=0}^{s=1} + \int_{T^0}^{T^1} \frac{\partial F_\rho}{\partial w^\sigma} \, dw^\sigma \, dt \tag{7:7b}$$

evaluated along x_0, where dw^σ is arbitrary. Let K be the convex hull of K'. It can be shown with the help of (7:4) that K is a derived cone of J_ρ on $\mathscr{C}$ at x_0. Consequently by Lemma 4:1 there exist multipliers λ_ρ not all zero such that

$$\lambda_\rho \, k_\rho \geq 0 \tag{7:8}$$

for all k in K and hence for all k in K'. Moreover, $\lambda_0 \geq 0$, $\lambda_\rho \geq 0$ $(1 \leq \rho \leq p')$, the equality holding in case $J_\rho(x_0) < 0$. Set

$$F = \lambda_\rho \, F_\rho, \quad G = \lambda_\rho \, G_\rho.$$

By (7:7a) and (7:8) we have

$$F(t,x_0(t),u,w_0) \geq F(t,x_0(t),u_0(t),w_0) \tag{7:9a}$$

for all (t,u,w_0) in $\mathscr{R}$. Using (7:8), (7:7b) and the fact that dw_σ is arbitrary, it is seen that on x_0

$$dG + \Big[F\, dT^s\Big]_{s=0}^{s=1} + \int_{T^0}^{T^1} \frac{\partial F}{\partial w^\sigma}\, dw^\sigma\, dt = 0 \qquad (7{:}9b)$$

for all dw^σ. These results are analogous to those given in the last section. Moreover, as before, the functions

$$p_j = \lambda_\beta\, q_{\beta_j} - \lambda_{p+i}\, P_{ij}$$

satisfy the relations

$$\dot{p}_i = - p_j\, A_i^{\,j} + \lambda_\beta\, B_{\beta j}\, .$$

The functions F and G are of the form

$$F = \lambda_\beta\, \overline{f}_\beta - p_j(t)\, \overline{f}^j, \quad G = \lambda_\beta\, g_\beta + \Big[p_i(T^s)X^{is}\Big]_{s=0}^{s=1}\, .$$

Defining H, g by (6:7) it is seen that (6:8), (6:9), (6:10) also hold. In fact Theorem 6:1 holds without change for problems nonlinear in the state variables, provided the region $\mathcal{R}$ of admissible element (t,u,w) is of the type here considered.

It remains to consider the case when the region $\mathcal{R}$ of admissible elements contains the state variables, and has the properties (1) and (2) relative to x_0 as described in Section 3. In this even we introduce the functions

$$r_j^{\,k}(t) = \frac{\partial U_0^{\,k}}{\partial x^j}, \quad v_\sigma^{\,k} = \frac{\partial U_0^{\,k}}{\partial w^\sigma} \quad \underline{\text{along}}\ \ x_0,$$

and set

$$A_j^{\,i}(t) = \frac{\partial f^j}{\partial x^j} + \frac{\partial f^i}{\partial u^k}\, r_j^{\,k}, \quad B_{\beta j} = \frac{\partial f_\beta}{\partial x^j} + \frac{\partial f_\beta}{\partial u^k}\, r_j^{\,k}$$

where the right members are evaluated along x_0. Then, proceeding as above, it is seen that Theorem 6:1 holds, if we replace the partial derivatives H_{x^i}, H_{w^σ} appearing in (6:11) by

$$H_{x^i} + H_{u^k}\, r_i^{\,k}, \quad H_{w^\sigma} + H_{u^k}\, v_\sigma^{\,k}$$

respectively, and if we restrict the set $(t,x_0(t),u,w_0)$ appearing in (6:12) to be in $\mathcal{R}$. The proof, however, is more complicated than in the previous cases. If $\mathcal{R}$ is defined by conditions (3:1) with (3:2) of rank m along x_0, then

$U_0(t,x,w)$ can be chosen so that multipliers μ_α exist so that the function $\tilde{H} = H - \mu_\alpha \varphi_\alpha$ has the properties described in Theorem 2:1.

8. <u>Second-order necessary conditions.</u> In the present section we shall consider problems without inequality constraints. Recall that inequality constraints can be eliminated by a device due to Valentine.

Consider now the problem of minimizing

$$I = g(w) + \int_{t^0}^{t^1} f(t,x,u)\, dt$$

in a class of state and control variables

$$x: \qquad x^i(t), \qquad u^k(t), \qquad w^\sigma \qquad (t^0 \leqq t \leqq t^1)$$

satisfying conditions of the form

$$\dot{x}^i = f^i(t,x,u), \quad \varphi_\alpha(t,x,u) = 0 \tag{8:1a}$$

$$t^s = T^s(w), \quad x^i(t^s) = X^{is}(w) \tag{8:1b}$$

$$I_\gamma = g_\gamma(w) + \int_{t^0}^{t^1} f_\gamma(t,x,u)\, dt = 0 \quad (\gamma=1, \ldots, p). \tag{8:1c}$$

As before, let

$$x_0: \qquad x_0{}^i(t), \qquad u_0{}^k(t), \qquad w_0{}^\sigma \qquad (t^0 \leqq t \leqq t^1)$$

denote a solution to our problem. Assume that the matrix (3:2) has rank m on $\mathcal{R}$. Let

$$y: \qquad y^i(t), \qquad v^k(t), \qquad \omega^\sigma \qquad (t^0 \leqq t \leqq t^1)$$

be a variation of x_0. The equations of variation of the system (8:1) along x_0 is given by the system

$$\dot{y}^i = f^i_{x^j}\, y^j + f^i_{u^k}\, v^k, \quad \varphi_{\alpha x^k}\, y^k + \varphi_{\alpha u^k}\, v^k = 0 \tag{8:2a}$$

$$y^i(t^s) = (X^{is}_\sigma - \dot{x}(t^s) T_\sigma{}^s)\omega^\sigma = c^{is}_\sigma\, \omega^\sigma \quad (s=0,1) \tag{8:2b}$$

$$I'_\gamma(y) = 0 \tag{8:2c}$$

where

$$I'_{\gamma}(y) = g_{\gamma\sigma}\omega^{\sigma} + \left[fT^{s}_{\sigma}\,\omega^{\sigma} \right]_{s=0}^{s=1} + \int_{t^0}^{t^1} \left\{ f_{\gamma x^i}\, y^i + f_{\gamma u^k}\, v^k \right\} dt$$

evaluated along x_0. Here and elsewhere the subscripts σ, τ denote derivatives with respect to w^{σ}, w^{τ} at $w = w_0$.

If x_0 satisfies the multiplier rule described in Theorem 2:1 with functions H and G, then the second variation of I along x_0 is expressible in the form

$$I''(y) = b_{\sigma\tau}\,\omega^{\sigma}\,\omega^{\tau} + \int_{t^0}^{t^1} 2\Omega(t,y,v)\, dt$$

where

$$2\Omega = H_{x^i x^j}\, y^i y^j + 2H_{x^i u^k}\, y^i v^k + H_{u^h u^k}\, v^h v^k ,$$

$$b_{\sigma\tau} = G_{\sigma\tau} + \left[-\,H\,T^{s}_{\sigma\tau} + p_i\, X^{is}_{\sigma\tau} \right]_{s=0}^{s=1}$$

$$-\left[(H - \dot{x}_0^{\,i}\, H_{x^i})\, T_{\sigma}^{\,s}\, T_{\tau}^{\,s} + H_{x^i} (X^{is}_{\sigma}\, T_{\tau}^{\,s} + X^{is}_{\tau}\, T_{\sigma}^{\,s}) \right]_{s=0}^{s=1},$$

where all derivatives are evaluated along x_0.

Using the results obtained by Mary Jane Cox (12) one can establish the following

THEOREM 8:1. SUPPOSE THAT x_0 HAS NO CORNERS AND MINIMIZES I SUBJECT TO (8:1). THEN FOR EVERY VARIATION y SATISFYING THE CONSTRAINTS (8:2) THERE IS A SET OF MULTIPLIERS λ_{β}, $p_i(t)$, $\mu_{\alpha}(t)$ WITH WHICH x_0 SATISFIES THE MULTIPLIER RULE AND SUCH THAT $I''(y) \geq 0$.

If x_0 has corners, discontinuous variations must be admitted. The corresponding result for this case can be obtained from that here given by a transformation of variables.

If there exists a set of $N = 2n+p$ variations y_j satisfying (8:2a) and having the determinant

$$\begin{vmatrix} c_\sigma^{i0} \; \omega_j^{\;\sigma} \\ c_\sigma^{i1} \; \omega_j^{\;\sigma} \\ I_\gamma \; (y_j) \end{vmatrix}$$

is different from zero, then x_0 will be said to be normal. If x_0 is normal, there is a unique set of multipliers with which x_0 satisfies the multiplier rule. Moreover, $\lambda_0 > 0$ and hence one can choose $\lambda_0 = 1$.

REFERENCES

(1) F. A. Valentine, The problem of Lagrange with differential inequalities as side conditions, dissertation, University of Chicago, 1937. See also contributions to the Calculus of Variations (1933-1937), 403-407.

(2) L. D. Berkowitz, Variational Methods in Problems of Control and Programming, Journal of Mathematical Analysis and Applications, volume 3 (1961), 122, 131; On control problems with bounded state variables, volume 4 (1962), 488-498.

(3) See The mathematical theory of optimal control processes, by L. S. Pontryagin, V. G. Boltyanskii, R. V. Gamkrelidze, E. F. Mishchenko, Interscience Publishers (1962).

(4) T. Guinn, On first order necessary conditions for variational and control problems, dissertation, University of California, Los Angeles, 1964.

(5) Bliss and Underhill, The minimum of a definite integral for unilateral variations in space, Transactions of the American Mathematical Society, volume 15 (1914), 291-310.

(6) M. R. Hestenes, A general problem in the calculus of variations with applications to paths of least time, Rand Corporation RM-100, Astia Document No. AD 112382.

(7) G. A. Bliss, Lectures on the Calculus of Variations, The University of Chicago Press, 1946.

(8) G. A. Bliss, The Evolution of Problems of the Calculus of Variations, American Mathematical Monthly, volume 43 (1936), 598-609.

(9) L. S. Pontryagin, Optimal Control Processes, Uspekhi Mat. Nauk., volume 14 (1959); see also Reference 3.

(10) R. Bellman, Dynamic Programming, Princeton University Press, Princeton, N. J., 1957. Bellman and Dreyfuss, Applied dynamic programming, Princeton University Press, Princeton, N. J., 1962.

(11) E. J. McShane, On multipliers for Lagrange problems, American Journal of Mathematics, volume 61 (1939), 809-19.

(12) M. J. Cox, On necessary conditions for relative minima, American Journal of Mathematics, volume 66 (1944), 170-178.

ON THE COMPUTATION OF THE OPTIMAL TEMPERATURE PROFILE IN A TUBULAR REACTION VESSEL

C. Storey
I.C.I. Central Instrument Laboratory
Boyedown House, Pangbourne, Berks, England

H.H. Rosenbrock
Cambridge University - present address:
Massachusetts Institute of Technology,
Cambridge 39, Mass.

1. THE PROBLEM AND ITS MATHEMATICAL FORMULATION

Consider a reaction scheme of the kind shown below:

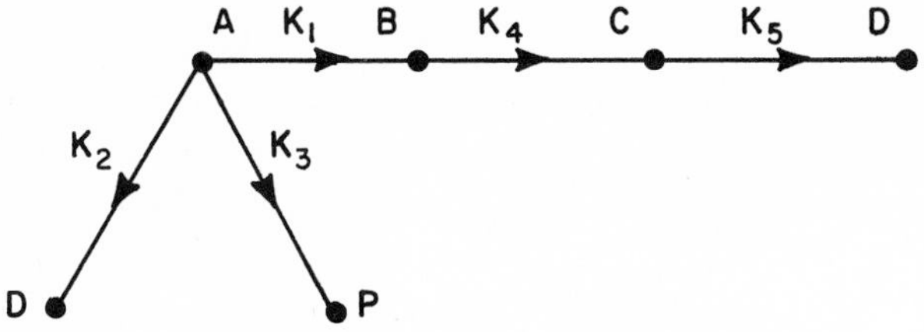

FIGURE 1

where A is the feed material, B a transient intermediate, C the required product and D an unwanted side product. The kinetic rate constants k_i are assumed to obey the usual law

$$k_i = k^o_i \exp \frac{-E_i}{RT} \tag{1.1}$$

in which the k_i are frequency factors, the E_i activation energies, R is the gas constant and T the absolute temperature.

The reaction is assumed to take place in a tubular reaction vessel with plug flow conditions. The problem is to select a temperature profile along the tube which will maximize some measure of the reactor performance.

The effect of a non-isothermal temperature will depend very much on the nature of the reaction that is taking place. Thus with an exothermic reversible reaction the yield may be increased by favouring the forward rate at one end of the tube and the equilibrium yield at the other. With a reaction of the type shown in Figure 1, the yield can often be increased (depending on the relative ratios of the rate constants) by favouring production of the required product at the expense of the side products.

On the other hand, with an endothermic reversible reaction the higher the temperature the larger the yield and the upper limit to the temperature is determined purely by what is physically possible.

Attention is confined in this paper to a specific example of the reaction scheme of Figure 1 in which the rate constants are given in the form

$$k_i = k_i^o \exp\left\{ -\frac{E_i}{R}\left(\frac{1}{T} - \frac{1}{658}\right)\right\} \tag{1.2}$$

where the k_i and E_i are shown in Table 1. Consideration of the ratios of the various activation energies indicates a falling temperature profile for optimum yield. Considerations

TABLE 1

	1	2	3	4	5
k_i^o	1.02	0.93	0.386	3.28	0.084
E_i	16,000	14,000	15,000	10,000	15,000

of catalyst stability impose an upper limit of 550°C on the temperature. It is also important to notice that as the useful product C is itself being reacted to D there will be an optimal contact time. This is in opposition to the case where C does not react and the yield continually increases with the contact time [Denbigh, 1958].

Mathematical Formulation

Stated mathematically the problem is as follows: given the set of differential equations (kinetic equations)

$$\left.\begin{aligned} \frac{dx_1}{dt} &= -(k_1 + k_2 + k_3)x_1 \\ \frac{dx_2}{dt} &= k_1x_1 - k_4x_2 \\ \frac{dx_3}{dt} &= k_4x_2 - k_5x_3 \end{aligned}\right\} \tag{1.3}$$

with the initial conditions

$$x_1(0) = 1 \qquad x_2(0) = 0 \qquad x_3(0) = 0 \tag{1.4}$$

and the k_i given by Equation (1.2), find the temperature profile $T(t)$, and the final time t_f, so that $x_3(t_f)$ is a maximum.

(The concentrations of A, B, C have been denoted by x_1, x_2, x_3.) The object of this paper is to examine critically a number of different techniques for the solution of this problem.

2. BEST ISOTHERMAL YIELD

For an isothermal reactor the kinetic equations can be integrated analytically to give for x_3, the yield of C,

$$x_3 = \frac{k_1 k_4 e^{-k_5 t}}{k - k_4} \left\{ \frac{1 - e^{-(k_4 - k_5)t}}{k_4 - k_5} - \frac{1 - e^{-(k - k_5)t}}{k - k_5} \right\}$$

where $(k_1 + k_2 + k_3)$ has been replaced by k. The best isothermal yield is found by maximizing this expression with respect to the contact time t and the temperature T. It is obvious that to do this analytically by setting $\partial x_3/\partial T = \partial x_3/\partial t = 0$ would involve some heavy algebra and result in a pair of complicated non-linear equations. The maximization was therefore carried out using the hill-climbing technique described by Rosenbrock (1960) with the results given in Table 2.

TABLE 2

	Run 1			Run 2			Run 3		
	T^oK	t secs	$x_3\%$	T^oK	t secs	$x_3\%$	T^oK	t secs	$x_3\%$
Initial Guess	1073	0.50	1.9	773	0.5	40.6	873	0.5	28.2
1st Stage	909	0.10	41.4	773	0.45	40.9	867	0.19	41.9
5th Stage	915	0.12	42.2	773	0.435	40.9	867	0.18	41.95
16th Stage	983	0.076	42.3	858	0.19	41.9	867	0.18	41.95
29th Stage	983	0.076	42.3	983	0.076	42.3	867	0.18	41.95
35th Stage	983	0.076	42.3	983	0.076	42.3	867	0.18	41.95

An examination of these results shows that the optimal isothermal yield is about 42.3% at a temperature of 710°C and a holding time of 0.076 sec. The last run shows how insensitive the yield is to changes in T and t in the neighbourhood of the maximum: so much so, in fact, that the hill-climbing routine can make no further progress. This illustrates the need for starting the hill-climbing procedure from a number of different points. It also shows how a hill-climbing method may succeed better if it is allowed to start further away from the optimum. The direction of a ridge can then be determined at a point where its upward trend is greater, and used near the optimum where the direction would be less easy to find. Table 3 gives a fuller picture of the results of Run 2. The first part of this table shows the difficulties involved in deciding on a criterion for stopping a run: from trials 22 to 51 there has been virtually no change in the yield. The constant γ is explained in Appendix 2.

TABLE 3

No. of Trials	$T^{o}K$	t secs	$x_3\%$	γ
0	773	0.50	0.40596	0
6	772.95000	0.45000	0.40876	.707
22	772.93757	0.43591	0.40893	.062
29	772.93852	0.43566	0.40893	.894
37	772.94115	0.43530	0.40893	.124
42	772.94709	0.43500	0.40893	.083
51	772.99050	0.43423	0.40894	.034
62	773.89143	0.42165	0.40900	.004
75	775.37409	0.42536	0.40932	.016
85	776.72113	0.42398	0.40951	.004
93	799.23578	0.30825	0.41196	.004
104	810.92610	0.27221	0.41320	.002
112	817.50201	0.28803	0.41484	.005
125	818.73502	0.27323	0.41523	.014
137	818.90841	0.27258	0.41525	.008
149	824.10999	0.25994	0.41582	.001
163	852.34282	0.18848	0.41888	.000
169	862.78651	0.18530	0.41924	.001
179	883.66320	0.16125	0.42031	.000
187	922.98464	0.11323	0.42221	.000
198	926.14816	0.11033	0.42229	.000
206	935.63875	0.10309	0.42253	.000
214	956.99255	0.09006	0.42293	.000
226	978.01272	0.07907	0.42306	.000
234	984.76920	0.07502	0.42308	.008
281	983.05517	0.07589	0.42308	.009
400	983.05517	0.07589	0.42308	.014

Subsequently an upper limit $T^*=550^oC$ was imposed on the temperature and with this restriction the best isothermal yield was found to be 41.6% at 550^oC with a contact time of 0.26 secs.

3. FIRST METHOD OF SOLUTION: DISCRETE APPROXIMATION

The first approach was to write the Equations (1.3) in finite difference form to obtain

$$\begin{aligned} x_{1r} - x_{1,r-1} &= -t_r(k_{1r} + k_{2r} + k_{3r})x_{1r} \\ x_{2r} - x_{2,r-1} &= t_r(k_{1r}x_{1r} - k_{4r}x_{2r}) \\ x_{3r} - x_{3,r-1} &= t_r(k_{4r}x_{2r} - k_{5r}x_{3r}) \end{aligned} \tag{3.1}$$

It is apparent that these equations are physically equivalent to approximating the tube by a series of completely stirred tanks; they represent a mass balance on the rth tank.

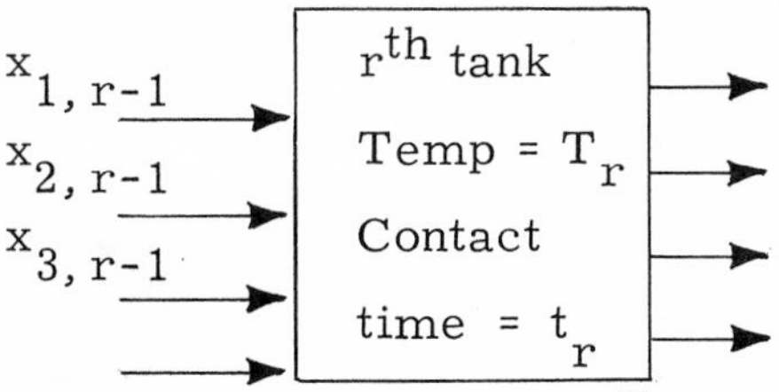

In these equations, $k_{ir} = k_i^o \exp\left\{-\frac{E_i}{R}\left(\frac{1}{T_r} - \frac{1}{658}\right)\right\}$ (3.2)

with T_r the temperature and t_r the holding time in the rth tank.

From the sets of algebraic equations (3.1) it is possible by elimination to write the yield of C, i.e., $x_3(t_f)$, as a function of the t_r and T_r. The value of $x_3(t_f)$ can then be maximized directly by hill-climbing simultaneously on these 2r variables (r is the number of tanks). This was done using the method of Rosenbrock [1960]. Table 4 shows the variation of the maximum yield with the number of tanks. With eight tanks the hill-climbing routine was dealing simultaneously with 16 variables and it is of interest to look briefly into the convergence to the optimum.

TABLE 4

No. of Tanks	Best yield%
2	37.2
3	39.7
4	40.0
8	43.4

Table 5 shows the results of a run starting with each tank at a temperature of 375°C and a contact time of 0.25 sec. The machine (Ferranti Mercury) was stopped after 20 minutes computing time. It is obvious from the Table that the best yield has not been reached so a further run was started with approximately the times and temperatures given at the end of Table 5. Table 6 shows the results of this run which took 60 minutes of machine time and appears to have converged. The final profile is so unlikely, however, that a further run was carried out with only the temperature and contact time of the third tank changed to 475°C and 0.10 secs respectively. The results are shown in Table 7. In this case there were 100 perturbations per variable and machine time was 36 minutes.

These results further illustrate the difficulty of finding the direction of a ridge near a maximum, and bring out clearly the need for starting the hill-climbing technique from a number of different points. To test the significance of the long residence time required in the 8th tank a short run was carried out with temperatures and times the same as in the last row of Table 7 except for the time in the last tank which was put equal to 0.1 secs. The starting value for the yield was .42011 and after 50 trials in each variable the contact time in the last tank had gone back to 20 secs, the other variables had changed very slightly, and the final yield was .43455. Since in the previous runs the contact time in each tank had been constrained to lie between 0 and 20 secs, a further run was carried out with this restriction removed.

The final best profile is shown in Table 8.

4. SECOND METHOD OF SOLUTION: PARAMETRIC EXPANSION

With this method a shape was assumed for the

TABLE 5

No. of Trials	T_1	T_2	T_3	T_4	T_5	T_6	T_7	T_8	t_1	t_2	t_3	t_4	t_5	t_6	t_7	t_8	$x_3(t_f)$	γ
0	375	375	375	375	375	375	375	375	0.25	0.25	0.25	0.25	0.25	0.25	0.25	0.25	0.3627	0
143	484.3	429.6	338.5	338.0	372.1	320.4	356.8	320.3	0.200	0.200	0.200	0.284	0.284	0.308	0.270	0.256	0.3942	0.686
372	548.8	448.2	292.5	344.1	382.6	328.1	329.7	293.8	0.091	0.160	1.272	0.253	0.200	0.431	0.307	0.101	0.4120	0.644
558	550.0	463.0	290.0	390.6	395.0	361.0	313.8	281.5	0.076	0.136	0.802	0.172	0.112	0.387	0.474	1.859	0.4145	1.000
787	550.0	473.6	316.0	378.3	399.4	366.6	307.0	270.6	0.077	0.115	0.302	0.208	0.107	0.207	0.905	2.261	0.4164	1.000

TABLE 6

No. of Trials	T_1	T_2	T_3	T_4	T_5	T_6	T_7	T_8	t_1	t_2	t_3	t_4	t_5	t_6	t_7	t_8	$x_3(t_f)$	γ
0	549	474	316	378	399	367	307	271	0.076	0.115	0.302	0.208	0.107	0.207	0.905	2.261	0.4163	0
125	549.8	510.4	334.2	384.0	411.1	365.6	288.8	265.0	0.064	0.093	0.308	0.214	0.132	0.232	1.024	2.492	0.4197	1.000
336	550.0	515.9	329.2	372.6	403.3	352.6	282.6	222.7	0.064	0.081	0.296	0.197	0.136	0.293	1.619	7.982	0.4225	0.989
566	550.0	518.4	300.2	412.4	399.9	346.6	273.5	187.1	0.063	0.073	0.040	0.150	0.168	0.377	1.724	19.813	0.4252	0.879
781	550.0	542.3	303.5	414.7	401.8	346.7	270.9	187.3	0.061	0.069	0.017	0.146	0.163	0.384	1.893	19.987	0.4259	0.999
932	550.0	528.3	301.4	414.3	400.6	347.0	272.9	188.1	0.061	0.068	0.002	0.142	0.160	0.379	1.969	19.967	0.4260	0.977
1147	550.0	529.2	301.4	414.2	400.6	347.0	273.1	188.3	0.060	0.064	0.001	0.144	0.163	0.373	1.969	19.987	0.4262	0.434
1357	550.0	532.6	302.0	413.3	401.1	347.2	273.1	188.9	0.059	0.062	0.005	0.148	0.173	0.360	1.889	19.917	0.4264	0.199
1495	550.0	547.9	304.8	409.4	403.4	347.8	273.3	191.7	0.056	0.056	0.006	0.159	0.168	0.351	1.591	19.588	0.4274	0.009
1981	550.0	550.0	305.3	409.1	403.7	347.9	273.3	192.0	0.055	0.055	0.003	0.156	0.155	0.379	1.803	19.638	0.4276	0.382
2649	550.0	550.0	305.4	409.2	403.7	347.9	273.3	192.0	0.055	0.055	0.002	0.150	0.158	0.362	1.931	19.708	0.4277	0.997
2737	550.0	550.0	305.4	409.2	403.7	347.9	273.3	192.0	0.055	0.055	0.001	0.150	0.158	0.361	1.931	19.707	0.4277	1.000

TABLE 7

No. of Trials	T_1	T_2	T_3	T_4	T_5	T_6	T_7	T_8	t_1	t_2	t_3	t_4	t_5	t_6	t_7	t_8	$x_3(t_f)$	γ
0	549	549	475	409	403	348	273	192	0.055	0.055	0.100	0.150	0.158	0.360	1.930	19.700	0.4274	0
125	549.8	549.8	484.0	418.0	412.0	342.0	254.8	186.0	0.052	0.052	0.069	0.100	0.108	0.385	1.955	19.856	0.4316	1.000
376	550.0	550.0	502.2	417.9	410.8	347.2	254.5	185.2	0.046	0.045	0.055	0.108	0.112	0.314	2.967	19.992	0.4327	0.963
670	550.0	550.0	507.2	418.7	408.5	348.0	255.6	185.6	0.044	0.043	0.055	0.106	0.115	0.309	2.925	19.990	0.4329	0.461
839	550.0	550.0	534.2	423.8	394.7	351.6	262.9	188.3	0.040	0.035	0.049	0.098	0.137	0.302	2.518	19.976	0.4334	0.056
963	550.0	550.0	543.4	425.9	389.1	352.5	266.0	189.5	0.039	0.042	0.041	0.098	0.146	0.284	2.268	19.982	0.4340	0.093
1166	550.0	550.0	549.9	426.9	386.1	353.6	267.6	190.0	0.039	0.039	0.039	0.100	0.161	0.270	2.217	19.998	0.4342	0.156
1311	550.0	550.0	550.0	426.9	386.2	353.6	267.5	190.0	0.039	0.039	0.039	0.100	0.161	0.270	2.217	19.998	0.4342	0.998
1496	550.0	550.0	550.0	426.9	386.2	353.6	267.5	190.0	0.039	0.039	0.039	0.100	0.160	0.270	2.218	19.998	0.4342	0.984
1596	550.0	550.0	550.0	426.9	386.2	353.6	267.5	190.0	0.039	0.039	0.039	0.101	0.159	0.270	2.214	19.988	0.4342	0.998
1600	550.0	550.0	550.0	426.9	386.2	353.6	267.5	190.0	0.039	0.039	0.039	0.101	0.159	0.270	2.214	19.988	0.4342	0.998

TABLE 8

Best yield 0.44204

Tank	1	2	3	4	5	6	7	8
Temp: °C	549.95	549.91	549.95	549.96	430.36	408.47	162.18	135.08
time: secs	0.034	0.033	0.033	0.033	0.096	0.128	28.08	120.69

temperature profile in the form of an expression (straight line, quadratic, exponential, etc.) with a number of adjustable parameters. This expression was then substituted into the kinetic equations (1.3) and hill-climbing carried out on the parameters (and on the total contact time t_f) until $x_3(t_f)$ was maximized.

The trapezoidal rule was used for integrating the kinetic equations, the finite difference equations taking the particularly simple form below (see Appendix 1 for the derivation).

$$x_{1r} = x_{1,r-1} \frac{1-hk_{r-1}/2}{1+hk_r/2}$$

$$x_{2r} = x_{2,r-1} \frac{1-hk_{4,r-1}/2}{1+hk_{4r}/2} + x_{1,r-1} \frac{hk_{1,r-1}/2}{1+hk_{4r}/2} + x_{1r} \frac{hk_{1r}/2}{1+hk_{4r}/2}$$

$$x_{3r} = x_{3,r-1} \frac{1-hk_{5,r-1}/2}{1+hk_{5r}/2} + x_{2,r-1} \frac{hk_{4,r-1}/2}{1+hk_{5r}/2} + x_{2r} \frac{hk_{4r}/2}{1+hk_{5r}/2} \tag{4.1}$$

To get the feel of the problem, a simple straight line relationship

$$T(^{\circ}K) = a_2 - a_1 t \tag{4.2}$$

was used first with a fixed t_f of 0.5 secs. The interval of integration h was 0.01 secs and Rosenbrock's method was used for the optimization.

With starting values of a_2 = 800, a_1 = 500 (i.e., a straight-line profile going from 527°C at the inlet to 277°C at the outlet) the yield was 34.8%. After 50 perturbations (by the hill-climbing program) in each variable, the best yield was 42.57% with a_2 at its upper limit of 823 (corresponding to 550°C) and a_1 = 312. Computer time was 18 minutes and this, of course, had involved solving the set of differential equations (1.3) one hundred times.

The simple exponential relationship

$$T = a_1 \exp(-a_2 t) \tag{4.3}$$

was then tried and the results are shown in Table 9.

TABLE 9

	a_1	a_2	$x_3(0.5)\%$
Start	750	0	40.3
After 50 trials per variable (19 mins)	822.9	0.39	42.55

In a similar manner a quadratic expression

$$T = a_1 + a_2 t + a_3 t^2 \tag{4.4}$$

gave the results in Table 10.

TABLE 10

	a_1	a_2	a_3	$x_3(0.5)\%$
Start	750	0	0	40.3
After 50 trials per variable (26 mins)	822.9	-288.3	-55.9	42.58

The quadratic approximation was also tried from a different set of starting values, namely

$$a_1 = 822.93 \qquad a_2 = -135.1 \qquad a_3 = -578.7$$

this time converging to 42.67. Other starting values were also tried but with no improvement in the yield.

These results are another good illustration of the difficulty in finding a criterion for stopping a hill-climbing technique. The results shown in Table 10 were, in fact, continued for at least 4 stages of the hill-climb without any increase in yield (up to the 5th decimal place) whereas as shown above, a change of 0.1% was achieved by starting from a different point.

From the tank approximations it appeared that the first part of the reactor should be at the upper temperature limit and that a profile of the type shown in Figure 2 was required. This suggested using a composite expression consisting of say two straight lines, or a straight line and an exponential,

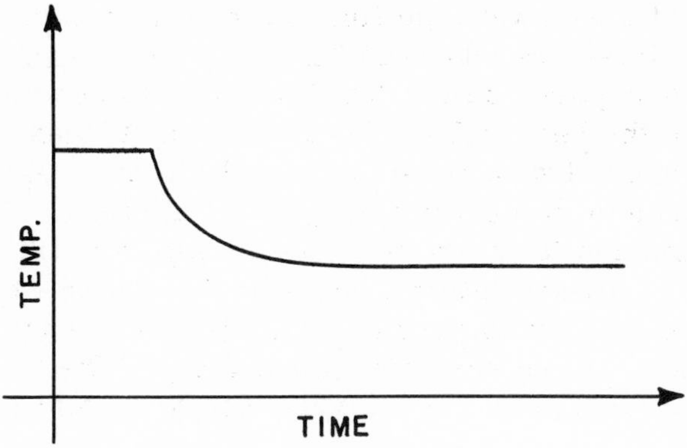

FIGURE 2

with the point of intersection of the two parts regarded as one of the parameters.

The hill-climb was therefore repeated for the two forms of T(r):

$$T = \begin{cases} a_2 - a_1 t, & t < a_4 \\ a_2 + a_4(a_3 - a_1) - a_3 t, & t > a_4 \end{cases} \qquad (4.5)$$

(a_2 and a_1 the intercept and slope of first straight line, a_3 slope of second straight line and a_4 the variable point of intersection.) The second form is

$$T = \begin{cases} a_2 - a_1 t, & t < a_4 \\ (a_2 - a_4 a_1) \exp\left\{a_3(t - a_4)\right\}, & t > a_4 \end{cases} \qquad (4.6)$$

(a_3 is now the exponent in the exponential part).

The results obtained, however, were not significantly better (for a fixed time of 0.5 secs) than those obtained before; the straight line and exponential, for example, giving a best yield of 42.85%.

One important benefit of the parametric expansion technique is the ease with which it can deal with a variable final time. The time is simply regarded as an extra parameter to be adjusted in the hill-climbing routine. The results of a run with the final time left variable and a pair of straight lines are shown in Table 11. An upper limit of 10 secs was imposed on t_f. The starting values used in this run were the best values for two straight lines and a fixed t_f of 0.5 secs. There were 50 perturbations in each of the five variables and computer time was 77 minutes. One difficulty in this method is in choosing a suitable integration step length. If a fixed interval suitable for a small t_f is taken (which will be small because the rates of change of the x_i are large) this can be very time consuming if the final time is long at any stage in the convergence to the optimum.

TABLE 11

No of trials	a_1	a_2	a_3	a_4	a_5	$x_3(t_f)$	γ
0	310	820	294	20.0	0.5	0.4281	0
46	337.3	819.1	131.9	12.9	6.5	0.4370	0.986
89	376.4	821.4	83.1	11.1	8.0	0.4405	0.487
142	399.8	823.0	65.1	11.2	8.8	0.4424	0.242
158	401.4	822.8	64.2	11.2	8.8	0.4426	0.196
186	409.2	822.6	60.4	11.1	9.1	0.4431	0.132
205	423.6	822.8	53.1	10.7	9.5	0.4441	0.035
243	431.6	822.9	48.8	10.6	9.9	0.4446	0.016
250	434.2	822.9	47.5	10.5	10.0	0.4446	0.016

Exactly the same program was run starting from the final values in Table 11 but with the restriction of an upper limit of 10 secs on t_f removed. After roughly 100 minutes of computer time the total time t_f was 41 secs and the best yield 0.4469. Convergence had not been attained since only 75 trials had been made.

5. THIRD METHOD OF SOLUTION: PONTRYAGIN'S MAXIMUM PRINCIPLE

The next step was to try the formal solution of the problem given by Pontryagin's maximum principle. The analytical results are simply stated here and are discussed in Appendix 2. The maximum principle states that the optimum profile problem can be solved by integrating the kinetic equations (1.3) together with the "adjoint" equations

$$\left.\begin{aligned} \frac{d\Psi_1}{dt} &= (k_1 + k_2 + k_3)\,\Psi_1 - k_1\Psi_2 \\ \frac{d\Psi_2}{dt} &= k_4\Psi_2 - k_4\Psi_3 \\ \frac{d\Psi_3}{dt} &= k_5\Psi_3 \end{aligned}\right\} \tag{5.1}$$

with boundary conditions

$$\Psi_1(t_f) = \Psi_2(t_f) = 0, \Psi_3(t_f) = 1$$

at each instant selecting the temperature by maximizing H with respect to T, where

$$\begin{aligned} H &= \sum \Psi_i f_i \\ &= -(k_1 + k_2 + k_3)\,\Psi_1 x_1 + k_1\Psi_2 x_1 - k_4 x_2(\Psi_2 - \Psi_3) \\ &\quad -k_5\Psi_3 x_3 \end{aligned} \tag{5.2}$$

If T has upper and lower limits T^* and T_*, the maximization of T is equivalent to taking T^*, T_* or a solution of the equation $\partial H/\partial T = 0$, whichever makes H greatest. This makes the selection of T definite even if H has a number of local maxima.

It will be noticed that the boundary conditions for the kinetic equations are given at the reactor inlet and those for the adjoint equations are given at the outlet - thus a two-point boundary value problem is encountered. It is possible, therefore, to proceed in either of two ways as follows:

1. Guesses can be made for the outlet concentrations and the kinetic and adjoint equations integrated from the outlet to the inlet. The differences between the actual and desired concentrations at the outlet can then be used to correct the guesses at the inlet. The successive iterations in this method give the best profile for the correct performance index (since this depends

only on the boundary values of the adjoint equations) but for a reactor with different initial concentrations.

2. The boundary values for the adjoint equations can be estimated at the inlet, the equations integrated forward, and the estimates adjusted until the boundary values of the adjoints at the outlet are correct. Successive iterations in this case give the best temperature profile for a reactor with the correct inlet concentrations but a wrong performance index. If, in fact, the outlet conditions for the adjoints are $\Psi_1(t_f)$, $\Psi_2(t_f)$, $\Psi_3(t_f)$ for any specific iteration the profile that has been chosen by the maximum principle will maximize

$$F(t_f) = \Psi(t_f)\, x_1(t_f) + \Psi_2(t_f)\, x_2(t_f) + \Psi_3(t_f)\, x_3(t_f)$$

In the present work the first method was used and adjustments made to the outlet concentrations by hill-climbing on the function

$$G = \{1 - x_1(0)\}^2 + \{x_2(0)\}^2 + \{x_3(0)\}^2$$

Two different methods were used for finding the maximum value of H. In the first method the equation $\partial H/\partial T = 0$ was solved by the rule of false position. In the second method a direct search was made by varying T by a small quantity (usually $1^{o}C$) and calculating H. The Runge-Kutta technique was used for integration in both cases. In the first method, however, the temperature was taken to be constant over the interval of integration while in the second method the maximum value of H was calculated at those points within the interval which are used by the Runge-Kutta integration formulae.

A fixed t_f of 0.5 secs was taken with an integration interval of 0.005. The first difficulty encountered was the extreme sensitivity of the temperature profile to the initial guesses for $x_1(t_f)$, $x_2(t_f)$ and $x_3(t_f)$. This sensitivity is demonstrated in Table 12 where the results of starting with two different sets of initial values is shown.

The results from a typical run are shown in Table 13. Here it will be noticed that some of the concentrations have gone negative and that although the concentrations at 0.025

TABLE 12

	Run 1							Run 2						
Time (secs)	Temp ^ok	x_1	x_2	x_3	Ψ_1	Ψ_2	Ψ_3	Temp ^ok	x_1	x_2	x_3	Ψ_1	Ψ_2	Ψ_3
0.50	381.5	0.004	0.016	0.425	0.000	0.000	1.000	346.2	0.002	0.013	0.430	0.000	0.000	1.000
0.40	385.1	0.005	0.022	0.422	0.016	0.297	0.991	347.1	0.002	0.016	0.429	0.004	0.184	0.996
0.30	390.1	0.006	0.030	0.417	0.049	0.486	0.983	348.2	0.003	0.019	0.427	0.016	0.336	0.992
0.20	397.3	0.008	0.042	0.408	0.098	0.636	0.973	349.4	0.003	0.024	0.424	0.033	0.460	0.987
0.10	408.9	0.011	0.061	0.393	0.159	0.746	0.962	350.7	0.003	0.029	0.421	0.054	0.561	0.983
0.05	418.2	0.013	0.075	0.380	0.195	0.789	0.956	351.4	0.003	0.032	0.418	0.066	0.604	0.981
0.02	425.8	0.015	0.087	0.370	0.220	0.811	0.951	351.9	0.004	0.035	0.417	0.073	0.628	0.980
0.01	550.0	0.016	0.095	0.362	0.253	0.825	0.964	352.0	0.004	0.035	0.416	0.075	0.635	0.979
0.00	550.0	0.018	0.104	0.354	0.283	0.836	0.942	352.2	0.004	0.036	0.415	0.078	0.643	0.979

TABLE 13

Time (secs)	Temp ^ok	x_1	x_2	x_3	Ψ_1	Ψ_2	Ψ_3
0.50	419	0.005	0.020	0.430	0.000	0.000	1.000
0.40	428	0.008	0.031	0.424	0.037	0.390	0.984
0.30	441	0.013	0.051	0.409	0.122	0.639	0.966
0.20	474	0.026	0.093	0.372	0.234	0.794	0.942
0.175	499	0.034	0.112	0.352	0.271	0.823	0.933
0.150	550	0.056	0.144	0.315	0.327	0.852	0.917
0.125	550	0.101	0.184	0.259	0.374	0.869	0.898
0.100	550	0.183	0.220	0.186	0.402	0.875	0.880
0.075	550	0.330	0.234	0.102	0.419	0.874	0.862
0.050	550	0.596	0.183	0.021	0.426	0.867	0.844
0.025	550	1.078	-0.021	-0.017	0.428	0.857	0.826
0.000	550	1.984	-0.552	0.078	0.427	0.844	0.809

secs are reasonably close to their required values of 1, 0, 0 they are much further from these values at t=0. Computer time for the run of Table 13 was 6 minutes.

Attempts to minimize the function G by hill-climbing with respect to the guesses at the exit concentrations were quite unsuccessful (also very time consuming on the computer).

6. FOURTH METHOD OF SOLUTION: GRADIENT METHOD IN FUNCTION SPACE

In this method the solution to the problem is given in the following form. Make a guess at the temperature profile T(t): say, isothermal or a straight line between the upper and lower limits or the best estimate from some other technique. Then integrate the kinetic equations,

$$\begin{aligned} \frac{dx_1}{dt} &= -(k_1 + k_2 + k_3)x_1 & x_1(0) &= 1 \\ \frac{dx_2}{dt} &= k_1x_1 - k_4x_2 & x_2(0) &= 0 \\ \frac{dx_3}{dt} &= k_4x_2 - k_5x_3 & x_3(0) &= 0 \end{aligned} \tag{6.1}$$

from the inlet to the outlet of the reactor. Integrate the adjoint equations

$$\begin{aligned} \frac{d\Psi_1}{dt} &= (k_1 + k_2 + k_3)\Psi_1 - k_1\Psi_2 & \Psi_1(t_f) &= 0 \\ \frac{d\Psi_2}{dt} &= k_4\Psi_2 - k_4\Psi_3 & \Psi_2(t_f) &= 0 \\ \frac{d\Psi_3}{dt} &= k_5\Psi_3 & \Psi_3(t_f) &= 1 \end{aligned} \tag{6.2}$$

in the opposite direction from outlet to inlet. Now calculate $\partial H/\partial T$ for each time step from

$$H = -(k_1+k_2+k_3)\Psi_1x_1+k_1\Psi_2x_1-k_4x_2(\Psi_2-\Psi_3)-k_5\Psi_3x_3 \tag{6.3}$$

$$\frac{\partial H}{\partial T} = -\frac{1}{RT^2}\{-(k_1E_1+k_2E_2+k_3E_3)\Psi_1x_1+k_1E_1\Psi_2x_1 - k_4E_4x_2(\Psi_2-\Psi_3) - k_5E_5\Psi_3x_3\} \tag{6.4}$$

and take $T + \epsilon\ \partial H/\partial T$ as the next guess for the temperature profile, where ϵ is a suitable constant. The whole process is then repeated until there is no further change in the profile. For a discussion of the basis of this technique see Appendix 2.

The method of integration used in this case was the trapezoidal rule as in Section 4. For the adjoint equations the finite difference equations are as follows (Appendix 1).

$$\left.\begin{aligned}
\Psi_{3,r} &= \Psi_{3,r-1}\frac{1+h/2\,k_{5,r-1}}{1-h/2\,k_{5,r}}\\
\Psi_{2,r} &= \Psi_{2,r-1}\frac{1+h/2\,k_{4,r-1}}{1-h/2\,k_{4,r}} - \Psi_{3,r-1}\frac{h/2\,k_{4,r-1}}{1-h/2\,k_{4,r}}\\
&\quad - \Psi_{3,r}\frac{h/2\,k_{4,r}}{1-h/2\,k_{4,r}}\\
\Psi_{1,r} &= \Psi_{1,r-1}\frac{1+h/2\,k_{r-1}}{1-h/2\,k_{1,r}} - \Psi_{2,r-1}\frac{h/2\,k_{1,r-1}}{1-h/2\,k_r}\\
&\quad - \Psi_{2,r}\frac{h/2\,k_{1,r}}{1-h/2\,k_r}
\end{aligned}\right\} \tag{6.5}$$

The main difficulty in the method is the selection of the constant ϵ. If this is too large instability results: if it is too small convergence is slow or fails completely.* The

*Although convergence proofs can be given for the gradient method in certain conditions, these do not take account of the discrete nature of variables held in a digital computer. In no practical case is convergence assumed, even with a finite number of parameters.

effect of varying ϵ will become clearer from the numerical work.

In all numerical work on this method a fixed total time was taken, and to find the best final time a number of runs with different final times could be considered. We begin with a value of 1.0 secs for t_f and Tables 14, 15, 16 and 17 show how the iterations proceed for values of ϵ equal to 0.1, 0.2, 0.5 and 0.75. In each case the initial guess at the profile was isothermal at 400°C and if the temperature tried to exceed 550°C it was set equal to this value.

TABLE 14

t_f = 1.0 secs   h = 0.05 secs ϵ = 0.1

time per iteration   0.09 mins.   (Mercury)

Time secs		0	0.2	0.4	0.6	0.8	1.0
Start	T	400	400	400	400	400	400
	x_3	0	0.006	0.173	0.261	0.321	0.357
1st Iter.	T	400.4	400.1	400.0	400.0	400.0	400.0
	x_3	0	0.066	0.173	0.261	0.321	0.357
10th Iter.	T	404.3	400.9	400.2	400.0	400.0	400.0
	x_3	0	0.069	0.177	0.265	0.324	0.359
50th Iter.	T	427.1	404.3	400.8	400.1	400.0	400.0
	x_3	0	0.088	0.199	0.283	0.336	0.367
100th Iter.	T	493.3	408.2	401.5	400.3	400.0	400.0
	x_3	0	0.145	0.257	0.328	0.368	0.390

TABLE 15

t_f = 1.0 secs   h = 0.05 secs ϵ = 0.2

time per iteration   0.09 mins.

Time secs		0	0.2	0.4	0.6	0.8	1.0
Start	T^oC	400	400	400	400	400	400
	x_3	0	0.066	0.173	0.261	0.321	0.357
1st Iter.	T^oC	400.8	400.2	400.0	400.0	400.0	400.0
	x_3	0	0.066	0.0173	0.0262	0.322	0.357
10th Iter.	T^oC	408.9	401.7	400.3	400.1	400.0	400.0
	x_3	0	0.073	0.182	0.269	0.326	0.361
50th Iter.	T^oC	491.2	408.2	401.5	400.3	400.0	400.0
	x_3	0	0.143	0.256	0.326	0.368	0.389
100th Iter.	T^oC	550.0	412.0	402.1	400.4	400.1	400.0
	x_3	0	0.246	0.346	0.394	0.417	0.425

TABLE 16

t_f = 1.0 secs   h = 0.05 secs ϵ = 0.5

time per iteration   0.09 mins.

Time secs		0	0.2	0.4	0.6	0.8	1.0
Start	T^oC	400	400	400	400	400	400
	x_3	0	0.066	0.173	0.261	0.321	0.357
1st Iter.	T^oC	402.0	400.4	400.1	400.0	400.0	400.0
	x_3	0	0.067	0.175	0.263	0.322	0.358
10th Iter.	T^oC	426.3	404.3	400.8	400.1	400.0	400.0
	x_3	0	0.088	0.199	0.282	0.336	0.367
23rd Iter.	T^oC	533.5	409.2	401.7	400.3	400.0	400.0
	x_3	0	0.191	0.302	0.363	0.395	0.409
26th Iter.	T^oC	-4680.5	409.6	401.7	400.3	400.0	400.0
	x_3	0	1.5×10^4	1.7×10^4	1.6×10^4	1.5×10^4	1.3×10^4

TABLE 17

t_f = 1.0 secs h = 0.05 secs ϵ = 0.75

time per iteration 0.09 mins.

Time secs		0	0.2	0.4	0.6	0.8	1.0
Start	T°C	400	400	400	400	400	400
	x_3	0	0.066	0.173	0.261	0.321	0.357
1st Iter.	T°C	403.1	400.7	400.1	400.0	400.0	400.0
	x_3	0	0.068	0.176	0.264	0.323	0.358
10th Iter.	T°C	446.9	406.4	401.2	400.2	400.0	400.0
	x_3	0	0.105	0.218	0.297	0.346	0.374
16th Iter.	T°C	545.1	409.6	401.7	400.3	400.0	400.0
	x_3	0	0.208	0.318	0.375	0.404	0.417
18th Iter.	T°C	-7449.1	409.9	401.8	400.3	400.0	400.0
	x_3	0	7.4×10^3	8.2×10^3	7.7×10^3	7.0×10^3	8.4×10^3

The effect of increasing ϵ is clearly shown: rate of convergence is increased but instability can occur. This, of course, means that ϵ should be reduced before the onset of instability. The next step was to take another guess at the profile based on results obtained so far and carry out some further iterations to see if convergence had in fact taken place. The results are shown in Tables 18 and 19. A more detailed comparison of the final profile and concentration of x_3 for these last two runs is shown in Table 20. As a further check twenty five iterations were carried out with ϵ = 0.01 starting with the final profile from Table 18. The results showed no further improvement.

Thus at this stage we seem to have exhausted the resources of the method. Yet the final profile is plainly not optimal, for larger values of x_3 occur in Table 20 at t = 0.8 sec than at t = 1.0 sec. If the temperature after t = 0.8 sec

TABLE 18

t_f = 1.0 secs h = 0.05 secs ϵ = 0.2

Time secs		0	0.2	0.4	0.6	0.8	1.0
Start	T°C	496	456	402	400	400	400
	x_3	0	0.254	0.350	0.390	0.409	0.415
1st Iter.	T°C	513.9	456.1	402.0	400.0	400.0	400.0
	x_3	0	0.272	0.362	0.399	0.415	0.419
2nd Iter.	T°C	540.0	456.2	402.0	400.0	400.0	400.0
	x_3	0	0.299	0.381	0.413	0.425	0.427
10th Iter.	T°C	550.0	456.7	402.0	400.0	400.0	400.0
	x_3	0	0.336	0.403	0.427	0.434	0.433
50th Iter.	T°C	550.0	458.0	402.1	400.0	400.0	400.0
	x_3	0	0.366	0.419	0.435	0.438	0.435

TABLE 19

t_f = 1.0 secs h = 0.05 secs ϵ = 0.1

Time secs		0	0.2	0.4	0.6	0.8	1.0
Start	T°C	496	456	402	400	400	400
	x_3	0	0.254	0.350	0.390	0.409	0.415
1st Iter.	T°C	505	456.1	402.0	400.0	400.0	400.0
	x_3	0	0.262	0.355	0.394	0.412	0.417
2nd Iter.	T°C	515.7	456.1	402.0	400.0	400.0	400.0
	x_3	0	0.273	0.363	0.399	0.415	0.420
10th Iter.	T°C	550	456.4	402.0	400.0	400.0	400.0
	x_3	0	0.318	0.393	0.421	0.430	0.431
50th Iter.	T°C	550.0	457.2	402.1	400.0	400.0	400.0
	x_3	0	0.361	0.417	0.434	0.438	0.435

TABLE 20

t: secs	Temperature °C		x_3	
	$\epsilon = 0.1$	$\epsilon = 0.2$	$\epsilon = 0.1$	$\epsilon = 0.2$
0	550.0	550.0	0	0
0.05	550.0	550.0	0.101	0.101
0.10	489.4	500.9	0.247	0.250
0.15	469.7	472.2	0.319	0.325
0.20	457.2	458.0	0.361	0.366
0.25	408.3	408.5	0.385	0.389
0.30	406.2	406.3	0.398	0.402
0.35	404.1	404.2	0.409	0.411
0.40	402.1	402.1	0.417	0.419
0.45	401.1	401.1	0.423	0.425
0.50	401.0	401.1	0.428	0.429
0.55	400.0	400.0	0.432	0.433
0.60	400.0	400.0	0.434	0.435
0.65	400.0	400.0	0.436	0.437
0.70	400.0	400.0	0.437	0.437
0.75	400.0	400.0	0.438	0.438
0.80	400.0	400.0	0.438	0.438
0.85	400.0	400.0	0.438	0.438
0.90	400.0	400.0	0.437	0.437
0.95	400.0	400.0	0.436	0.436
1.00	400.0	400.0	0.435	0.435

were dropped to a very low value, the reaction would be frozen and the value of x_3 at 1.0 sec would be significantly improved. It appears in fact from all the results so far, that the gradient $\partial H/\partial T$ is excessively small near $t = 1.0$ sec. Horn's technique of making ϵ a function of t would evidently be useful here [Horn, 1963]. The value of ϵ would be made small for small t in order to avoid instability, and large for larger t in order to speed up convergence.

An examination of what can happen if the initial guess at the profile is poor was then carried out. Table 21 is the result of starting with a profile which was almost optimal for a final time of $t_f = 0.5$ instead of $t_f = 1.0$. A similar run with $\epsilon = 0.5$ produced the same temperature and x_3 concentration profiles in 25 iterations as in the last line of Table 21.

TABLE 21

$\epsilon = 0.1$ $h = 0.05$ secs $t_f = 1.0$ secs

Time secs	0	0.2	0.4	0.6	0.8	1.0
Start T^oC	547	547	463	423	383	343
Start x_3	0	0.405	0.419	0.407	0.399	0.394
5th Iter. T^oC	550.0	547.4	463.0	423.0	383.0	343.0
5th Iter. x_3	0	0.409	0.418	0.406	0.398	0.394
10th Iter. T^oC	550.0	547.9	463.0	423.0	383.0	343.0
10th Iter. x_3	0	0.409	0.418	0.406	0.398	0.393
50th Iter. T^oC	550	550	463.0	423.0	383.0	343.0
50th Iter. x_3	0	0.409	0.418	0.405	0.397	0.393

It will be seen from Table 21 that x_3 has been slightly reduced, rather than increased. This is because the increased temperatures near the inlet of the reactor produce larger values of the rate constants. These lead to increased truncation errors in the integration process with fixed h. For constant truncation error it would be necessary to adjust h as the hill-climb proceeded. Limitations of fast storage (570 words) in the machine prevented this and sometimes (see below) led to complete breakdown of the procedure. The important points are that the method makes relatively large demands on fast storage, and that the slope of the "hill" in function space is small in the region covered by the Table.

An isothermal profile of 300°C was also tried as the initial guess with an ϵ of 0.2. There was virtually no progress after 100 iterations.

Now a series of tests with different values for t_f was undertaken. The first value chosen for the final time was $t_f = 0.5$, since some idea of the best profile in this case had been obtained from the parametric expansion methods. Table 22 gives a summary of the results of starting from what was considered a reasonable guess and using values of 0.1 and 0.2 for ϵ. The number of iterations was 50 in each case and good results were obtained.

TABLE 22

Time secs	Starting Temp.	Starting x_3	Final Temp. 50 iterations		Final x_3 50 iterations	
			$\epsilon = 0.1$	$\epsilon = 0.2$	$\epsilon = 0.1$	$\epsilon = 0.2$
0	550	0	550.0	550.0	0	0
0.025	542		550.0	550.0	0.036	0.036
0.05	534		550.0	550.0	0.116	0.116
0.075	526		550.0	550.0	0.189	0.199
0.10	518	0.236	525.2	532.4	0.264	0.265
0.125	510		512.6	515.0	0.309	0.312
0.150	502		503.1	504.0	0.342	0.344
0.175	494		494.5	494.9	0.365	0.368
0.200	489	0.367	489.2	489.4	0.383	0.385
0.225	482		482.1	482.2	0.396	0.397
0.250	475		475.1	475.1	0.405	0.406
0.275	468		468.0	468.1	0.412	0.413
0.300	461	0.409	461.0	461.0	0.417	0.418
0.325	454		454.0	454.0	0.421	0.421
0.350	447		447.0	447.0	0.427	0.424
0.375	440		440.0	440.0	0.425	0.425
0.400	433	0.422	433.0	433.0	0.426	0.427
0.425	426		426.0	426.0	0.427	0.427
0.450	419		419.0	419.0	0.428	0.428
0.475	412		412.0	412.0	0.428	0.428
0.500	405	0.426	405.0	405.0	0.429	0.429

Then a t_f of 2 secs was tried and this proved to be much more difficult because of the stringent limitation in the available fast storage. The first attempt was with an isothermal profile of 450°C and an ϵ of 0.1. The process broke down completely, and reducing ϵ to 0.001 was not much better. Even reducing ϵ to 0.0001 did not improve the situation as is apparent from Table 23. Comparison of the first iteration and starting values in Table 23 with profiles obtained earlier (e.g. Table 7) shows clearly that the direction of steepest ascent does not lead in the direction of the "summit". In fact the gradient method in no case succeeded in changing the temperatures towards the end of the reactor.

This is typical of all methods relying only on the gradient when there is a steep "ridge". Such methods are able to climb the side of the ridge, but not to make progress along its spine.

TABLE 23

$\epsilon = 0.0001$ $\qquad h = 0.1$ secs $\qquad t_f = 2.0$ secs

Time secs		0	0.4	0.8	1.2	1.6	2.0
Start	T^oC	450	450	450	450	450	450
	x_3	0	0.330	0.400	0.367	0.343	0.313
1st Iter.	T^oC	535.4	450.3	450.0	450.0	450.0	450.0
	x_3	0	0.429	0.425	0.390	0.355	0.323
2nd Iter.	T^oC	-2.2×10^5	450.3	450.0	450.0	450.0	450.0
	x_3	0	4.6×10^3	3.3×10^3	2.0×10^3	2.6×10^3	2.4×10^3

7. FIFTH METHOD OF SOLUTION: DYNAMIC PROGRAMMING

7.1 Discrete Methods

Consider an n-tank approximation to the continuous reactor, numbering the tanks backwards from last to first as in Figure 8.

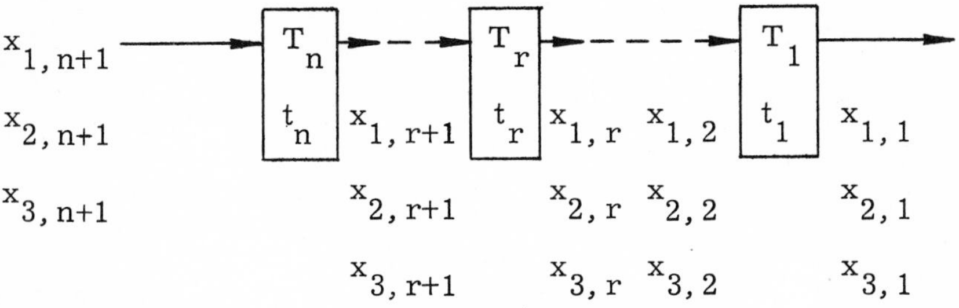

FIGURE 8

Then with the notation of Section 3, the mass balance for the rth tank gives

$$\left.\begin{aligned} x_{1,r}-x_{1,r+1} &= -(k_{1,r}+k_{2,r}+k_{3,r})x_{1,r}t_r \\ x_{2,r}-x_{2,r+1} &= (k_{1,r}x_{1,r}-k_{4,r}x_{2,r})\,t_r \\ x_{3,r}-x_{3,r+1} &= (k_{4,r}x_{2,r}-k_{5,r}x_{3,r})\,t_r \end{aligned}\right\} \quad (7.1)$$

The objective is to select the 2n variables T_r and t_r so as to maximize the quantity

$$Y_n = (x_{3,1} - x_{3,n+1}) \quad (7.2)$$

or

$$Y_n = \sum_{r=1}^{n} y_r = \sum_{r=1}^{n} (x_{3,r} - x_{3,r+1}) \quad (7.3)$$

Now let $f_n = \max Y_n$; then f_n is a function only of $\underline{x}_{n+1}$, the vector of the inlet concentration $(x_{1,n+1}, x_{2,n+1}, x_{3,n+1})$. By the "principle of optimality" (see Appendix 2) it follows that

$$\begin{aligned} f_n(\underline{x}_{n+1}) &= \max \{ y_n + f_{n-1}(\underline{x}_n) \} \\ &= \max \{ (x_{3,n} - x_{3,n+1}) + f_{n-1}(\underline{x}_n) \} \end{aligned} \quad (7.4)$$

where the maximization must now only be carried out with respect to T_n and t_n. Thus, the problem of maximization with respect to 2n variables simultaneously has been reduced to that of n maximizations with respect to two parameters.

There are now two methods of proceeding: one is the tabular method used by Aris [1961] and the other is an analytical method due to Pismen and Ioffe [1963]. Unfortunately the tabular method, for the problem discussed here, requires the tabulation of two variables for each tank. These are the ratios of the compositions and have a range from zero to infinity. The computing time would obviously be prohibitive and this method is therefore discussed no further.

It is of interest to remark, however, that for the problem discussed by Denbigh [1958] it is only necessary to tabulate with respect to a single variable. In a private communication, Westerterp has compared the dynamic programming solution with a solution based on direct hill-climbing [Storey, 1962] showing that the temperatures and yields agree closely but agreement between the residence times is not so good. Westerterp concludes that the series of stirred tanks is somewhat insensitive to variation of residence time: a conclusion borne out by the results of Section 3.

Returning to the analytical method, this proceeds in the following manner. Differentiating the expression in (7.4) with respect to t_n and T_n gives, for an internal maximum,

$$\sum_{i=1}^{3} \left\{ \delta_{i,3} + \frac{\partial f_{n-1}}{\partial x_{i,n}} \right\} \frac{\partial x_{i,n}}{\partial t_n} = 0 \tag{7.5}$$

$$\sum_{i=1}^{3} \left\{ \delta_{i,3} + \frac{\partial f_{n-1}}{\partial x_{i,n}} \right\} \frac{\partial x_{i,n}}{\partial T_n} = 0 \tag{7.6}$$

where δ is the Kronecker delta $\left(\text{i.e.}, \ \delta_{ij} = \begin{cases} 0, & i \neq j \\ 1, & i = j \end{cases}\right)$. But from Equations (7.1) by implicit differentiation

$$\frac{\partial x_{1,n}}{\partial t_n} = -(k_{1,n}+k_{2,n}+k_{3,n})x_{1,n} - (k_{1,n}+k_{2,n}+k_{3,n})t_n \frac{\partial x_{1,n}}{\partial t_n}$$

$$\frac{\partial x_{2,n}}{\partial t_n} = (k_{1,n}x_{1,n} - k_{4,n}x_{2,n}) + t_n k_{1,n} \frac{\partial x_{1,n}}{\partial t_n} - t_n k_{4,n} \frac{\partial x_{1,n}}{\partial t_n}$$

$$\frac{\partial x_{3,n}}{\partial t_n} = (k_{4,n}x_{2,n} - k_{5,n}x_{3,n}) + t_n k_{4,n} \frac{\partial x_{2,n}}{\partial t_n} - t_n k_{5,n} \frac{\partial x_{3,n}}{\partial t_n}$$

(7.7)

On rearranging, writing k for $k_1 + k_2 + k_3$, and denoting partial differentiation with respect to t_n by a prime, these equations become

$$x'_{1,n} = \frac{-k_n x_{1,n}}{1+t_n k_n}$$

(7.8)

$$x'_{2,n} = \frac{k_{1,n}x_{1,n} - k_{4,n}x_{2,n}}{1 + t_n k_{4,n}} - \frac{t_n k_{1,n} x'_{1,n}}{1 + t_n k_{4,n}}$$

$$x'_{3,n} = \frac{k_{4,n}x_{2,n} - k_{5,n}x_{3,n}}{1 + t_n k_{5,n}} + \frac{t_n k_{4,n} x'_{2,n}}{1 + t_n k_{5,n}} \tag{7.8 (cont.)}$$

Again, on implicit differentiation of (7.1) with respect to T_n and rearrangement, the following results are obtained:

$$x''_{1,n} = \frac{k''_n t_n x_{1,n}}{1+t_n k_n}$$

$$x''_{1,n} = \frac{t_n\left(k''_{1,n}x_{1,n} - k''_{4,n}\right)}{1+t_n k_{4,n}} + \frac{t_n k_{1,n} x''_{1,n}}{1+t_n k_{4,n}} \tag{7.9}$$

$$x''_{3,n} = \frac{t_n\left(k''_{4,n}x_{2,n} - k''_{5,n}x_{3,n}\right)}{1+t_n k_{5,n}} + \frac{t_n k_{4,n} x''_{2,n}}{1+t_n k_{5,n}}$$

where two primes denote partial differentiation with respect to T_n.

Now it is necessary to have a recurrence relationship for the partial derivatives of f_n. Thus,

$$\frac{\partial f_n}{\partial x_{j,n+1}} = \sum_{i=1}^{3}\left(\delta_{i,3} + \frac{\partial f_{n-1}}{\partial x_{i,n}}\right)\frac{\partial x_{i,n}}{\partial x_{j,n+1}} - \delta_{j,3} \tag{7.10}$$

and, on writing,

$$R_{j,n} = \delta_{j,3} + \frac{\partial f}{\partial x_{j,n+1}} \tag{7.11}$$

there follows

$$R_{j,n} = \sum_{i=1}^{3} R_{i,n-1}\frac{\partial x_{1,n}}{\partial x_{j,n+1}} \tag{7.12}$$

which is the required relationship.

Finally, the partial derivatives of the outlet concentration (of the nth tank) with respect to the inlet concentrations are required. By differentiation of the mass balance equations (7.1), and denoting partial differentiation with respect to $x_{j,n+1}$ by three primes, the following formulae are found.

$$
\begin{aligned}
x''_{1,n} &= \frac{\delta_{ij}}{1+t_n k_n} \\
x''_{2,n} &= \frac{\delta_{2,j}}{1+t_n k_{4,n}} + \frac{t_n k_{1,n} x_{1,n}}{1+t_n k_{4,n}} \\
x''_{3,n} &= \frac{\delta_{3,j}}{1+t_n k_{5,n}} + \frac{t_n k_{4,n} x_{2,n}}{1+t_n k_{5,n}}
\end{aligned}
\tag{7.13}
$$

It is now possible to proceed with the computation which is organized on the following lines. Guesses are made at the outlet concentrations $x_{1,1}$, $x_{2,1}$, $x_{3,1}$ and Equations (7.5) and (7.6) are solved for t_n and T_n using Equations (7.8) and (7.9). The starting values for the R are given by $R_{j,0} = \delta_{j,3}$, since $f_0 \equiv 0$ and $\partial f_0 / \partial x_{i,1} = 0$. The mass balance equations are now used to find the inlet concentrations for the last tank; the relation (7.12) and Equations (7.13) give new values for the R. The computation proceeds in this manner from the last tank to the first. The initial guesses at the outlet concentrations are then adjusted in some manner (e.g., by hill-climbing) until the correct values for the inlet concentrations $x_{1,n+1}$, $x_{2,n+1}$, $x_{3,n+1}$ are obtained.

The first difficulty that arose in actual computation was in solving the equations for t_n and T_n. First the Newton-Raphson technique was tried but this ran into trouble since the variables t_n, T_n could not easily be constrained. Consequently in the approach to a solution the contact time often went negative with drastic effects on the subsequent calculations. This method was therefore abandoned in favour of minimizing the sum of the squares of the left-hand sides of Equations (7.5) and (7.6) by hill-climbing (using Rosenbrock's method). It was then much easier to constrain t_n and T_n.

Further difficulty was then encountered, this time through the insensitivity of the solution to variations in t_n and T_n. Table 25 shows an attempt at solving the problem with eight tanks using what was thought to be a reasonable guess (taken from previous calculations) at the outlet concentrations. Only the results for the first 5 tanks are shown since one of the concentrations had gone negative by then.

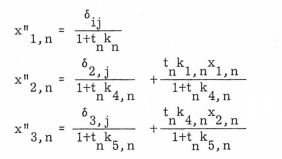

TABLE 25

TANK 1			TANK 2			TANK 3			TANK 4		
EXIT CONCENTRATIONS			EXIT CONCENTRATIONS			EXIT CONCENTRATIONS			EXIT CONCENTRATIONS		
x_1	x_2	x_3	x_1	x_2	x_3	x_1	x_2	x_3	x_1	x_2	x_3
0.011	0.0099	0.4343	0.012	0.024	0.041	0.019	0.195	0.257	0.029	0.323	0.130
No. of Trials	t_n (secs)	T_n (^{o}k)	No. of Trials	t_n (secs)	T_n (^{o}k)	No. of Trials	t_n (secs)	T_n (^{o}k)	No. of Trials	t_n (secs)	T_n (^{o}k)
0	121.0	407.0	0	28.0	435.0	0	0.13	681.0	0	0.10	703.0
53	127.6	373.1	58	116.7	430.1	63	0.13	685.4	51	0.10	707.2
105	127.7	373.0	110	123.4	428.8	102	0.13	683.2	100	0.10	707.2
150	138.4	373.1	152	146.9	424.7	153	0.14	678.2	152	"	"
205	149.1	373.1	199	150.9	424.3	201	0.16	673.9	198	"	"
255	150.0	"	253	150.0	"	247	0.17	670.5	253	"	"
304	"	"	299	"	"	305	0.18	667.3	298	"	"
352	"	"	349	"	"	352	0.18	666.8	355	"	"
400	"	"	400	"	"	400	0.20	661.8	400	0.10	707.2
INLET CONCENTRATIONS			INLET CONCENTRATIONS			INLET CONCENTRATIONS			INLET CONCENTRATIONS		
x_1	x_2	x_3	x_1	x_2	x_3	x_1	x_2	x_3	x_1	x_2	x_3
0.012	0.024	0.421	0.019	0.195	0.257	0.029	0.323	0.130	0.044	0.497	-0.049

For each tank the hill-climbing routine carried out 200 iterations in each of the two variables but it was almost impossible to tell whether convergence had taken place and even less possible to ensure convergence to the right root. Computer time for a single run for eight tanks was just over 30 minutes. Thus even if it could have been assumed that the correct roots had been obtained for each tank (in 200 iterations per variable per tank) any form of iteration on the outlet concentrations from the 1st tank would have been prohibitively time consuming on the computer.

For this particular problem, some alternative way of applying the dynamic programming method might perhaps have proved feasible. In general, however, the method does not look attractive for this type of problem

7.2 Continuous Methods

It is shown in Appendix 2 that in the continuous case the dynamic programming approach results in a partial differential equation. Because of the lack of success of applying the technique in the discrete case, no attempt was made to carry out calculations for the continuous case.

8. CONCLUSIONS

The broad conclusions to be drawn from this study are that the direct methods of stirred tank approximation and expansion of the temperature function are relatively trouble free and easy to use. They are, however, liable to use a lot of computer time. Convergence is less sure if the hill-climb is started close to the maximum, and it is always difficult to distinguish between convergence to the maximum and failure of the hill-climbing technique.

The gradient method in function space is fast and reliable when a good initial guess has been made at the profile. It is inefficient when the initial profile is far from the optimum. The final yield from the tube, in the problem studied, is insensitive to the profile for a good part of its length. Hence, different values of ϵ should be used for different parts of the tube. This brings the gradient method closer to such methods as Newton-Raphson.

Because of their contrasted properties, a combination of direct hill-climbing, followed by the gradient method in function space would seem to be attractive. Even better might be a direct hill-climb followed by an analogue in function space of the Newton-Raphson method.

Neither dynamic programming nor Pontryagin's maximum principle can compete with the other two methods for the problem studied.

APPENDIX I

THE TRAPEZOIDAL RULE FOR INTEGRATION

The trapezoidal rule applied to the general set of equations

$$\frac{dx_i}{dt} = \phi_i(x_i, t) \qquad i = 1, 2, \ldots, r \tag{1}$$

gives

$$x_{ir} - x_{i,r-1} = \frac{h}{2}\phi_{ir} + \frac{h}{2}\phi_{i,r-1} \tag{2}$$

where

$$t_r - t_{r-1} = h$$

With the kinetic equations of the problem discussed here

$$\phi_1 = -kx_1 \tag{3}$$

$$\phi_2 = k_1x_1 - k_4x_2 \tag{4}$$

$$\phi_3 = k_4x_2 - k_5x_3 \tag{5}$$

Writing Equation (2) in the form

$$x_{ir} - \frac{h}{2}\phi_{ir} = x_{i,r-1} + \frac{h}{2}\phi_{i,r-1} \tag{6}$$

and using (3) gives

$$x_{1r}(1 + \frac{h}{2}k_r) = x_{1,r-1}(1 - \frac{h}{2}k_{r-1})$$

or

$$x_{1r} = x_{1,r-1}\frac{1 - h/2\, k_{r-1}}{1 + h/2\, k_r} \tag{7}$$

In a similar manner,

$$x_{2r} - \frac{h}{2}k_{1r}x_{1r} + \frac{h}{2}k_{4r}x_{2r} = x_{2,r-1} + \frac{h}{2}k_{1,r-1}x_{1,r-1} - \frac{h}{2}k_{4,r-1}x_{2,r-1}$$

or

$$x_{2r} = x_{2,r-1}\cdot\frac{1-h/2\, k_{4,r-1}}{1+h/2\, k_{4,r}} + x_{1,r-1}\cdot\frac{h/2\, k_{1,r-1}}{1+h/2\, k_{4r}} + x_{1r}\frac{h/2\, k_{1r}}{1+h/2\, k_{4r}} \tag{8}$$

Finally,

$$x_{3r}-\frac{h}{2}k_{4r}x_{2r}+\frac{h}{2}k_{5r}x_{3r}=x_{3,r-1}+\frac{h}{2}k_{4,r-1}x_{2,r-1}-\frac{h}{2}k_{5,r-1}x_{3,r-1}$$

or

$$x_{3r}=x_{3,r-1}\frac{1-h/2\,k_{5,r-1}}{1+h/2\,k_{5r}}+x_{2,r-1}\frac{h/2\,k_{4,r-1}}{1+h/2\,k_{5r}}+x_{2r}\frac{h/2\,k_{4r}}{1+h/2\,k_{5r}} \tag{9}$$

Equations (7), (8) and (9) are Equations (4.1). The finite difference form of the adjoint equations can be obtained in exactly the same way.

APPENDIX 2

DESCRIPTION AND COMPARISON OF TECHNIQUES

The purpose of this Appendix is not to derive the analytical results used in the paper, but simply to describe them briefly, give references, and indicate their connections.

The hill-climbing method used in the paper [Rosenbrock, 1960] has no analytical basis, but was empirically derived. A function $F(\underset{\sim}{a})$ is to be maximized by adjusting the elements $a_1, a_2, \ldots, a_n$ of $\underset{\sim}{a}$, subject to constraints

$$g_i(\underset{\sim}{a}) \leq A_i(\underset{\sim}{a}) \leq h_i(\underset{\sim}{a}), \quad i=1,2,\ldots,\ell \tag{1}$$

where $\ell \geq n$. In the first n of these constraints, $A_i = a_i$. Some or all of the g and h may be constant.

The machine stores a set of n orthogonal unit vectors $\underset{\sim}{v}_1, \underset{\sim}{v}_2, \ldots, \underset{\sim}{v}_n$ and a set of n constants $e_1, e_2, \ldots, e_n$. Initially the vectors $\underset{\sim}{v}_i$ are parallel to the coordinate axes of the a_i, and the e_i are set at 0.1. The values of $F(\underset{\sim}{a})$ and $F(\underset{\sim}{a}+e_1\underset{\sim}{v}_1)$ are evaluated. If the second is greater (success), $\underset{\sim}{a}$ is replaced by $\underset{\sim}{a}+e_1\underset{\sim}{v}_1$ and then e_1 is replaced by $3e_1$; if less (failure), $\underset{\sim}{a}$ is left unchanged and e_1 is replaced by $-\frac{1}{2}e_1$. This procedure is then repeated in turn with $\underset{\sim}{v}_2, \underset{\sim}{v}_3, \ldots, \underset{\sim}{v}_n, \underset{\sim}{v}_1, \ldots$, until for each $\underset{\sim}{v}$ a success has been achieved, and subsequently a failure.

The axes $\underset{\sim}{v}$ are then rotated in the following way. The sum of all successful steps parallel to $\underset{\sim}{v}_i$ is denoted d_i, and the following sums are formed

$$\begin{aligned}
\underset{\sim}{\alpha}_1 &= d_1\underset{\sim}{v}_1 + d_2\underset{\sim}{v}_2 + \ldots + d_n\underset{\sim}{v}_n \\
\underset{\sim}{\alpha}_2 &= \qquad\quad d_2\underset{\sim}{v}_2 + \ldots + d_n\underset{\sim}{v}_n \\
&\ldots\ldots \\
\underset{\sim}{\alpha}_n &= \qquad\qquad\qquad\qquad d_n\underset{\sim}{v}_n
\end{aligned} \tag{2}$$

A new set of vectors $\underset{\sim}{v}$ is now formed by the Schmidt procedure

$$\left.\begin{aligned}
\underset{\sim}{\beta}_i &= \underset{\sim}{\alpha}_i - \sum_{j=1}^{i=1} (\underset{\sim}{\alpha}_j' \underset{\sim}{v}_j)\, \underset{\sim}{v}_j \\
\underset{\sim}{v}_i &= \underset{\sim}{\beta}_i / \|\underset{\sim}{\beta}_i\|
\end{aligned}\right\} \quad i=1,2,\ldots,n \tag{3}$$

This terminates a stage of the process. Subsequent stages follow the same course.

At the end of each stage the values of F, $\underset{\sim}{x}$, $\|\underset{\sim}{\alpha}_1\|$ and $\gamma = \|\underset{\sim}{\alpha}_2\| / \|\underset{\sim}{\alpha}_1\|$ are printed. The last two quantities give respectively the total progress during the stage, and a measure of the rotation of the axis $\underset{\sim}{v}_1$ at the end of the stage. If a sharp ridge is encountered, $\|\underset{\sim}{\alpha}_1\|$ may remain small for a number of steps, until the direction of the ridge has been accurately determined: during this time γ will remain small. The value of γ therefore assists in judging whether the hill-climb is still proceeding systematically, or whether the search has become random. If γ is regularly less than 0.3 it should be suspected that better results can still be achieved, even if $\|\underset{\sim}{\alpha}_1\|$ is small. This is illustrated in Table 3.

Constraints such as (1) are dealt with by replacing F, in a narrow belt near the boundary of the permitted region, by a modified function. Details of the modification (which greatly affect the success or otherwise of the procedure) are given in the original paper.

The hill-climbing method just described deals with a function F of a vector $\underset{\sim}{a}$ with n elements. In the usual formulation of the problem of optimal temperature profiles we have to deal with a functional F depending on a function u(t): in the paper F is $x_3(t_f)$ which depends on the temperature T(t) for $0 \leq t \leq t_f$. Formally the functional can be regarded as the limit of a function $F(\underset{\sim}{a})$ as the number of elements in $\underset{\sim}{a}$ tends to infinity. Moreover, since functions must be represented in a digital computer by a set of n points, the distinction is largely one of viewpoint.

Posing our problem now in a continuous form, we have a set of differential equations

$$\dot{\underset{\sim}{x}} = \underset{\sim}{f}\,(\underset{\sim}{x}, u); \ \underset{\sim}{x}(o) = \underset{\sim}{c} \tag{3}$$

where $\underset{\sim}{x}$ is an m-vector and we wish to choose u(t), $0 \leq t \leq T$, so that $F[\underset{\sim}{x}(T)]$ is a maximum.

The dynamic programming approach to this problem [Bellman, 1957] can be stated in the following way. Let $S(\underset{\sim}{x}, t)$ be the best value of $F[\underset{\sim}{x}(T)]$ attainable from the state $\underset{\sim}{x}$ at time t by suitable choice of $u(\tau)$, $t \leq \tau \leq T$. By the "principle of optimality", this choice of $u(\tau)$, $t \leq \tau \leq T$, is precisely the choice we should have to make in the original problem if, having used the optimal $u(\tau)$ for $0 \leq \tau \leq t$, we arrived at the state $\underset{\sim}{x}$. The principle is intuitively appealing, but conceals some difficulties [Jackson, 1963].

If the optimal u(t) is used at all times, S will remain constant on the solution $\underset{\sim}{x}(t)$. If a non-optimal u is used at any time t, we shall be able to reach only smaller values of F at subsequent times. Thus S must be decreasing when non-optimal u is used, is constant when the optimal u is used, and can never increase. Hence,

$$\max_u \frac{dS}{dt} = 0 \tag{4}$$

or

$$\max_u \left\{ \frac{\partial S}{\partial t} + \sum_{i=1}^{m} \frac{\partial S}{\partial x_i} f_i(\underset{\sim}{x}, t) \right\} = 0 \tag{5}$$

There is an equivalent development when the differential equations (3) are replaced by difference equations (compare Section 7).

The above analysis can be carried out in the same way if u is constrained to be within certain bounds, $a \leq u \leq b$. The only difference in the result is that the maximum in (5) is to be sought within the permitted range of u.

By a simple development [Pontryagin, 1962, pp. 69-73] Equation (5) can be shown to be equivalent to the equations

$$\left.\begin{aligned}
&\dot{x}_i = f_i(\underset{\sim}{x}, u); \quad x_i(o) = c_i \\
\frac{d}{dt}\left(\frac{\partial S}{\partial x_i}\right) = &\dot{\psi}_i = -\sum_{j=1}^{m} \frac{\partial f_j}{\partial x_i}\psi_j; \quad \psi_i(T) = \frac{\partial F}{\partial x_i(T)} \\
&H = \sum_{i=1}^{m} \psi_i f_i(\underset{\sim}{x}, u) \\
u: \quad &\max_{a \le u \le b} H
\end{aligned}\right\} \qquad (6)$$

The first of these equations is Equations (3). The second is the adjoint equations. The third defines H and the fourth shows that u is to be chosen at each t, so as to maximize H. It is assumed that bounds are placed on u as above.

Equation (6) can also be found, under less restrictive assumptions, by a slight extension of the classical calculus of variations [Pontryagin, 1962]. The variables ψ_i can be identified with the Lagrange multipliers in this approach.

Returning now to the analogy between the function u(t) and a vector $\underset{\sim}{a}$ with many elements, we note that one method of hill-climbing (though not a very powerful one) is the gradient method. In this the direction of steepest ascent of the function $F(\underset{\sim}{a})$ is evaluated from the formula

$$\ell_i = \frac{\partial F}{\partial a_i} \Bigg/ \sqrt{\left\{\sum_{i=1}^{n}\left(\frac{\partial F}{\partial a_i}\right)^2\right\}} \qquad (7)$$

Here $\underset{\sim}{\ell}$ is a unit vector normal to the contour surfaces of F. The value of $\underset{\sim}{a}$ is then replaced by $\underset{\sim}{a} + \epsilon\underset{\sim}{\ell}$, and if ϵ is sufficiently small we shall have $F(\underset{\sim}{a} + \epsilon\underset{\sim}{\ell}) > F(\underset{\sim}{a})$ provided that $\partial F/\partial a_i \neq 0$.

It is natural to ask whether there is an analogous procedure for finding the function u(t) which maximizes a functional F[u(t)]. The gradient of F, by analogy, should be a function $\ell(t)$. Such a development has in fact been made by Horn [1960], Kelley [1962] and Bryson [1962] (compare also Courant [1953, pp. 222-224]).

The chief difficulty in the development is that F[u(t)] is defined indirectly by the differential equations (3). To overcome this difficulty the adjoint equations are again introduced, and it is found that

$$\ell(t) = \frac{\partial H}{\partial u} \Bigg/ \sqrt{\left\{ \int_0^T \left(\frac{\partial H}{\partial u}\right)^2 dt \right\}} \tag{8}$$

where H is defined in terms of $\underset{\sim}{\psi}$ and $\underset{\sim}{\dot{x}}$ by Equations (6).

The procedure is then, as described in the paper, to guess a function u(t), which will be non-optimal. The values of $\underset{\sim}{x}$ are then computed from 0 to T (which is the stable direction), and stored. Using the stored $\underset{\sim}{x}(t)$, $\underset{\sim}{\psi}$ can be computed from T back to 0 (again the stable direction), and $\partial H/\partial u$ can be formed at the same time. Then $u(t) + \epsilon\, \partial H/\partial u$ will improve the value of F if ϵ is sufficiently small. (The normalizing factor in (8) is generally absorbed into ϵ.)

This method, as Horn has remarked, uses an inefficient hill-climbing method, but nevertheless may perform well because the gradient is obtained with so little work. Horn [1963] has given a method for improving the performance of the hill-climbing process: the value of ϵ is no longer kept constant but is allowed to vary with t.

REFERENCES

R. Aris, The Optimal Design of Chemical Reactors (Academic Press), 1961.

R. Bellman, Dynamic Programming (Princeton University Press), 1957.

A.E. Bryson and W.F. Denham, "A Steepest-Ascent Method for Solving Optimum Programming Problems", J. Applied Mechanics, Trans. A.S.M.E., Series E, 29, pp. 247-257, 1962.

R. Courant and D. Hilbert, Methods of Mathematical Physics, Vol. 1 (Interscience), 1953.

K.G. Denbigh, "Optimum Temperature Sequences in Reactors", Chem. Eng. Sci., 8, pp. 125-131, 1958.

F. Horn, "Uber den Optimalen Temperaturverlauf in Reaktionsrohr", Chemie-Ingenieur-Technik, 32, pp. 382-293, 1960.

F. Horn, Uber das Problem der Optimalen Rührkesselkaskade für Chemische Reaktionen, Chem. Eng. Sci., 15, pp. 176-187, 1961.

F. Horn and U. Troltenier, "Zur Berechnung von Rührkesselnkaskaden mit Hilfe eines programmgesteuerten Rechenautomaten", Chemie-Ingenieur-Technik, 35, pp. 11-18, 1963.

R. Jackson, "Comments on the paper 'Optimum Cross-current Extraction with Product Recycle'", Chem. Eng. Sci., 18, pp. 215-217, 1963.

Kelley, in Optimization Techniques, ed. G. Leitmann, pp. 206-254 (Academic Press), 1962.

L.M. Pismen and I.I. Ioffe, "Calculation of the Optimal Process in Chemical Reactors by the Method of Dynamic Programming", Int. Chem. Eng., 3, pp. 24-32, 1963.

L.S. Pontryagin, V.G. Boltyanskii, R.V. Gamkrelidze and E.F. Mishchenko, The Mathematical Theory of Optimal Processes (Interscience), 1962.

H. H. Rosenbrock, "An Automatic Method for Finding the Greatest or Least Value of a Function", Computer Journal, 3, pp. 175-184, 1960.

C. Storey, "Applications of a Hill-Climbing Method of Optimization", Chem. Eng. Sci., 17, pp. 45-52, 1962.

SEVERAL TRAJECTORY OPTIMIZATION TECHNIQUES

Part I: Discussion

R. E. Kopp

R. McGill

Research Department
Grumman Aircraft Engineering Corporation
Bethpage, New York

Abstract

This paper discusses several numerical approaches for solving problems arising in optimizing trajectories. The basic concepts underlying the gradient method, the second variation method, and a generalized Newton-Raphson method are presented in a very elementary manner by considering an ordinary minimum problem with a side constraint. The results obtained when the basic concepts are extended to the variational problem and the computational algorithms are then discussed. Finally, in the concluding remarks, advantages and disadvantages of each method are reviewed, and a comparison is made between the second variation method, which might be considered a direct method, and the generalized Newton-Raphson method, normally considered as an indirect method. Part II of this paper provides an application of the three methods to a specific problem.

Introduction

The numerical methods for the solution of optimization problems have in the past taken two primary directions: the direct approach and the indirect approach. In the direct approach, which is usually associated with a steep descent technique, the constraining system differential equations are satisfied and an iteration made on the control signals such that each new iterate improves the function to be minimized. The indirect approach involves the development of an iterative technique for the solution of the system and Euler-Lagrange differential equations. Advantages usually associated with the steep descent techniques are that convergence does not depend upon the availability of a good initial estimate of the optimal trajectory as a starting point, and that the techniques seek out relative minima rather than merely functionals which are stationary. The main disadvantage associated with the steep descent techniques is that in many practical applications convergence slows as the optimum trajectory is approached. In contrast, the indirect methods usually exhibit good convergence as the optimal trajectory is approached if the method converges at all. However, a good initial estimate of the optimal trajectory may be needed to ensure convergence.

Part I of this paper presents a brief review of the first and second variation theory as associated with the steep descent methods. This is followed by a discussion of a generalized Newton-Raphson method as applied to the solution of the system and Euler-Lagrange equations. Finally, a comparison between the second variation method and the generalized Newton-Raphson method is made which suggests that the second variation method is equivalent to a special case of the generalized Newton-Raphson method.

Both the steep descent methods and the generalized Newton-Raphson method have been discussed in detail by the authors and others in previous papers, see (1) through (8). Here, the purpose is to review basic concepts. This can best be accomplished by considering an ordinary minimum problem with a single side constraint and then presenting the results derived in the above references when the theory is extended to the variational case.

Part II of this paper discusses the actual computational procedures using the gradient method, second variation method, and the generalized Newton-Raphson method to solve a specific problem.

Problem Formulation

The usual Mayer formulation is employed for the variational problem. Given a system of first order differential equations

$$\dot{x}_i = f_i(x_1, \ldots, x_n, y_1, \ldots, y_\ell, t) \tag{1}$$

find a solution of this system of equations which satisfies certain specified initial and terminal conditions and minimizes P, a function of the final unspecified terminal conditions and the terminal time.

$$P = P[x_{m+1_f}, \ldots, x_{n_f}, t_f] \tag{2}$$

The x variables are referred to as the state variables and the y variables as the control variables. Both the state and control variables may be subject to constraints; however, in this discussion we will deal primarily, though not exclusively, with the case where such constraints are absent.

It will be assumed for convenience that initial values of x_i are fixed at t_0

$$x_i(t_0) = \tilde{x}_{i_0} \quad , \quad i = 1, \ldots, n \tag{3}$$

as well as the first m of the terminal values

$$x_i(t_f) = \tilde{x}_{i_f} \quad , \quad i = 1, \ldots, m \tag{4}$$

The final time t_f may or may not be specified. In the gradient method it will be convenient to reformulate the problem such that all of the final state variables are open. This is done by employing a penalty function approximation:

$$P'(x_{1_f}, \ldots, x_{n_f}, t_f) = P(x_{m+1_f}, \ldots, x_{n_f}, t_f) + \frac{1}{2} \sum_{j=1}^{m} K_j^2 (x_{j_f} - \tilde{x}_{j_f})^2 \tag{5}$$

A minimum of P' is now sought without requiring the terminal values of the first m state variables to satisfy Eq. (4) exactly but rather paying a "penalty" for deviations. As the K_j becomes large the trajectory which minimizes P' is in some sense close to the trajectory which minimizes P with the final values of the first m state variables specified.

At this point it is advisable to digress from the variational problem and examine an ordinary minimum problem with a subsidiary constraint. Let us consider the problem of minimizing a function of two variables constrained such that a second function of the variables is equal to zero.

$$\text{Min } f(x_1, x_2) \quad \text{subject to} \quad g(x_1,x_2) = 0 \tag{6}$$

We further assume that both f and g and their first and second partial derivatives exist for all finite values of x_1 and x_2. Expanding both f and g in a Taylor series and retaining all terms up to and including second order gives:

$$f(x_1, x_2) = \bar{f}(\bar{x}_1, \bar{x}_2) + \bar{f}_{x_1}\Delta x_1 + \bar{f}_{x_2}\Delta x_2 + \tfrac{1}{2}\bar{f}_{x_1x_1}\Delta x_1^2 + \bar{f}_{x_1x_2}\Delta x_1\Delta x_2 + \tfrac{1}{2}\bar{f}_{x_2x_2}\Delta x_2^2 \tag{7a}$$

$$g(x_1, x_2) = \bar{g}(\bar{x}_1, \bar{x}_2) + \bar{g}_{x_1}\Delta x_1 + \bar{g}_{x_2}\Delta x_2 + \tfrac{1}{2}\bar{g}_{x_1x_1}\Delta x_1^2 + \bar{g}_{x_1x_2}\Delta x_1\Delta x_2 + \tfrac{1}{2}\bar{g}_{x_2x_2}\Delta x_2^2 = 0 \tag{7b}$$

where the barred functions are evaluated at a specific value of x_1 and x_2. We choose $\bar{x}_1$ and $\bar{x}_2$ such that the constraint $\bar{g}(\bar{x}_1, \bar{x}_2) = 0$ is satisfied and solve for Δx_1 in terms of Δx_2 retaining first and second order terms.

$$\Delta x_1 = -\frac{1}{\bar{g}_{x_1}}\left[\bar{g}_{x_2}\Delta x_2 + \tfrac{1}{2}\bar{g}_{x_1x_1}\left(-\frac{\bar{g}_{x_2}}{\bar{g}_{x_1}}\right)^2\Delta x_2^2 + \bar{g}_{x_1x_2}\left(-\frac{\bar{g}_{x_2}}{\bar{g}_{x_1}}\right)\Delta x_2^2 + \tfrac{1}{2}\bar{g}_{x_2x_2}\Delta x_2^2\right] \tag{8}$$

It is tacitly assumed that $\bar{g}_{x_1} \neq 0$. An expression for the change in f is then obtained by substituting Eq. (8) into Eq. (7a).

$$
\begin{aligned}
f(x_1, x_2) - \bar{f}(\bar{x}_1, \bar{x}_2) &= \left(\bar{f}_{x_2} - \frac{\bar{f}_{x_1}}{\bar{g}_{x_1}} \bar{g}_{x_2}\right) \Delta x_2 \\
&+ \tfrac{1}{2}\left(\bar{f}_{x_1x_1} - \frac{\bar{f}_{x_1}}{\bar{g}_{x_1}} \bar{g}_{x_1x_1}\right) \frac{\bar{g}^2_{x_2}}{\bar{g}^2_{x_1}} \Delta x_2^2 \\
&- \left(\bar{f}_{x_1x_2} - \frac{\bar{f}_{x_1}}{\bar{g}_{x_1}} \bar{g}_{x_1x_2}\right) \frac{\bar{g}_{x_2}}{\bar{g}_{x_1}} \Delta x_2^2 \\
&+ \tfrac{1}{2}\left(\bar{f}_{x_2x_2} - \frac{\bar{f}_{x_1}}{\bar{g}_{x_1}} \bar{g}_{x_2x_2}\right) \Delta x_2^2
\end{aligned}
\tag{9}
$$

Therefore, sufficient conditions for $\bar{f}(\bar{x}_1, \bar{x}_2)$ to be a minimum of $f(x_1, x_2)$ subject to $g(x_1, x_2)$ equal to zero are

(i) $$\bar{f}_{x_2} - \frac{\bar{f}_{x_1}}{\bar{g}_{x_1}} \bar{g}_{x_2} = 0 \quad , \quad \bar{g}_{x_1} \neq 0$$

(ii) $$
\begin{aligned}
&\tfrac{1}{2}\left(\bar{f}_{x_1x_1} - \frac{\bar{f}_{x_1}}{\bar{g}_{x_1}} \bar{g}_{x_1x_1}\right) \frac{\bar{g}^2_{x_2}}{\bar{g}^2_{x_1}} - \left(\bar{f}_{x_1x_2} - \frac{\bar{f}_{x_1}}{\bar{g}_{x_1}} \bar{g}_{x_1x_2}\right) \frac{\bar{g}_{x_2}}{\bar{g}_{x_1}} \\
&+ \tfrac{1}{2}\left(\bar{f}_{x_2x_2} - \frac{\bar{f}_{x_1}}{\bar{g}_{x_1}} \bar{g}_{x_2x_2}\right) > 0
\end{aligned}
\tag{10}
$$

Of course the conditions are symmetric with x_1 replaced with x_2 and x_2 replaced with x_1.

In the classical theory, the constraint $g(x_1, x_2) = 0$ is adjoined to $f(x_1, x_2)$ by means of a Lagrange multiplier

$$S(x_1, x_2, \lambda) = f(x_1, x_2) + \lambda g(x_1, x_2) \tag{11}$$

and S is expanded in the neighborhood of some point $\bar{x}_1$, $\bar{x}_2$, and $\bar{\lambda}$ considering all variables to have independent variations.

$$\begin{aligned} S(x_1, x_2, \lambda) &= \bar{S}(\bar{x}_1, \bar{x}_2, \bar{\lambda}) + \bar{S}_{x_1}\Delta x_1 + \bar{S}_{x_2}\Delta x_2 + \bar{g}\Delta\lambda \\ &+ \tfrac{1}{2}\bar{S}_{x_1x_1}\Delta x_1^2 + \bar{S}_{x_1x_2}\Delta x_1\Delta x_2 + \tfrac{1}{2}\bar{S}_{x_2x_2}\Delta x_2^2 \\ &+ (\bar{g}_{x_1}\Delta x_1 + \bar{g}_{x_2}\Delta x_2)\Delta\lambda \end{aligned} \tag{12}$$

Sufficient conditions for $\bar{S}(\bar{x}_1, \bar{x}_2, \bar{\lambda})$ to be a minimum of $S(x_1, x_2, \lambda)$ subject to $g(x_1, x_2)$ equal to zero are

$$\begin{aligned} &\text{(i)} && \bar{S}_{x_1} = \bar{f}_{x_1} + \bar{\lambda}\bar{g}_{x_1} = 0 \\ &\text{(ii)} && \bar{S}_{x_2} = \bar{f}_{x_2} + \bar{\lambda}\bar{g}_{x_2} = 0 \\ &\text{(iii)} && \bar{g}_{x_1}\Delta x_1 + \bar{g}_{x_2}\Delta x_2 = 0 \\ &\text{(iv)} && \tfrac{1}{2}\left(\bar{f}_{x_1x_1} + \bar{\lambda}\bar{g}_{x_1x_1}\right)\Delta x_1^2 + \left(\bar{f}_{x_1x_2} + \bar{\lambda}\bar{g}_{x_1x_2}\right)\Delta x_1\Delta x_2 \\ &&& + \tfrac{1}{2}\left(\bar{f}_{x_2x_2} + \bar{\lambda}\bar{g}_{x_2x_2}\right)\Delta x_2^2 > 0 \end{aligned} \tag{13}$$

These conditions are exactly equivalent to the sufficient conditions given in Eqs. (10i) and (10ii). Furthermore, it should be emphasized that S is merely stationary with respect to x_1, x_2, and λ and a minimum only when $g(x_1, x_2)$ is constrained to be equal to zero.

Gradient Techniques

The basis of the steep descent or gradient techniques is to search out the stationary value of S by an effective numerical iteration method. To complete the analogy between the ordinary minimum problem and the Mayer formulation of the variational problem either x_1 or x_2 is chosen as a control variable. Although Eq. (12) was used to determine the sufficient conditions for $\bar{f}(\bar{x}_1, \bar{x}_2)$ to be a minimum with $\bar{g}(\bar{x}_1, \bar{x}_2) = 0$, the expansion is valid for any value $\bar{x}_1$, $\bar{x}_2$, and $\bar{\lambda}$ and need not be at a stationary point of S.

In the gradient method initial estimates of x_1, x_2, and λ would be made that satisfy $g(x_1, x_2) = 0$ and Δx_1, Δx_2, and $\Delta\lambda$ determined from first order terms in Eq. (12) such that ΔS would decrease. Although usually one would not likely use a gradient method to solve an ordinary minimum problem of the type discussed, we will indicate how the computational algorithm might proceed so that we may see the analogy with the variational problem.

Let us assume that x_2 plays the role of the control variable. An initial guess is chosen for x_1, x_2, and λ such that $g(x_1, x_2) = 0$ and $S_{x_1} = 0$. This guess will be designated by the barred quantities in Eq. (12). We can then be sure that ΔS is negative if Δx_2 and $\bar{S}_{x_2}$ are of opposite sign.

$$\Delta S = S(x_1, x_2, \lambda) - \bar{S}(\bar{x}_1, \bar{x}_2, \bar{\lambda}) = \bar{S}_{x_2} \Delta x_2 \tag{14}$$

However, the magnitude of Δx_2 must be small enough to assure that the first order theory is valid. One could view the problem as one of minimizing ΔS subject to a constraint on the magnitude of Δx_2 if the constraint were known.

$$S' = \Delta S + \gamma(\Delta x_2^2 - K^2) = \bar{S}_{x_2} \Delta x_2 + \gamma(\Delta x_2^2 - K^2) \tag{15}$$

Here, γ acts as another Lagrange multiplier for a constrained auxiliary minimum problem. Solving for the stationary values of S' gives

$$\Delta x_2 = - \frac{\bar{S}_{x_2}}{2\gamma} \tag{16}$$

The magnitude of Δx_2 is still not determined, for γ is unspecified. A one dimensional search is normally made varying γ and calculating $S(x_1, x_2)$. In this simple problem one could just as well have performed the one dimensional search directly on Δx_2, however, in an n dimensional problem Eqs. (15) and (16) become

$$S' = \sum_{i=2}^{n} S_{x_i} \Delta x_i + \gamma \left(\sum_{i=2}^{n} \Delta x_i^2 - K^2 \right) \tag{17}$$

$$\Delta x_i = - \frac{\bar{S}_{x_i}}{2\gamma} \quad , \quad i = 2, \ldots, n \tag{18}$$

For the n dimensional problem we can appreciate how the gradient method received its name. If we consider the x_i, $i = 2, \ldots, n$ components of an $n-1$ vector, the $\vec{\Delta x}$ vector is in the negative gradient direction of S.

These concepts as applied to the variational problem have been discussed in detail in (1) through (4), and therefore, only the results are summarized here. The Lagrange multipliers become functions of time which obey the system of differential equations

$$\dot{\lambda}_i = - \sum_{j=1}^{n} \lambda_j \frac{\partial f_j}{\partial x_i} \quad , \quad \lambda_i(\bar{t}_f) = \frac{\partial P'}{\partial x_i} \quad , \quad i = 1, \ldots, n \tag{19}$$

For convenience the function $H(\vec{x}, \vec{\lambda}, \vec{y}, t)$ is defined:

$$H(\vec{x}, \vec{\lambda}, \vec{y}, t) = \sum_{i=1}^{n} \lambda_i f_i(\vec{x}, \vec{y}, t) \tag{20}$$

where

$$\vec{x}^T \equiv x_1, \ldots, x_n$$
$$\vec{\lambda}^T \equiv \lambda_1, \ldots, \lambda_n \qquad (21)$$
$$\vec{y}^T \equiv y_1, \ldots, y_\ell$$

The superscript denotes the transpose of the vector. Equations (1) and (19) can then be put in a canonical form:

$$\dot{x}_i = \frac{\partial H}{\partial \lambda_i}, \quad x_i(t_0) = \tilde{x}_{i_0}$$
$$\dot{\lambda}_i = -\frac{\partial H}{\partial x_i}, \quad \lambda_i(t_f) = \frac{\partial P'}{\partial x_i} \qquad (22)$$

From first order theory we may write an equation for $P'(\vec{x}_f, t_f)$

$$P'(\vec{x}_f, t_f) = \bar{P}'(\vec{\bar{x}}_f, \bar{t}_f) + \int_{t_0}^{t_f} \frac{\partial H}{\partial y_k} \delta y_k \, dt$$
$$+ \left[\frac{\partial \bar{P}'}{\partial x_{i_f}} \bar{f}_i(\vec{\bar{x}}, \vec{\bar{y}}, \bar{t}_f) + \frac{\partial \bar{P}'}{\partial t_f} \right] \delta t_f \qquad (23)$$

Necessary conditions for $\bar{x}(t)$ to be an optimum trajectory and $\bar{y}(t)$ the optimum control are

$$\frac{\partial \bar{H}}{\partial y_k} = 0 \qquad (24)$$

and if final time is open

$$\left.\frac{d\bar{P}'}{dt}\right|_{t=\bar{t}_f} = \frac{\partial \bar{P}'}{\partial x_{i_f}} \bar{f}_i(\vec{\bar{x}}, \vec{\bar{y}}, \bar{t}_f) + \frac{\partial \bar{P}'}{\partial t_f} = 0 \qquad (25)$$

In addition, of course, $\bar{x}$ and $\bar{\lambda}$ must satisfy Eq. (22).

As in the case of the ordinary minimum problem the barred variables in Eq. (22) need not be optimum trajectories. Therefore if $\vec{\bar{x}}$ is a nonoptimum trajectory, the gradient method provides an effective numerical iteration technique for choosing a $\vec{\delta y}$ vector to decrease the value of $P'(\vec{x}_f, t_f)$. Just as in the ordinary minimum problem we now consider an auxiliary minimum problem with a constraint on $\vec{\delta y}$ adjoined to ensure that the first order theory remains valid

$$\Delta P^{*'} = P'(\vec{x}_f, t_f) - P'(\vec{\bar{x}}_f, \bar{t}_f) + \sum_{k=1}^{\ell} \gamma_k \left\{ \int_{t_0}^{\bar{t}_f} w_k(t)\, \delta y_k^2 \, dt - a_k^2 \right\} \tag{26}$$

where $w_k(t)$ is a weighting function which in many cases is given the value of unity. A constraint could also be imposed on δt_f; however, in practice the determination of δt_f can best be accomplished in a different manner which will be explained when the actual computational procedure is discussed. The solution of the auxiliary minimum problem leads to an equation for $\vec{\delta y}$ as a function of time

$$\delta y_k = - \frac{1}{c_k w_k(t)} \frac{\partial \bar{H}}{\partial y_k} \tag{27}$$

As in the ordinary minimum problem the undetermined constants c_k appear and are found by an independent search procedure. For example, if there is only one control variable, P' would be calculated for several values of c and then a polynomial fit made to determine the value of c which gives the least value to P'.

The actual computer algorithm might proceed as follows:

1. Select an initial control time history as a first estimate and numerically integrate the system equations (1).

2. Terminate the trajectory calculations at the time t_f determined when P' reaches a minimum.
3. Integrate the adjoint system backwards using terminal values determined by $\lambda_i(\bar{t}_f) = \frac{\partial P'}{\partial x_{i_f}}$.

   During the backwards integration calculate $\delta y_k(t) = - \frac{1}{c_k w_k(t)} \frac{\partial H}{\partial y_k}$.
4. Integrate the system equations forward with $y_k = \bar{y}_k + \delta y_k$ for several values of c_k and evaluate $P'(\vec{x}_f, t_f)$ again terminating the trajectory when $\frac{dP'}{dt_f} = 0$.
5. Using a curve fitting technique find the best values for c_k and use this value to determine the next estimate for y_k: $y_k = \bar{y}_k + \delta y_k$. Return to step 1 and repeat.

This procedure has proved quite successful in the past. Several variations of the method are also used extensively. If constraints are imposed on the control variables a more general expression derived from the Pontryagin Maximum Principle, (9) and (10), is used for P' in place of Eq. (23).

$$P'(\vec{x}_f, t_f) = \bar{P}'(\vec{\bar{x}}_f, \bar{t}_f)$$

$$+ \int_{t_0}^{t_f} \left\{ H(\vec{\bar{x}}, \vec{\bar{\lambda}}, \vec{\bar{y}} + \vec{\delta y}, t) - H(\vec{\bar{x}}, \vec{\bar{\lambda}}, \vec{\bar{y}}, t) \right\} dt$$

$$+ \left\{ \bar{H}(\vec{\bar{x}}_f, \vec{\bar{\lambda}}_f, \vec{\bar{y}}_f, \bar{t}_f) + \frac{\partial \bar{P}'}{\partial t} \right\} \delta t_f \qquad (28)$$

Equation (27) is then replaced with the criterion that $H(\vec{\bar{x}}, \vec{\bar{\lambda}}, \vec{\bar{y}} + \vec{\delta y}, t) + \sum_{k=1}^{\ell} \gamma_k \delta y_k^2$ be a minimum within the admissible range of the control variables.

Although a quadratic constraint was used to assure that the new trajectory was neighboring to the estimated trajectory, many other constraints could also be used. One that is particularly useful when the optimum control is "bang-bang" or on-off is an integral absolute value constraint. In this case Eq. (27) is replaced with the criterion that $H(\vec{\bar{x}}, \vec{\bar{\lambda}}, \vec{\bar{y}} + \delta\vec{y}, t) + \sum_{k=1}^{\ell} \gamma_k |\delta y_k|$ be a minimum while satisfying the constraints on the control variables, $\vec{y} = \vec{\bar{y}} + \delta\vec{\bar{y}}$. It is easily seen that when the control variable δy_k appears linearly in H that every intermediate control estimate will be "bang-bang" or on-off. (The singular case is excluded where the coefficient y_k in H is identically zero over a finite interval of time.) The constants γ_k are determined by an independent search as before.

Another variation of the gradient method is discussed in (3) and referred to as the Min H method. Here $H(\vec{\bar{x}}, \vec{\bar{\lambda}}, \vec{\bar{y}} + \delta\vec{y}, t)$ is minimized by the choice of $\delta\vec{y}$ satisfying any constraints that might be imposed on $\vec{y}$. In place of the rather arbitrary absolute value and quadratic metrics previously used to ensure neighboring trajectories we set

$$y_k = \bar{y}_k + \alpha_k \delta y_k \tag{29}$$

and an independent search is made as before to determine α_k.

When constraints on the state variables are present some success has been experienced (11) when additional penalty function terms are added to the function to be minimized:

$$P'' = P' + \sum \beta_j \int_{t_0}^{t_f} U_{-1}[g_j(\vec{x}, t)]dt \tag{30}$$

where U_{-1} is the Heaviside step function and $g_j(\vec{x}, t) \leq 0$ the state constraints. The constants β_j are allowed to approach infinity as in the case when penalty function terms are used in place of satisfying terminal end conditions.

The principal advantage of the gradient method is that convergence is not contingent upon a good initial estimate of the trajectory. One is assured that the value of the function to be minimized is decreased in each succeeding iteration. There are three principal disadvantages of the method. First, the convergence, although usually relatively good in the beginning of the iterative sequence, often deteriorates severely as the optimum trajectory is approached. Second, the penalty function method required to solve problems with specified terminal conditions introduces arbitrary constants which are required to be "large" (certainly a relative measure) at least for the final iteration. If the constants are chosen too large at any point in the iteration cycle, the new control will tend to improve the specified terminal values without much weight being placed on improving the actual function to be minimized. If the constants are too small the specified terminal values will not be satisfied. Thus in practice, the success of the method depends to an appreciable extent upon past experience in making proper choices for the arbitrary constants associated with the penalty function terms. Third, regions of severe irregularity sometimes develop in the control variable functions. In extreme cases these are never smoothed out.

Second Variation Method

A natural extension of the gradient techniques which come from first order theory is a theory which would include second order terms in the expression for the function to be minimized. Let us return to the ordinary minimum problem and the expression for $S(x_1, x_2, \lambda)$ given in Eq. (12). Assuming, as before, that $\bar{x}_1$ and $\bar{x}_2$ satisfy $\bar{g} = 0$ we treat the auxiliary problem of finding the stationary value of S considering Δx_1, Δx_2, and $\Delta\lambda$ as independent variables:

$$\begin{aligned}
\bar{S}_{x_1} + \bar{S}_{x_1x_1}\Delta x_1 + \bar{S}_{x_1x_2}\Delta x_2 + \bar{g}_{x_1}\Delta\lambda &= 0 \\
\bar{S}_{x_2} + \bar{S}_{x_1x_2}\Delta x_1 + \bar{S}_{x_2x_2}\Delta x_2 + \bar{g}_{x_2}\Delta\lambda &= 0 \qquad (31) \\
\bar{g}_{x_1}\Delta x_1 + \bar{g}_{x_2}\Delta x_2 &= 0
\end{aligned}$$

One could also view the problem as that of finding the minimum of $S(x_1, x_2, \lambda)$ considering λ fixed and a constraint adjoined which requires $\bar{g}_{x_1} \Delta x_1 + \bar{g}_{x_2} \Delta x_2 = 0$. In this case the $\Delta\lambda$ would be viewed as another Lagrange multiplier. A step size constraint may also be required as in the first order theory to ensure that the second order theory is valid. Then in Eq. (31)

$$\begin{aligned} \bar{S}_{x_1x_1} &\rightarrow \bar{S}_{x_1x_1} + \gamma \\ \bar{S}_{x_2x_2} &\rightarrow \bar{S}_{x_2x_2} + \gamma \end{aligned} \tag{32}$$

It should be noted that Eq. (31) is a linearization of Eqs. (13i) and (13ii) and the constraint equation $g(x_1, x_2) = 0$.

In the variational problem we will first consider the case for which the penalty function technique is used in place of satisfying terminal conditions exactly. The penalty function terms will then be removed and the terminal conditions satisfied exactly. The actual derivation of the equations is quite involved and therefore we summarize the results derived in (5).

$$\delta\dot{x}_i = \sum_{j=1}^{n} \frac{\partial^2\bar{H}}{\partial\lambda_i\partial x_j}\,\delta x_j + \sum_{k=1}^{\ell} \frac{\partial^2\bar{H}}{\partial\lambda_i\partial y_k}\,\delta y_k \quad , \tag{33a}$$

$$\delta x_i(0) = 0$$

$$\delta\dot{\lambda}_i = -\sum_{j=1}^{n} \frac{\partial^2\bar{H}}{\partial x_i\partial x_j}\,\delta x_j - \sum_{k=1}^{\ell} \frac{\partial^2\bar{H}}{\partial x_i\partial y_k}\,\delta y_k$$

$$- \sum_{j=1}^{n} \frac{\partial^2\bar{H}}{\partial x_i\partial\lambda_j}\,\delta\lambda_j \tag{33b}$$

$$\Delta\lambda_i(\bar{t}_f) = \sum_{j=1}^{n} \frac{\partial^2 \bar{P}'}{\partial x_{j_f} \partial x_{i_f}} \Delta x_j(\bar{t}_f) + \frac{\partial^2 \bar{P}'_i}{\partial t_f \partial x_{i_f}} \delta t_f \tag{33c}$$

$$\Delta x_i(\bar{t}_f) = \delta x_i(\bar{t}_f) + \dot{\bar{x}}_i(t_f)\,\delta t_f \tag{33d}$$

$$\Delta\lambda_i(\bar{t}_f) = \delta\lambda_i(\bar{t}_f) + \dot{\bar{\lambda}}_i(t_f)\,\delta t_f \qquad i = 1, \ldots, n \tag{33e}$$

$$\frac{\partial \bar{H}}{\partial y_k} + \sum_{j=1}^{n} \frac{\partial^2 \bar{H}}{\partial y_k \partial x_j} \delta x_j + \sum_{j=1}^{n} \frac{\partial^2 \bar{H}}{\partial y_k \partial \lambda_j} \delta\lambda_j + \sum_{s=1}^{\ell} \frac{\partial^2 \bar{H}}{\partial y_k \partial y_s} \delta y_s = 0 \qquad k = 1, \ldots, \ell \tag{33f}$$

and the following equation evaluated at $\bar{t}_f$

$$\begin{aligned} &\sum_{i=1}^{n} \frac{\partial \bar{P}}{\partial x_{i_f}} \bar{f}_i + \frac{\partial \bar{P}}{\partial t_f} + \sum_{i,j=1}^{n} \frac{\partial^2 \bar{P}}{\partial x_{i_f} \partial x_{j_f}} \bar{f}_i \Delta x_j(\bar{t}_f) \\ &+ \sum_{i,j=1}^{n} \frac{\partial \bar{P}}{\partial x_{i_f}} \frac{\partial \bar{f}_i}{\partial x_{j_f}} \Delta x_j(\bar{t}_f) + \sum_{k=1}^{\ell} \sum_{i=1}^{n} \frac{\partial \bar{P}}{\partial x_{i_f}} \frac{\partial \bar{f}_i}{\partial y_{k_f}} \Delta y_k(\bar{t}_f) \\ &+ \sum_{i=1}^{n} \frac{\partial \bar{P}}{\partial x_{i_f}} \frac{\partial \bar{f}_i}{\partial t_f} \delta t_f + \sum_{i=1}^{n} \frac{\partial^2 \bar{P}}{\partial x_{i_f} \partial t_f} f_i \delta t_f \\ &+ \sum_{i=1}^{n} \frac{\partial^2 \bar{P}}{\partial x_{i_f} \partial t_f} \Delta x_i(\bar{t}_f) + \frac{\partial^2 P}{\partial t_p^2} \delta t_f = 0 \end{aligned} \tag{33g}$$

where

$$\Delta y_k(\bar{t}_f) = \delta y_k + \dot{\bar{y}}_k \delta t_f$$

These equations, as we might have anticipated from the analysis of the ordinary minimum problem, are a linearization of the necessary condition for a minimum as derived from the first order theory. Again, an integral step size constraint may be required for $\delta \vec{y}$ in which event the diagonal terms of the array $(\partial^2 H)/(\partial y_k \partial y_s)$ would have positive constants added to them.

The actual computational procedure might proceed as follows:

1. Select an initial control time history as a first estimate and numerically integrate the system equations (1) as in the gradient method. Terminate the calculation at time $\bar{t}_f$ determined such that $(dP')/(dt_f) = 0$.
2. Integrate the adjoint system backwards using terminal values determined by $\lambda_i(\bar{t}_f) = (\partial P')/(\partial x_{i_f})$ and store the initial values of $\lambda_i(t_0)$.
3. Generate a partitioned transition matrix for the linearized system and linearized adjoint system by n simultaneous integrations of linearized systems with one of the $\delta\lambda_i(0)$ equal to 1 and the remaining $\delta\lambda(0)$ equal to zero for each integration. The $\delta x_i(0)$ are all equal to zero. The homogeneous part of the control law as obtained from Eq. (33f) is substituted in the linearized systems equations for the calculation of the partitioned transition matrix.
4. The linearized system and adjoint system are integrated once again for the inhomogeneous part of the solution due to the term $(\partial \bar{H})/(\partial y_k)$ in the control law. For this integration all the $\delta\lambda_i(0)$ are equal to zero.
5. By linear algebraic operations the $\delta\lambda_i(t_0)$ are determined so as to satisfy Eqs. (33c), (33d), (33e), and (33g).
6. Another integration of the combined systems is performed with these values of $\delta\lambda_i(t_0)$ and

δy_k calculated and added to $\bar{y}_k$. Return to step 1 and repeat the process.

The process continues until the decrements in P' become small. The penalty function technique is then dropped in preference to satisfying terminal conditions exactly. Equations (33) are modified appropriately. The $\Delta x_i(\bar{t}_f)$ for the first m state variables are chosen to make $x_i(\bar{t}_f + \delta t)$ equal to $\tilde{x}_{i_f}$.

$$\Delta x_i(\bar{t}_f) = \tilde{x}_{i_f} - \bar{x}_i(\bar{t}_f) \quad , \quad i = 1, \ldots, m \tag{34}$$

Equation (33c) remains the same for $i = m+1, \ldots, n$. Of course the appropriate summation indices are changed throughout Eq. (33) to be consistent with the payoff P (the prime is dropped) being only a function of last n-m state variables and final time.

The computational procedure is quite similar to the procedure sketched earlier when the penalty function technique was used. The adjoint system is integrated numerically forward with initial values $\bar{\lambda}_{i_0} + \delta\lambda_{i_0}$, $i = 1, \ldots, n$ of the preceding cycle. The modified terminal conditions of the linearized system and adjoint system are satisfied using linear algebraic procedures as before.

One advantage of the second variation method is that in the final stages of the computational procedure the penalty function technique is no longer needed and each successive approximation attempts to satisfy the boundary conditions exactly. Thus the undetermined constants associated with the penalty function terms are eliminated. A second advantage is that in both phases (penalty function and nonpenalty functions) the step size is automatically determined thus eliminating the independent search procedure needed in the gradient methods. In addition to the two main advantages listed above, most of the information necessary to perform the generalized Jacobi test is available. Also, the matrix elements for the second variational guidance scheme discussed in (12) are available as an end result of the computational process.

The disadvantages of the method lie chiefly in the additional programming effort needed to formulate the computing algorithm. However, the over-all actual computing time is considerably less as discussed in (5) and

Part II of this paper. In the present state of the art, the method is applicable only to problems where the control signal is unbounded and continuous. Extensions to bounded control variables which lead to an on-off type control signal are being investigated.

Generalized Newton-Raphson Method

We will now proceed to discuss an indirect method which on the surface does not appear to be related to the steep descent techniques or variations thereof. The method couched in the framework of functional analysis is developed in (6) from an application of the Contraction Mapping Principle. In essence, it is a generalization of a Newton-Raphson method applied to the system and Euler-Lagrange equations, and contrasts sharply with the more usual indirect approach which has had such a dismal computational past. For example, in the usual procedure sets of initial conditions are successively mapped into new sets of initial conditions and the differential constraints satisfied whereas in the generalized Newton-Raphson technique a mapping is produced which transforms sets of functions into improved sets of functions which do not necessarily satisfy the differential constraints and thus, as one might expect, yields a greater tenacity of convergence.

Let us again consider the ordinary minimum problem with a single constraint. The Euler-Lagrange equations (13i) and (13ii) and the constraint condition which is analogous to the system equations are repeated below.

$$\begin{aligned} S_{x_1} &= f_{x_1} + \lambda g_{x_1} = 0 \\ S_{x_2} &= f_{x_2} + \lambda g_{x_2} = 0 \\ S_{\lambda} &= g(x_1, x_2) = 0 \end{aligned} \tag{35}$$

A Newton-Raphson approach to the solution of these equations might proceed as follows. Select an initial x_1, x_2, and λ which need not satisfy any of the equations given in Eq. (35). Designate these values as barred variables as before and expand Eq. (35) in a Taylor series keeping only zero and first order terms

$$\begin{aligned}
&\bar{S}_{x_1} + \bar{S}_{x_1x_1}\Delta x_1 + \bar{S}_{x_1x_2}\Delta x_2 + \bar{g}_{x_1}\Delta\lambda = 0 \\
&\bar{S}_{x_2} + \bar{S}_{x_1x_2}\Delta x_1 + \bar{S}_{x_2x_2}\Delta x_2 + \bar{g}_{x_2}\Delta\lambda = 0 \\
&\bar{g}(x_1x_2) + \bar{g}_{x_1}\Delta x_1 + \bar{g}_{x_2}\Delta x_2 = 0
\end{aligned} \tag{36}$$

Equations (36) would then be solved for Δx_1, Δx_2, and $\Delta\lambda$ and new values of x_1, x_2, and λ determined.

$$\begin{aligned}
x_1 &= \bar{x}_1 + \Delta x_1 \\
x_2 &= \bar{x}_2 + \Delta x_2 \\
\lambda &= \bar{\lambda} + \Delta\lambda
\end{aligned} \tag{37}$$

The procedure continues until Eqs. (35) are satisfied or until some measure of error has decreased sufficiently.

When this technique is applied to the variational problem, the following equations result.

$$\delta\dot{x}_i = \frac{\partial\bar{H}}{\partial\lambda_i} - \dot{\bar{x}}_i + \sum_{j=1}^{n} \frac{\partial^2\bar{H}}{\partial\lambda_i\partial x_j}\delta x_j + \sum_{k=1}^{\ell} \frac{\partial^2\bar{H}}{\partial\lambda_i\partial y_k}\delta y_k \tag{38a}$$

$$\delta x_i(0) = 0 \quad , \quad i = 1, \ldots, n$$

$$\Delta x_i(t_f) = \tilde{x}_{i_f} - \bar{x}_{i_f} \tag{38b}$$

$$\Delta x_i(t_f) = \delta x_i(\bar{t}_f) + \dot{\bar{x}}_i\delta t_f \quad , \quad i = 1, \ldots, m \tag{38c}$$

$$\delta\dot{\lambda}_i = -\frac{\partial\bar{H}}{\partial x_i} - \dot{\bar{\lambda}}_i - \sum_{j=1}^{n} \frac{\partial^2\bar{H}}{\partial x_i \partial x_j}\delta x_j - \sum_{k=1}^{\ell} \frac{\partial^2\bar{H}}{\partial x_i \partial y_k}\delta y_k$$

$$- \sum_{j=1}^{n} \frac{\partial^2\bar{H}}{\partial x_i \partial \lambda_j}\delta\lambda_j \quad , \quad i = 1, \ldots, n \tag{38d}$$

$$\Delta\lambda_i(t_f) = \frac{\partial\bar{P}}{\partial x_{i_f}} - \bar{\lambda}_i(\bar{t}_f) + \sum_{j=1}^{n} \frac{\partial^2\bar{P}}{\partial x_{i_f}\, \partial x_{j_f}} \Delta x_j(\bar{t}_f)$$

$$+ \frac{\partial^2\bar{P}_i}{\partial x_{i_f}\, \partial t_f}\delta\bar{t}_f \tag{38e}$$

$$\Delta\lambda_i(t_f) = \delta\lambda_i(t_f) + \dot{\bar{\lambda}}_i \delta t_f \quad , \quad i = m+1, \ldots, n \tag{38f}$$

$$\frac{\partial\bar{H}}{\partial y_k} + \sum_{j=1}^{n} \frac{\partial^2\bar{H}}{\partial y_k \partial x_j}\delta x_j + \sum_{j=1}^{n} \frac{\partial^2\bar{H}}{\partial y_k \partial \lambda_j}\delta\lambda_j$$

$$+ \sum_{s=1}^{\ell} \frac{\partial^2\bar{H}}{\partial y_k \partial y_s}\delta y_s = 0 \quad , \quad k, \ldots, \ell \tag{38g}$$

and

$$\sum_{i=1}^{n} \frac{\partial\bar{P}}{\partial x_{i_f}}\bar{f}_i + \frac{\partial\bar{P}}{\partial t_f} + \sum_{i,j=1}^{n} \frac{\partial^2\bar{P}}{\partial x_{i_f}\, \partial x_{j_f}}\bar{f}_i \Delta x_j(\bar{t}_f)$$

$$+ \sum_{i,j=1}^{n} \frac{\partial\bar{P}}{\partial x_{i_f}} \frac{\partial\bar{f}_i}{\partial x_{j_f}} \Delta x_j(\bar{t}_f) + \sum_{k=1}^{\ell}\sum_{j=1}^{n} \frac{\partial\bar{P}}{\partial x_{i_f}} \frac{\partial\bar{f}_i}{\partial y_k}\Delta y_k(t_f) = 0 \tag{38h}$$

evaluated at $\bar{t}_f$. The penalty function technique has not been used in this formulation. It should be noted that the initial estimates for trajectories or the Lagrange multiplier time histories need not satisfy their respective differential equations.

A computational procedure might proceed as follows.

1. Analytically solve for y_k in terms of x_i, λ_i, and t and substitute the control law into the system and adjoint system equations. Select a system trajectory and ajoint trajectory that need not satisfy the differential constraints, but that does satisfy the initial conditions and perhaps, although not necessarily, the specified terminal conditions.
2. Calculate a partitioned transition matrix for the homogeneous linearized systems and adjoint system as in the second variation method by setting $\delta x_i(0) = 0$ and letting the $\delta\lambda_i(0)$ take on unity values as before.
3. Solve the system and adjoint system again for the nonhomogeneous part of the solutions.
4. Using linear algebraic relationships determine the $\delta\lambda_i(0)$ required to satisfy boundary conditions in Eqs. (38).
5. With these values for $\delta\lambda_i(0)$ integrate both linearized systems and add the $\delta\vec{x}(t)$ and $\delta\vec{\lambda}(t)$ to obtain new estimates of $\vec{x}(t)$ and $\vec{\lambda}(t)$.
6. Return to step 1 and repeat.

Because of the additional degree of freedom given by not requiring the trajectories or the adjoint system to satisfy the differential constraints there are many variations for the computational procedure. In (6) some discussion has been given to sufficient conditions for convergence using as a metric the maximum deviation between the approximate trajectory and the actual trajectory. However, in practice it has been found that the region of convergence is somewhat larger than that described by these sufficient conditions. A few examples of the numerical application of the Newton-Raphson operator technique are described in (13).

Conclusions

Several methods have been described for the numerical solution of optimization problems. The gradient technique and possibly the second variation method might be described as direct methods while the generalized

Newton-Raphson technique would no doubt be considered of the indirect type.

The advantages of the gradient method and variations of this method are in its simplicity. The convergence of the method is not contingent upon a good initial estimate as a starting condition. It is assured that the function to be minimized is decreased after each iteration cycle. There is no difficulty in handling constraints imposed on the control variables. Successful results have also been obtained when constraints were imposed on the state variables by employing an integral type penalty function. The major disadvantage of the method is in the way specified terminal conditions must be treated using penalty functions which introduce undetermined constants and often slows convergence as the optimal trajectory is approached. In addition, the step size is unspecified which also introduces additional constants which must be evaluated by independent search techniques.

Original motivation for the second variation method was to improve the iteration technique and eliminate the shortcomings of the gradient method. In the final stages of the second variation method, the penalty function technique is dropped in preference to satisfying specified terminal conditions exactly which improves convergence properties of the iterative technique as the optimal trajectory is approached. In addition, the step size is inherently determined by the method eliminating the need for evaluating undetermined constants by an independent search as is required in the gradient methods. As a by-product, the Jacobi test can be performed with little additional computation and the matrix coefficients needed for the second variation guidance are available from the final iteration cycle. The over-all saving in computer time seems to be in the order of 50 per cent, at least for the limited experience available. The disadvantages of the method are that the computer program is significantly more complicated and the method as it presently stands is not directly applicable to the case where constraints are imposed on the control signals.

The Generalized Newton-Raphson method is an indirect approach which iterates to a solution of the system and Euler-Lagrange equations which have mixed boundary conditions. An examination of the ordinary minimum problem with a single side constraint, illustrates that the significant difference between the second variation method and the generalized Newton-Raphson method is that in the former the constraint is satisfied exactly while in the latter the constraint is satisfied when the method converges to the optimum value. However, both methods systematically search out the stationary value of S. One should be able to take advantage of the additional degree of freedom available in the Newton-Raphson method to improve the computing algorithm. However, in the second variation method one can argue certain convergence properties since a minimum of the function or functional is being sought when the constraints are satisfied (at least when the penalty function is used) rather than seeking out merely stationary values of function or functional as is done in the generalized Newton-Raphson method. In summary, one might say that the generalized Newton-Raphson method is a more general form of the second variation method or conversely, the second variation method is a specific approach to the generalized Newton-Raphson method. This seems to be a common meeting ground for a direct and indirect approach to the solution of optimization problems.

As is usually the case, it is difficult to state dogmatically the superiority of any one method over another. Each method should be used where its advantages can be maximized and disadvantages minimized. A combination of two or more of the methods in practice might well be used to advantage. For example, one might initially use a gradient method or the second variation method with penalty functions to satisfy terminal constraints so as to be assured of convergence and then switch to the generalized Newton-Raphson procedure as the optimum trajectory is approached to take advantage of the possible improved rate of convergence of the latter method in the terminal phase of the iteration technique.

In Part II of this paper the application of all three methods to a specific problem will be discussed. Some of the salient features of the actual computational procedures will be brought out and a comparison made of actual computing time for the different methods.

Acknowledgments

The work reported in this paper was partly supported by the USAF Office of Scientific Research, Applied Mathematics Division, under Contract AF49(638)-1207 and by NASA Marshall Space Flight Center, Aero-Astrodynamics Laboratory, under Contract NAS 8-1549.

References

(1). Kelley, H.J., "Gradient Theory of Optimal Flight Paths," presented at Am. Rocket Soc. Semi-Annual Meeting, Los Angeles, California, May 9-12, 1960, ARS Journal 30, 947-954, 1960.

(2). Bryson, A.E., Carroll, F.J., Mikami, K., and Denham, W.F., "Determination of the Lift or Drag Program that Minimizes Re-entry Heating with Acceleration or Range Constraints Using a Steepest Descent Computation Procedure," presented at IAS 29th Annual Meeting, New York, New York, January 23-25, 1961.

(3). Kelley, H.J., Kopp, R.E., and Moyer, H.G., "Successive Approximation Techniques for Trajectory Optimization," presented at the IAS Vehicle Systems Optimization Symposium, Garden City, New York, November 28-29, 1961.

(4). Kelley, H.J., "Methods of Gradients," Chapt. 6 of Optimization Techniques, edited by G. Leitmann, Academic Press, 1962.

(5). Kelley, H.J., Kopp, R.E., and Moyer, H.G., "A Trajectory Optimization Technique Based Upon the Theory of the Second Variation," presented at the AIAA Astrodynamics Conference, Yale University, New Haven Conn., August 19-21, 1963.

(6). McGill, R., and Kenneth, P., "A Convergence Theorem on the Iterative Solution of Nonlinear Two-Point Boundary Value Systems," presented at the XIVth International Astronautical Congress, Paris, France, September 1963.

(7). Kalaba, R., "On Nonlinear Differential Equations, the Maximum Operation, and Monotone Convergence," Journal of Mathematics and Mechanics, Vol. 8, No. 4, July 1959.

(8). Hestenes, M.R., Numerical Methods of Obtaining Solutions of Fixed End Point Problems in the Calculus of Variations, RM-102, The Rand Corporation, August 1949.

(9). Rozonoer, L.I., "L.S. Pontryagin Maximum Principle in the Theory of Optimum Systems," Automat. i Telemekh. 20 (1959). (English Translation: Automation and Remote Control 1288-1302, 1405-1421, 1517-1532, 1960.)

(10). Kopp, R.E., "Pontryagin Maximum Principle," Chapt. 7, Optimization Techniques, edited by G. Leitmann, Academic Press, 1962.

(11). Kelley, H.J., Falco, M., and Ball, D.J., "Air Vehicle Trajectory Optimization," presented at the Symposium on Multivariable System Theory, Fall Meeting of SIAM, Cambridge, Massachusetts, 1962.

(12). Kelley, H.J., "Guidance Theory and Extremal Fields," IRE Transactions on Automatic Control, Vol. AC-7, No. 5, October 1962.

(13). McGill, R., and Kenneth, P., "Solution of Variational Problems by Means of a Generalized Newton-Raphson Operator," to be published.

SEVERAL TRAJECTORY OPTIMIZATION TECHNIQUES

Part II: Application

H. Gardner Moyer

Gordon Pinkham

Research Department
Grumman Aircraft Engineering Corporation
Bethpage, New York

Abstract

This paper discusses the application of the three optimization methods — steepest descent, second variation, and generalized Newton-Raphson — to the problem of minimum time, low thrust, circle-to-circle transfer. Details of computational techniques that have proved successful in practice are presented. The number of iteration cycles and the time used by the computer are given for each method.

Introduction and Statement of Problem

This paper describes the application of the three basic optimization schemes covered in Part I: Discussion to a specific problem. This problem is that of minimizing the transfer time of a low-thrust ion rocket between the orbits of Earth and Mars. Applications of the gradient method and of the second variation method to this problem have been reported in (1), (2), and (4), and therefore only a brief sketch of interesting variations in these computational procedures and of the results will be included here.

To simplify the problem as much as possible the rocket's thrust level was assumed constant, and thus the single control variable is the thrust direction. Further, the orbits of Earth and Mars were assumed to be circular and coplanar, and the gravitational attractions of the two planets on the vehicle were neglected. The following system parameters for the low-thrust vehicle were adopted from (1).

Initial Mass, m_o	46.58 slugs
Specific Impulse	5700 sec
Propellant Consumption, $\dot{m}$,	-6.937×10^{-7} slugs/sec
Thrust, T,	0.127 lb
Thrust/Initial Weight	0.9×10^{-4}

The equations of motion were given by:

Radial Velocity

$$\dot{r} = f^{(1)} = u \tag{1}$$

Radial Acceleration

$$\dot{u} = f^{(2)} = \frac{v^2}{r} - \frac{\mu}{r^2} + \frac{T \sin \theta}{m_0 + \dot{m}t} \tag{2}$$

Circumferential Acceleration

$$\dot{v} = f^{(3)} = - \frac{uv}{r} + \frac{T \cos \theta}{m_0 + \dot{m}t} \tag{3}$$

where u and v are the radial and circumferential velocities respectively; r is the radius; and θ is the thrust direction angle measured from the local horizontal. All the initial and final values of the state variables were specified, and the quantity to be minimized was t_f, the final time.

The Three Methods as Applied to the Sample Problem

Gradient Method

As stated in Part I, the gradient methods utilize a penalty function which for this problem becomes

$$P' = t + \tfrac{1}{2} \sum_{i=1}^{3} k_i (x_{i_f} - \tilde{x}_i)^2 \tag{4}$$

As was also stated in Part I, the criterion for the termination of a trajectory is

$$\dot{P}' = 1 + \sum_{i=1}^{3} k_i (x_{i_f} - \tilde{x}_i) f_f^{(i)} = 0 \tag{5}$$

Utilizing

$$\lambda_{i_f} = \frac{\partial P'}{\partial x_i} = k_i (x_{i_f} - \tilde{x}_i) \tag{6}$$

we have

$$1 + \sum_{i=1}^{3} \lambda_{i_f} f_f^{(i)} = 0 \tag{7}$$

This equation scales the multipliers.

Since by the "multiplier rule" all the final λ's cannot vanish, the extremal that minimizes P' must deviate from the desired values $\tilde{x}_i$. We will present two methods of reducing the deviation to within tolerable limits.

We will assume that the errors are small enough so that the extremal that minimizes P' is close to the extremal that passes through the desired end-point. By close we mean that the two extremals have approximately the same final λ's. If we increase the k's and reconverge, this new extremal will also have approximately the same final λ's. It then follows from Eq. (6) that the deviations will be reduced in proportion to the increase in the k's.

Thus the first method of reducing the errors is to "build up the k's." This method was often unsuccessful however, due to inexact interpolation for the final values and other numerical errors that prevented convergence. Therefore, the method of "shifting boundary values" was devised and has proved invariably successful.

After convergence, the boundary values are redefined by subtracting $\Delta x_i = x_{i_f} - \tilde{x}_i$ from $\tilde{x}_i$. We then apply the gradient process to obtain the minimum of

$$P' = t + \sum_{i=1}^{3} k_i (x_{i_f} - \tilde{x}_i + \Delta x_i)^2 \tag{8}$$

If the final λ's were unchanged, the extremal would pass directly through the desired end-point. In practice, several boundary shifts may be necessary.

Applying a gradient scheme incorporating the boundary shift technique to the above problem of minimizing the time of low-thrust Earth to Mars trajectories, it was found that attainment of the minimum t of 193 days with convergence to within 0.1% of the boundary values was possible in 5 shifts with an average of 20 descents per shift. As programmed, a descent was a one dimensional search for a minimum of P' versus control variations calculated from the adjoint equations, and it required the computation of one adjoint solution and at most four trajectories. Figure 1 shows the initial, some intermediate, and the final θ time-histories preceding the first boundary shift. As indicated in the figure, the first boundary shift took place after 25 descents. The converged curve, labeled F, is also included.

Second Variation Method

As explained in Part I, the first stage of the second variation method also depends on a penalty function, P'. However, in this case P' is expanded to second order terms, and among these are terms in δt_f, the change in the final time. Because these terms greatly complicate an already lengthy numerical calculation, δt_f was set equal to zero in the expansion of P' when the second variation method was coded for the computer. This implies that the control variable increment $\delta\theta(t)$ was then calculated to obtain the maximum reduction in P' at the nominal final time $\bar{t}_f$ instead of $\bar{t}_f + \delta t_f$. Of course when the trajectory with control variable $\theta + \delta\theta$ was computed, it was not terminated at time $\bar{t}_f$ but rather at that point of the trajectory with minimum P', as is done in the gradient programs. With respect to over-all computational time this technique represents a compromise between a true second variation calculation and additional programming complexity. For this particular problem it was advantageous to treat the problem as a

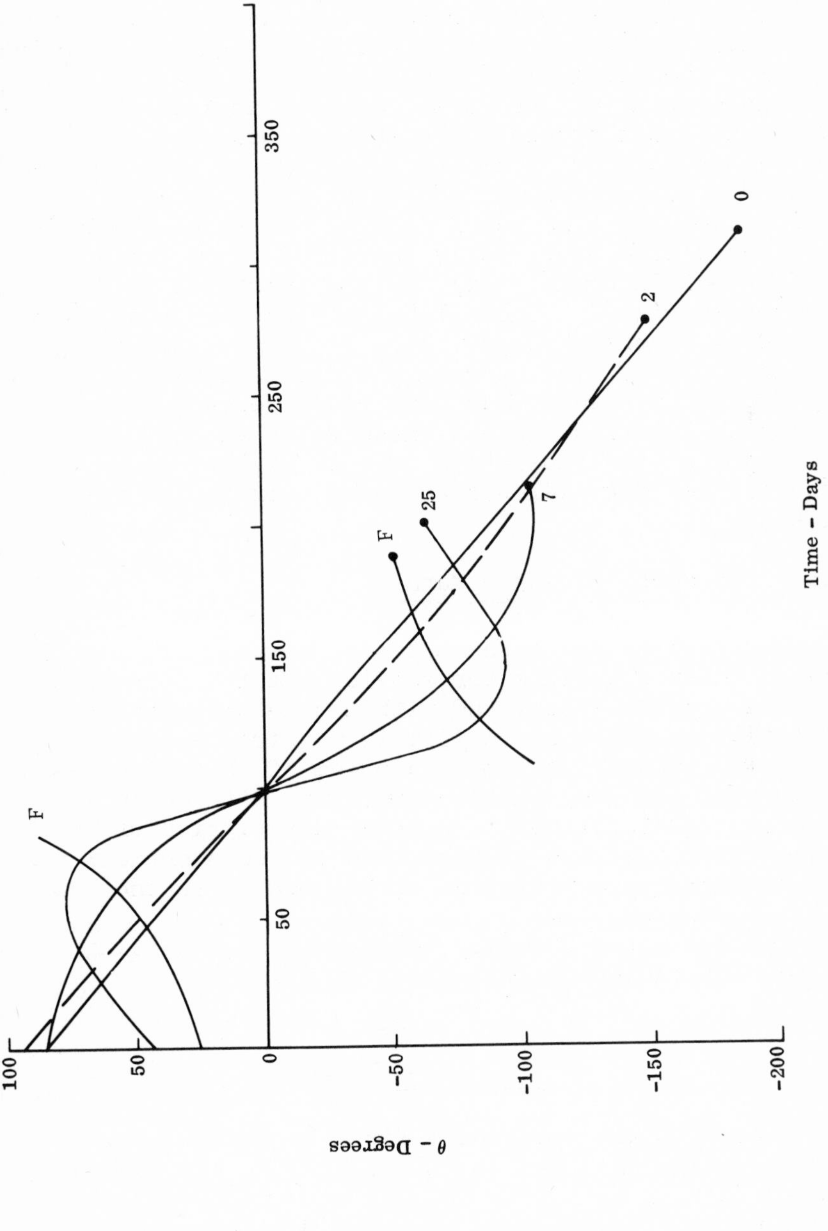

Fig. 1 Control Angle Programs From Gradient Technique

fixed time problem when computing $\delta\theta$ using penalty functions.

The initial $\theta(t)$ function in this case corresponds to constant circumferential thrust. This resulted in terminal boundary value errors that averaged 20 per cent. After 6 descent cycles, using the penalty function procedure, the terminal errors averaged 3 per cent with the transfer time at 180 days. After 5 additional cycles of the refinement process, the average boundary value error was reduced to 0.05 per cent and the transfer time had reached its minimum of 193 days. The over-all IBM 7094 computer time was 2 minutes, representing half the computer time required by the first order gradient program. Intermediate $\theta(t)$ curves (numbered by descent) are shown in Fig. 2. Those labeled 6 or less come from the penalty function stage. The F-4 curve typifies the refinement stage. The converged curve is labeled F.

Experiments were made with fewer descent cycles in the penalty function stage. These cases all required more computer time indicating that it is best to be close to the desired extremal before going over to the refinement stage.

Generalized Newton-Raphson Method[1]

The last of the three methods discussed in Part I is based on an algorithm for solving the two-point boundary value problem associated with the Euler-Lagrange equations. As outlined in (3), it required a fixed final time. Since the sample problem of this paper is a minimum time problem, the procedure was altered to suit this case. What follows is a brief description of the modified procedure and a discussion of the numerical results obtained by application of the method to the sample orbit transfer problem.

The two-point boundary value problem resulting from the Euler-Lagrange equations is given by

---

[1] This algorithm was apparently first suggested for boundary value problems by Hestenes (5), and was developed further by Kalaba (6). A convergence proof for N dimensional systems was given by McGill and Kenneth (3).

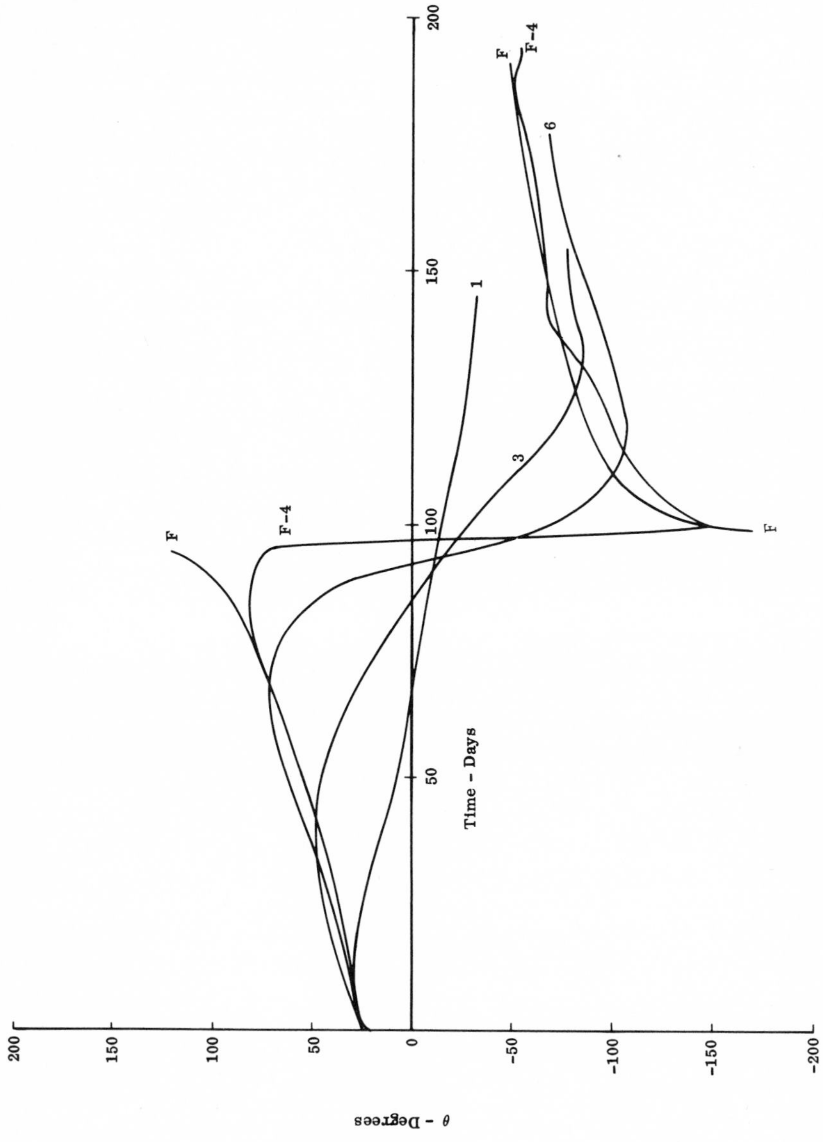

Fig. 2 Control Angle Programs From Second Variation Technique

$$\dot{r} = u = f^{(1)} \tag{9}$$

$$\dot{u} = \frac{v^2}{r} - \frac{\mu}{r^2} + a(t)\frac{\lambda_u}{\left(\lambda_u^2 + \lambda_v^2\right)^{\frac{1}{2}}} = f^{(2)} \tag{10}$$

$$\dot{v} = -\frac{uv}{r} + a(t)\frac{\lambda_v}{\left(\lambda_u^2 + \lambda_v^2\right)^{\frac{1}{2}}} = f^{(3)} \tag{11}$$

$$\dot{\lambda}_r = \left(\frac{v^2}{r^2} - 2\frac{\mu}{r^3}\right)\lambda_u - \frac{uv}{r^2}\lambda_v = f^{(4)} \tag{12}$$

$$\dot{\lambda}_u = -\lambda_r + \frac{v}{r}\lambda_v = f^{(5)} \tag{13}$$

$$\dot{\lambda}_v = -2\frac{v}{r}\lambda_u + \frac{u}{r}\lambda_v = f^{(6)} \tag{14}$$

where

$$a(t) = \frac{T}{m_0 + \dot{m}t} \tag{15}$$

and the boundary conditions are

$$\begin{aligned} t &= 0 & t &= t_f \text{ (unspecified)} \\ r(0) &= r_0 & r(t_f) &= r_f \\ u(0) &= u_0 & u(t_f) &= u_f \\ v(0) &= v_0 & v(t_f) &= v_f \end{aligned} \tag{16}$$

Equations (9) through (14) may be written as

$$\dot{X} = F(X, t) \tag{17}$$

where

$$X = (x^{(1)}, \ldots, x^{(6)})$$
$$F = (f^{(1)}, \ldots, f^{(6)}) \qquad (18)$$

and

$$x^{(1)}(t) = r(t) \quad , \quad x^{(2)}(t) = u(t) \quad , \quad x^{(3)}(t) = v(t)$$
$$x^{(4)}(t) = \lambda_r(t) \quad , \quad x^{(5)}(t) = \lambda_u(t) \quad , \quad x^{(6)}(t) = \lambda_v(t)$$

The method proceeds by solving the following sequence of linear two-point problems.

$$\dot{X}_{n+1} = J(X_n, t)\left[X_{n+1} - X_n\right] + F(X_n, t) \qquad n = 0, 1, \ldots (19)$$

where $J(X,t)$ is the Jacobian matrix of partial derivatives of the $f^{(i)}$ with respect to the $x^{(j)}$, $i = 1, \ldots, 6$, $j = 1, \ldots, 6$. A starting vector, $X_0(t)$ and an estimated final time, t_{f_0}, are assumed and the sequence of linear boundary value problems is solved numerically by the procedure outlined in (3). Altering the original boundary conditions so that the final r is maximized at $t_{f_k}(k=0)$ we have:

$$\begin{array}{ll}
t = 0 & t = t_{f_k} \\
x_n^{(1)}(0) = r_n(0) = r_0 & \\
x_n^{(2)}(0) = u_n(0) = u_0 & x_n^{(2)}(t_f) = u_n(t_f) = u_f \\
x_n^{(3)}(0) = v_n(0) = v_0 & x_n^{(3)}(t_f) = v_n(t_f) = v_f \\
x_n^{(4)}(0) = \lambda_{r_n}(0) = 1 &
\end{array} \qquad (20)$$

$$n = 1, 2, \ldots$$

Setting $\lambda_r(0) = 1$ accomplished the scaling of the multipliers. The iteration proceeds until $\bar{\rho}(X_{n+1}, X_n) \leq \epsilon$ where

$$\bar{\rho}(X_{n+1}, X_n) = \sum_{i=1}^{6} \max_{t \in [0, t_{f_k}]} |x_{n+1}^{(i)} - x_n^{(i)}| \tag{21}$$

At this stage the final time, t_{f_k}, is adjusted automatically according to the difference $[r_f - r(t_{f_k})]$ by a scalar application of the Newton-Raphson procedure:

$$t_{f_{k+1}} = t_{f_k} + \frac{(t_{f_k} - t_{f_{k-1}})}{r(t_{f_k}) - r(t_{f_{k-1}})}[r_f - r(t_{f_k})] \tag{22}$$

The above iteration on X_n now continues for the new final time $t_{f_{k+1}}$ until $\bar{\rho}$ is again $\leq \epsilon$. The over-all process proceeds until $\rho \leq \epsilon$ where

$$\rho = \bar{\rho} + \frac{1}{b}|t_{f_{k+1}} - t_{f_k}| \tag{23}$$

and b is a scaling factor. The corresponding iterate X_{n+1} is accepted as the solution to the minimum time problem, and a final check is run by integrating the nonlinear Euler-Lagrange equations with a complete set of initial conditions taken from the final iterate.

For the purpose of numerical precision the data for the sample problem were normalized to obtain

$$\begin{array}{llll} r_0 = 1.000 & & v_f = .8098 & \\ r_f = 1.525 & & u_f = 0.000 & \\ \mu = 1.000 & & m_0 = 1.000 & \\ v_0 = 1.000 & & \dot{m} = -.07487 & \\ u_0 = 0.000 & & T = .1405 & \end{array} \tag{24}$$

This resulted in a time unit of 58.18 days. The starting vector $X_0(t)$ was chosen rather crudely as follows:

$$
\begin{aligned}
t_{f_0} &= 178.0 \text{ days, or } 3.060 \text{ of our time units} \\
x_0^{(1)}(t) &= r_0(t) = r_0 + \frac{r_f - r_0}{t_{f_0}}\, t \\
x_0^{(2)}(t) &= u_0(t) \equiv 0 \\
x_0^{(3)}(t) &= v_0(t) = \left(\frac{\mu}{r_0(t)}\right)^{\frac{1}{2}} \\
x_0^{(4)}(t) &= \lambda_{r_0}(t) \equiv 1.000 \\
x_0^{(5)}(t) &= \lambda_{u_0}(t) \equiv \begin{cases} .5200 & \text{for } t \in [0, \tfrac{1}{2} t_{f_0}] \\ -.5000 & \text{for } t \in [\tfrac{1}{2} t_{f_0}, t_{f_0}] \end{cases} \\
x_0^{(6)}(t) &= \lambda_{v_0}(t) \equiv \begin{cases} .3000 & \text{for } t \in [0, \tfrac{1}{2} t_{f_0}] \\ 0.000 & \text{for } t \in [\tfrac{1}{2} t_{f_0}, t_{f_0}] \end{cases}
\end{aligned}
\qquad (25)
$$

The final two starting functions $\lambda_{u_0}(t)$ and $\lambda_{v_0}(t)$ correspond to a control angle $\theta_0(t)$ which is constant at $60°$ above the local horizontal for the first half of the transit time, and constant inward along the local vertical for the remaining half of the transit time (see Fig. 3).

The sequence $\{X_n\}$ converged uniformly to an accuracy of 5 significant figures in 13 total iterations with 4 shifts of the final time. The resultant minimum time was found to be 193.2 days; in agreement with the results of the gradient and second variation solutions. The total computer time (IBM 7094) required was 36 seconds. Figure 3 illustrates the behavior of the control angle program, where $\theta_0(t)$ is the starting function,

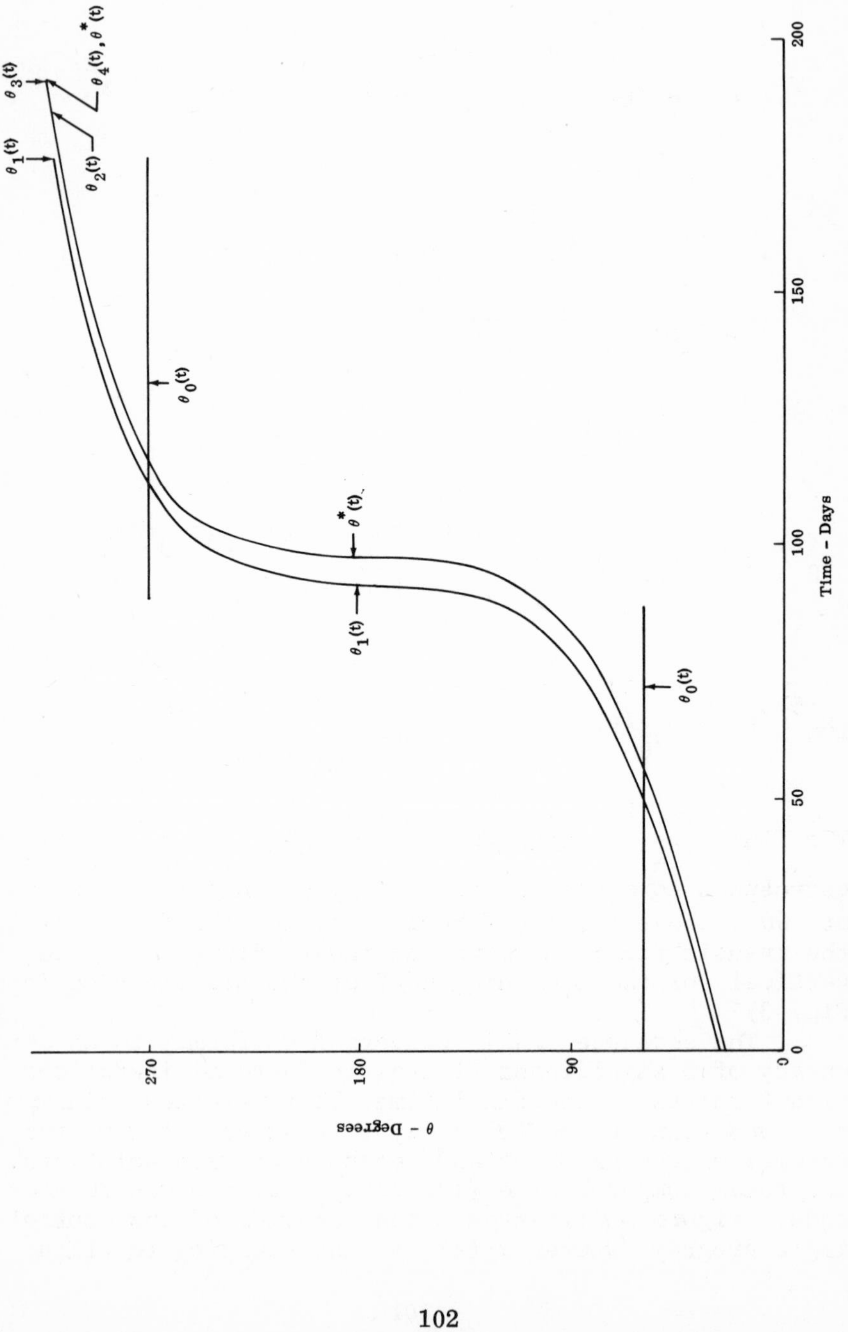

Fig. 3 Control Angle Programs From Generalized Newton-Raphson Method

$\theta_1(t)$ through $\theta_4(t)$ correspond to the 4 shifts of the final time t_f, and $\theta^*(t)$ results from the integration of the nonlinear Euler-Lagrange equations with the initial values taken from the final iterate. The curves for $\theta_2(t)$, $\theta_3(t)$, and $\theta_4(t)$ lie, within our plotting accuracy, on the solution curve $\theta^*(t)$; except for the final segments as indicated on the figure. Figure 4 illustrates the behavior of the metrics, ρ, and $\bar{\rho}$.

We observe that for this particular example the approach just described is systematic, simple to apply, and yields rapid convergence from crude a priori starting functions.[1] However, it is possible that for other variational problems a priori starting functions sufficient to produce convergence may not be easily obtainable. In such a case one might consider the possibility of using a hybrid approach, that is, a combination of one of the gradient procedures, or a crude application of dynamic programming; and the technique just described. Such a hybrid approach is currently under study.

Acknowledgments

The work reported in this paper was partly supported by the USAF Office of Scientific Research, Applied Mathematics Division, under Contract AF 49(638)-1207 and by NASA Marshall Space Flight Center, Aero-Astrodynamics Laboratory, under Contract NAS 8-1549.

The authors wish to express their appreciation to Dr. Henry J. Kelley for valuable discussions and suggestions concerning this work; and to Gerald E. Taylor whose able programming made the numerical example for the generalized Newton-Raphson method possible.

References

(1). Lindorfer, W., and Moyer, H.G., "Application of a Low Thrust Trajectory Optimization Scheme to Planar Earth-Mars Transfer," ARS Journal, February 1962.

---

[1]For additional numerical examples see (7).

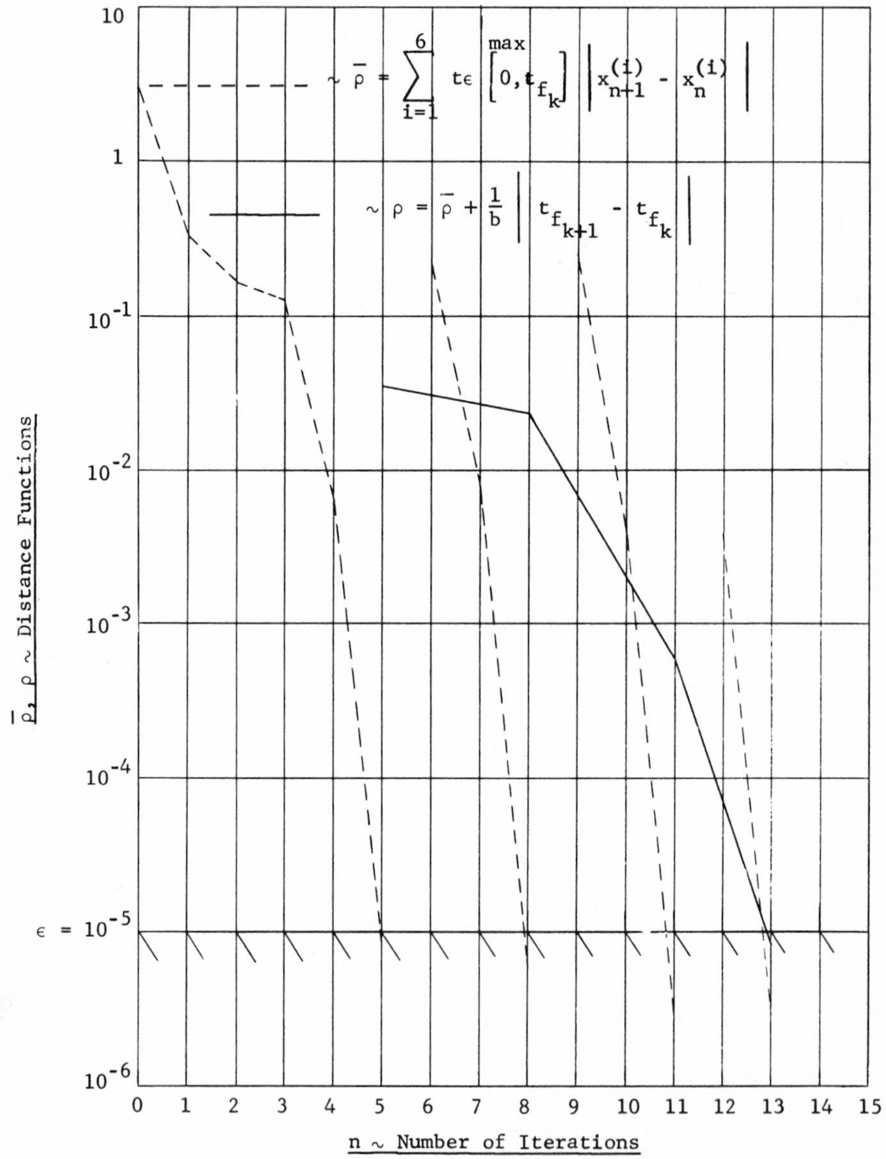

Fig. 4 $\bar{\rho}$, ρ Versus n For The Newton-Raphson Method

(2). Kelley, H.J., Kopp, R.E., and Moyer, H.G., "A Trajectory Optimization Technique Based upon the Theory of the Second Variation," presented at the AIAA Astrodynamics Conference, Yale University, Connecticut, August 1963.

(3). McGill, R., and Kenneth, P., "A Convergence Theorem on the Iterative Solution of Nonlinear Two-Point Boundary Value Systems," presented at the XIVth IAF Congress, Paris, France, September 1963.

(4). Kelley, H.J., "Method of Gradients," Chapter 6 of Optimization Techniques, edited by G. Leitmann, Academic Press, 1962.

(5). Hestenes, M.R., Numerical Methods of Obtaining Solutions of Fixed End Point Problems in the Calculus of Variations, RM-102, The Rand Corporation, August 1949.

(6). Kalaba, R., "On Nonlinear Differential Equations, the Maximum Operation, and Monotone Convergence," Journal of Mathematics and Mechanics, Vol. 8, No. 4, pp. 519-574, July 1959.

(7). McGill, R., and Kenneth, P., "Solution of Variational Problems by Means of a Generalized Newton-Raphson Operator," to be published.

A STEEPEST-ASCENT TRAJECTORY OPTIMIZATION METHOD WHICH REDUCES MEMORY REQUIREMENTS

by

Dr. R. H. Hillsley
Dr. H. M. Robbins

International Business Machines Corporation
Federal Systems Division
Space Guidance Center
Oswego, New York

This paper describes an iterative process for steepest-ascent optimization of orbit transfer trajectories. The method is designed to minimize storage requirements, at the expense of a small amount of additional computation. The reduced memory requirements eliminate the need for tape operations on the 7090 when the method is used to compute nominal trajectories. In-flight use, by a guidance computer of limited memory, appears feasible.

The method has the following features:

The adjoint equations are integrated forward with the equations of motion. Forward integration of the adjoint equations presents no problems because the equations of perturbed motion are self-adjoint. This procedure produces the values of the state variables at the same time they are needed in the adjoint equations; as a result no state variable values have to be stored.

Instead of storing the control schedule as a function of time, the control schedule is generated by segment-wise integration of certain differential equations. The initial conditions inserted in these equations at each of the segment beginnings constitute a finite set of control parameters that may be iteratively adjusted to alter the trajectory toward optimality and make it meet terminal conditions. This works out particularly well in the orbit transfer application. Each burn can be made a segment because burn times are short compared to the relevant Schuler periods.

Kepler arcs and an explicit expression for the corresponding Jacobian matrix are used in place of numerical integration during coast periods on runs neglecting quadrapole fields.

The initial trajectory is determined by a modification procedure to be applied to the minimum fuel rendezvous trajectory computed for impulse thrusts.

The metric used to define step size is a Euclidean metric determined by the control increments which maximize the local Hamiltonian.

Step size is modified by comparing the predicted and actual increment in terminal states.

The computations are first derived and then summarized. The first section gives expressions for the changes in terminal mass, position, and velocity in terms of changes in the control variables. These expressions involve a complete set of adjoint variables produced by forward integration of the adjoint equations. The second section gives the extremum necessary conditions and the Hamiltonian. The third section gives the second order expression for changes in the Hamiltonian and uses it to compute the control increments for the steepest-ascent method. The fourth section discusses computation procedures. The fifth section reviews the computations.

1. Adjoint Equations

The set of system equations are:

$$\ddot{\overline{R}} - \overline{g}(\overline{R}) - SF\hat{e}/m = 0$$

$$\dot{m} + SF/c = 0 \qquad (1\text{-}1)$$

where $\overline{R}$ is the position vector, $\dot{\overline{R}}$ is velocity, m is mass, and thrust F and effective exhaust velocity c are given constants. $\overline{g}(\overline{R})$ is the gravity vector. $\hat{e}$ is the unit steering vector which gives the direction of the thrust. $S = S(t)$ is the switch function.

$S = 1$ during burn periods

$S = 0$ during coast periods

The next step is to form six independent combinations of the system equations, and integrate these combinations from t_o to t_f. That is, we form

$$0 = \int_{t_o}^{t_f} \left\{ \Lambda^T(t) \left[\ddot{\overline{R}} - \overline{g}(\overline{R}) - SF\hat{e}/m \right] + \overline{N}(t) \left[\dot{m} + SF/c \right] \right\} dt \tag{1-2}$$

where Λ^T is the transpose of a 3 x 6 matrix Λ, and $\overline{N}$ is a 6 x 1 vector. (All vectors will be indicated by bars and represent column vectors.)

A seventh equation is

$$0 = \int_{t_o}^{t_f} (\dot{m} + SF/c)\, dt \tag{1-3}$$

The function S(t) is completely defined by specifying a sequence of burn-begin times t_b and burn end times t_e. Perturbing $\overline{R}$, $\hat{e}$, m and the switch times t_b, t_e gives

$$0 = \int_{t_o}^{t_f} \left\{ \Lambda^T \left[\delta\ddot{\overline{R}} - G\,\delta\overline{R} - (SF/m)\,\delta\hat{e} + (SF\hat{e}/m^2)\,\delta m \right] + \overline{N}\,\delta\dot{m} \right\} dt + \sum_b \left(\Lambda^T \hat{e}F/m - \overline{N}F/c \right)_b dt_b - \sum_e \left(\Lambda^T \hat{e}F/m - \overline{N}F/c \right)_e dt_e \tag{1-4}$$

and

$$\delta m_f = (F/c) \left[\sum_b dt_b - \sum_e dt_e \right] \tag{1-5}$$

In Eq. (1-4), $(\;\;)_b$ means that the quantity in parenthesis is evaluated at time t_b, and $(\;\;)_e$ similarly means evaluation at time t_e. G is the 3 x 3 gravity gradient matrix, whose elements are

$$G_{ij} = \partial g_i / \partial x_j = - \frac{\partial^2 \gamma}{\partial x_i\, \partial x_j} \quad \text{for } ij = 1, 2, 3 \tag{1-6}$$

where γ is the gravity potential. It is evident that $G = G^T$. Integrating Eq. (1-4) by parts, and requiring $\Lambda(t)$ and $\overline{N}(t)$ to obey

$$\ddot{\Lambda}^T = \Lambda^T G \qquad (1\text{-}7)$$

$$\dot{\overline{N}} = \Lambda^T \hat{e}\, SF/m^2 \qquad (1\text{-}8)$$

gives

$$(\overline{N}\,\delta m + \Lambda^T\, \delta\dot{\overline{R}} - \dot{\Lambda}^T\, \delta\overline{R})_f = \int_{t_o}^{t_f} (\Lambda^T SF/m)\, \delta\hat{e}\, dt +$$

$$- \sum_b (\Lambda^T \hat{e} F/m - \overline{N}F/c)_b\, dt_b + \sum_e (\Lambda^T \hat{e} F/m - \overline{N}F/c)\, dt_e \qquad (1\text{-}9)$$

where $(\;)_f$ means evaluation at time t_f, and the perturbations of m, $\overline{R}$, and $\dot{\overline{R}}$ at time t_o are assumed zero. Multiplying Eq. (1-5) by $\overline{N}_f$ and subtracting from Eq. (1-9) gives

$$(\Lambda^T\, \delta\dot{\overline{R}} - \dot{\Lambda}^T\, \delta\overline{R})_f = \int_{t_o}^{t_f} (\Lambda^T SF/m)\, \delta\hat{e} dt - \sum_b \overline{K}_b\, dt_b +$$

$$\sum_e \overline{K}_e\, dt_e \qquad (1\text{-}10)$$

where $\overline{K}_b = \overline{K}(t_b)$, $\overline{K}_e = \overline{K}(t_e)$, and

$$\overline{K}(t) = \Lambda^T \hat{e}(t)\, F/m(t) + \left[\overline{N}_f - \overline{N}(t)\right] F/c \qquad (1\text{-}11)$$

Eqs. (1-5) and (1-10) give δm_f and six independent combinations of $\delta\overline{R}_f$, $\delta\dot{\overline{R}}_f$ in terms of control changes. Eq. (1-10) could readily be solved for $\delta\overline{R}_f$ and $\delta\dot{\overline{R}}_f$ explicitly, but this step is unnecessary for our purpose.

Since the adjoint variables Λ and $\overline{N}$ are to be generated by forward integration of Eqs. (1-7) and (1-8), it is necessary to specify initial conditions. A convenient choice for Λ is

$$\begin{bmatrix} \Lambda(t_o) \\ \dot{\Lambda}(t_o) \end{bmatrix} = \begin{bmatrix} I & 0 \\ 0 & I \end{bmatrix} \qquad (1\text{-}12)$$

where I is a 3 x 3 unit matrix and 0 is a 3 x 3 zero matrix. The initial value of $\overline{N}$ is unimportant, since it cancels out in the function $\overline{K}(t)$. We choose

$$\overline{N}(t_o) = 0 \tag{1-13}$$

2. Necessary Conditions and the Hamiltonian

Necessary conditions for the optimality of a rocket trajectory have been given many times, but are rederived here for convenience. From the system equations written as first-order equations

$$\dot{\overline{R}} = \overline{V} \tag{2-1a}$$

$$\dot{\overline{V}} = \overline{g}(\overline{R}) + SF\hat{e}/m \tag{2-1b}$$

$$\dot{m} = -SF/c \tag{2-1c}$$

we form the Hamiltonian

$$H = \overline{q}^T \overline{V} + \overline{p}^T \left[\overline{g}(\overline{R}) + SF\hat{e}/m \right] - r\, SF/c \tag{2-2}$$

where the new variables $\overline{q}$, $\overline{p}$, and r are conjugate, in the Hamiltonian sense, to $\overline{R}$, $\overline{V}$, m respectively.

It is easy to see that this Hamiltonian generates the system equations in the standard manner.

$$\dot{\overline{R}} = \partial H / \partial \overline{q}^T = \overline{V}$$

$$\dot{\overline{V}} = \partial H / \partial \overline{p}^T = \overline{g}(\overline{R}) + SF\hat{e}/m$$

$$\dot{m} = \partial H / \partial r = -SF/c$$

It also generates the adjoint equations

$$\dot{\overline{q}}^T = - \partial H / \partial \overline{R} = -\overline{p}^T G \tag{2-3}$$

$$\dot{\overline{p}}^T = - \partial H / \partial \overline{V} = -\overline{q}^T \tag{2-4}$$

$$\dot{r} = - \partial H / \partial m = \overline{p}^T \hat{e}\, SF/m^2 \tag{2-5}$$

Eqs. (2-3) and (2-4) can be combined and transposed to give

$$\ddot{\bar{p}} = G\bar{p} \tag{2-6}$$

The necessary conditions are derived by forming

$$0 = J = \int_{t_o}^{t_f} \left[\bar{q}^T (\dot{\bar{R}} - \bar{V}) + \bar{p}^T (\dot{\bar{V}} - \bar{g} - SF\hat{e}/m) + r(\dot{m} + SF/c) \right] dt \tag{2-7}$$

and varying $\bar{R}$, $\bar{V}$, m, $\hat{e}$ and S, keeping $\bar{q}$, $\bar{p}$, r fixed. The variations of $\bar{R}$, $\bar{V}$ and m are assumed to vanish at time t_o. Integration by parts after variation, and use of the adjoint equations, gives

$$r_f \, \delta m_f = -(\bar{q}^T \delta\bar{R} + \bar{p}^T \delta\bar{V})_f + \delta \Big|_{\hat{e},S} \int_{t_o}^{t_f} H \, dt \tag{2-8}$$

where the last term represents the variation of the integral of the Hamiltonian, with respect to the controls $\hat{e}$ and S. We choose $r_f > 0$. This is always possible by proper choice of the additive constant in the general solution of Eq. (2-5). Then Eq. (2-8) says that m_f cannot be maximal unless two conditions are satisfied. Firstly, the final values of $\bar{p}$ and $\dot{\bar{p}} = -\bar{q}$ must be such that

$$(\bar{p}^T \delta\bar{V} - \dot{\bar{p}}^T \delta\bar{R})_f = 0 \tag{2-9}$$

for every variation of $\bar{R}_f$ and $\bar{V}_f = \dot{\bar{R}}_f$ that is compatible with the final conditions imposed on the trajectory. For a fixed end point, $\delta\bar{V}_f = \delta\dot{\bar{R}}_f = 0$ so $\bar{p}_f$ and $\dot{\bar{p}}_f$ may have any values, but for a variable end point, $\bar{p}_f$ and $\dot{\bar{p}}_f$ would be subject to one or more transversality equations. Secondly, the controls $\hat{e}$ and S must be chosen to maximize H at every instant (which automatically maximizes the integral). The "optimum" controls which satisfy this condition are evidently given by

$$\hat{e}_{opt} = \bar{p}/|\bar{p}| \tag{2-10}$$

and

$$S_{opt} = \begin{cases} 1 \text{ if } \bar{p}^T \hat{e}/m - r/c > 0 \\ 0 \text{ if } \bar{p}^T \hat{e}/m - r/c < 0 \end{cases} \tag{2-11}$$

Putting $\hat{e}_{opt}$ into this equation simplifies it by reducing $\bar{p}^T \hat{e}$ to $|\bar{p}|$. A useful relation, derived from Eqs. (2-1c) and (2-5), is

$$\frac{d}{dt}\left(|\bar{p}|/m - r/c\right) = |\bar{p}|^{\cdot}/m \tag{2-12}$$

3. Steepest-Ascent Method

Since no analytic method is known for obtaining trajectories that satisfy the necessary conditions for optimality, numerical methods must be used. The chosen method is a "steepest-ascent" method in that it proceeds by iterative modification of trial trajectories to make them more nearly optimum; it can be regarded as essentially Bryson's steepest-ascent method (Bryson, A. E., "A Steepest-Ascent Method for Solving Optimum Programming Problems," Raytheon Report BR-1303) with a particular choice of metric. However, the method is unique in that reduced memory requirements eliminate the need for tape operations on the 7090. Furthermore, in flight use by a guidance computer of limited memory appears feasible.

The reduced memory requirements are realized by eliminating state variable storage and control schedule storage. Forward integration of the adjoint equations, as described in Section 1, eliminates the need for state variable storage; generating the control by segment-wise integration of certain differential equations eliminates the need of control schedule storage.

The control schedule is generated during burns by computing the controls which maximize a local Hamiltonian.

From Eq. (2-2)

$$\hat{e} = \bar{p}/|\bar{p}| \tag{3-1}$$

where $\hat{e}$ is the unit steering vector which maximizes the local Hamiltonian, and

$$\ddot{\bar{p}} = G\bar{p} \tag{3-2}$$

Unlike the $\bar{p}(t)$ considered in Section 2 in connection with the necessary conditions for optimality, this $\bar{p}(t)$ is defined independently for each burn. This procedure insures that the control is generated for a short period. This requirement arises because the new $\bar{p}(t)$ is generated by Eq. (3-2) using gravity gradient G evaluated on the new trajectory, not on the old trajectory where Λ was computed. The consequent change in G causes an additional change in $\bar{p}$ besides that due to change in the initial conditions, $\bar{p}$ and $\dot{\bar{p}}$ at burn-beginning. The effect can be approximately corrected or made negligible by breaking up the control program into short segments. However, for a high thrust vehicle in the orbit transfer case, this is generally not necessary when each burn represents a control segment. Thus, the initial conditions $\bar{p}(t_b)$ and $\dot{\bar{p}}(t_b)$ at burn beginning constitute a set of six control parameters which completely define the steering schedule for the burn in question.

We now proceed to determine new $\bar{p}(t_b)$, $\bar{p}(t_b)$, t_b, and t_e which produce a specified change in terminal position, velocity, and mass; minimize a Euclidean metric; and satisfy the constraint that $\delta\hat{e}$ is perpendicular to $\hat{e}$.

A suitable measure of step size is the change in the integral of the Hamiltonian when the control variables $\hat{e}(t)$, t_b and t_e are perturbed from their optimal values which maximize the integral. (These are not truly optimal values unless $\bar{p}$ and r obey Eqs. (2-5) and (2-6), with coefficients evaluated on an optimal trajectory.) This expression is:

$$\delta/\hat{e}, S \int_{t_o}^{t_f} H\,dt = -\frac{1}{2} \int_{t_o}^{t_f} (SF/m)\,|\bar{p}|\,|\delta\hat{e}|^2\,dt - \frac{1}{2} \sum_s \frac{1}{|\beta_s|} (dt_s)^2 \qquad (3\text{-}3)$$

where s is an index of all "switch times," i.e., all burn-begin times t_b and all burn-end times t_e, and

$$\beta_s = (m/F\ |\bar{p}|^{\cdot})_s \qquad (3\text{-}4)$$

so by Eq. (2-12),

$$1/\beta_s = F\left[\frac{d}{dt}(|\bar{p}|/m - r/c)\right]_s \tag{3-5}$$

To derive the first term of Eq. (3-3), note that the only term in H (as given in Eq. (2-2)) that involves e is:

$$(SF/m)\,\bar{p}^T\hat{e} = (SF/m)\,|\bar{p}|\cos\theta \tag{3-6}$$

where θ is the angle between the vectors $\bar{p}$ and $\hat{e}$, and use has been made of the fact that $|\hat{e}| = 1$. For "optimal" $\hat{e}$, $\theta = 0$. For $\hat{e}$ perturbed from optimal by a change $\delta\hat{e}$,

$$\theta = |\delta\hat{e}| \tag{3-7}$$

$$\cos\theta \approx 1 - \frac{1}{2}\theta^2 = 1 - \frac{1}{2}|\delta\hat{e}|^2$$

Substituting Eq. (3-7) into (3-6), and the result into the H integral, gives the first term of Eq. (3-3). To derive the second term note, in Eq. 2-2, that S enters into the Hamiltonian in the combination.

$$SF\,(|\bar{p}|/m - r/c)$$

assuming optimal e. So

$$\delta|_S \int H\,dt = F\int (S - S_{opt})(|\bar{p}|/m - r/c)\,dt \tag{3-8}$$

S differs from the optimal S by changing from 0 to 1, or vice versa, at a switch time $t_S + \Delta t_S$ which is slightly different from the optimal switch time t_S. In the vicinity of such a switch time,

$$F\,(|\bar{p}|/m - r/c) \approx (t - t_s)/\beta_s \tag{3-9}$$

Also

$$S_{opt} = 1 \quad \text{if} \quad (t - t_s)/\beta_s > 0$$

$$\phantom{S_{opt}} = 0 \quad \text{if} \quad (t - t_s)/\beta_s < 0$$

S disagrees with S_{opt} for values of t between t_s and $t_s + \Delta t_s$. In this interval

$$\begin{aligned} S - S_{opt} &= 0 - 1 = -1 \qquad \text{if} \quad (t - t_s) / \beta_s > 0 \\ &= 1 - 0 = +1 \qquad \text{if} \quad (t - t_s) / \beta_s < 0 \\ &= -\operatorname{sgn}\left[(t - t_s) / \beta_s \right] \quad \text{always} \end{aligned} \tag{3-10}$$

Combining Eqs. (3-9) and (3-10) shows that the integrand of Eq. (3-8) is approximately

$$- \left| (t - t_s) / \beta_s \right|$$

between t_s and $t_s + \Delta t_s$, and zero elsewhere. In each interval of width $|\Delta t_s|$ in which it is non zero it changes linearly from zero to $-|\Delta t_s| / |\beta_s|$, so its average value in the interval is $-\frac{1}{2} |\Delta t_s| / |\beta_s|$ and its integral over the interval is

$$-\frac{1}{2} \frac{1}{|\beta_s|} (\Delta t_s)^2$$

Summing over all switch times, and changing the notation so the perturbation of switchtime t_s is denoted by dt_s rather than Δt_s, gives the second term of Eq. (3-3), completing its derivation.

The next step is to seek control increments $\delta\hat{e}(t)$ and dt_s, such that the integral of H is maximized subject to the constraints given by requiring the control-change to induce specified changes in the final values of $\overline{R}$, $\dot{\overline{R}}$, and m. This is possible in general, if the initial trajectory is non-optimal and the specified changes are sufficiently small. Introducing the abbreviation

$$\begin{aligned} (dL)^2 &= \int_{t_o}^{t_f} (SF/m) \, |\overline{p}| \, \delta\hat{e}^T \, \delta\hat{e} \, dt + \sum_s \frac{1}{|\beta_s|} (dt_s)^2 \\ &= -2 \, \delta \Big|_{\hat{e}, S} \int H \, dt \end{aligned} \tag{3-11}$$

the stated problem reduces to that of minimizing the quantity

$$J = \frac{1}{2} (dL)^2 - (c/F)\, k\, \delta m_f - \overline{v}^T (\Lambda^T \delta \dot{\overline{R}} - \dot{\Lambda}^T \delta \overline{R})_f - \int Sn(t)\, \hat{e}^T \delta \hat{e}\, dt \qquad (3\text{-}12)$$

with respect to $\delta \hat{e}(t)$ and dt_s. The scalar constant k and the 6 x 1 vector constant $\overline{v}$ are Lagrange multipliers introduced to enforce the desired final-value changes. The integral involving n(t) is similarly introduced to enfore the constraint

$$\hat{e}^T \delta \hat{e} = 0 \qquad (3\text{-}13)$$

Rewriting Eqs. (1-5) and (1-10) as

$$(c/F)\, \delta m_f = \sum_s (\text{sgn}\, \beta_s)\, dt_s \qquad (1\text{-}5')$$

and

$$(\Lambda^T \delta \dot{\overline{R}} - \dot{\Lambda}^T \delta \overline{R})_f = \int (\Lambda^T SF/m)\, \delta \hat{e}\, dt - \sum_s (\text{sgn}\, \beta_s)\, \overline{K}_s\, dt_s \qquad (1\text{-}10')$$

and substituting these expressions into Eq. (3-12) gives J in terms of $\delta \hat{e}$ and dt_s. Requiring the partial of J with respect to $\delta \hat{e}$ to vanish gives

$$|\overline{p}|\, \delta \hat{e} = \Lambda \overline{v} + (m/F)\, n(t)\, \hat{e} \qquad (3\text{-}14)$$

when $S \neq 0$. At other times, $\delta \hat{e}$ is indeterminate and irrelevant. Requiring the vanishing of the partial of J with respect to dt_s gives

$$dt_s = \beta_s (k - \overline{K}_s^T \overline{v}) \qquad (3\text{-}15)$$

The Lagrange multipliers k, $\overline{v}$, n are determined by substituting these results into the constraint equations. Eq. (3-13) gives

$$0 = \hat{e}^T \Lambda \overline{v} + (m/F)\, n(t)$$

which may be used to eliminate n from Eq. (3-12), giving

$$|\bar{p}| \, \delta\hat{e} = \Lambda\bar{v} - \hat{e}\hat{e}^T \Lambda\bar{v} = (I - \hat{e}\hat{e}^T) \, \Lambda\bar{v} \tag{3-16}$$

Then Eqs. (1-5′) and (1-10′) give

$$(c/F) \, \delta m_f = \sum_s |\beta_s| \, (k - \bar{K}_s^T \, \bar{v}) \tag{3-17}$$

and

$$(\Lambda^T \delta\dot{\bar{R}} - \dot{\Lambda}^T \delta\bar{R})_f = - \bar{U}k + M\bar{v} \tag{3-18}$$

where

$$\bar{U} = \sum_s |\beta_s| \bar{K}_s \tag{3-19}$$

and

$$M = \int_{t_o}^{t_f} \frac{SF}{m|\bar{p}|} \, \Lambda^T (I - \hat{e}\hat{e}^T) \, \Lambda \, dt + \sum_s |\beta_s| \bar{K}_s \, \bar{K}_s^T \tag{3-20}$$

Introducing the further abbreviation $u = \sum_s |\beta_s|$, Eq. (3-17) can be written as

$$(c/F) \, \delta m_f = uk - \bar{U}^T \bar{v} \tag{3-21}$$

Defining

$$\bar{B}_\psi = (\Lambda^T \delta\dot{\bar{R}} - \dot{\Lambda}^T \delta\bar{R})_f \tag{3-22}$$

and solving Eq. (3-18) for $\bar{v}$ gives

$$\bar{v} = M^{-1} (\bar{B}_\psi + \bar{U}k) \tag{3-23}$$

Substituting this into Eqs. (3-15), (3-16), and (3-21) gives

$$dt_s = - \beta_s \bar{K}_s^T \, M^{-1} \, \bar{B}_\psi + k \, \beta_s (1 - \bar{K}_s^T \, M^{-1} \, \bar{U}) \tag{3-24}$$

$$\delta\hat{e} = |\bar{p}|^{-1} (I - \hat{e}\hat{e}^T) \, \Lambda M^{-1} (\bar{B}_\psi + k\bar{U}) \tag{3-25}$$

$$(c/F) \, \delta m_f = - \bar{U}^T M^{-1} \bar{B}_\psi + k \left[u - \bar{U}^T M^{-1} \bar{U} \right] \tag{3-26}$$

The value of $(dL)^2$ is found to be

$$(dL)^2 = \overline{B}_\psi^T M^{-1} \overline{B}_\psi + k^2 \left[u - \overline{U}^T M^{-1} \overline{U} \right] \tag{3-27}$$

which implies that the bracketed quantity must be non-negative. For $(dL)^2$ is minimized subject to constraints, and cannot increase if one of these constraints is removed by setting $k = 0$ (which abolishes the constraint on δm_f). This argument, together with Eq. (3-26), shows that k should always be chosen positive to increase m_f.

Eq. (3-25), together with

$$\text{new } \hat{e}(t) = \hat{e}(t) + \delta\hat{e}(t) \tag{3-28}$$

gives a new steering schedule for the next iteration. To avoid having to store this schedule as a tabulated function of time, we resort to the control generating technique described at the beginning of this section. We compute $\delta \dot{\overline{p}}(t_b)$ and $\delta \overline{p}(t_b)$ in order to determine the new $\overline{p}(t_b)$ and $\dot{\overline{p}}(t_b)$ from the equation

$$\text{new } \overline{p} = \overline{p} + \delta\overline{p} \tag{3-29}$$

If we assume $|\delta\overline{p}| << |\overline{p}|$ and use $|\overline{p}| = \hat{e}^T\overline{p}$, (Eq. (3-1)), this gives

$$\delta\hat{e} = (\text{new } \hat{e}) - \hat{e} = |\overline{p}|^{-1} (I - \hat{e}\hat{e}^T)\, \delta\overline{p} \tag{3-30}$$

to first order in $\delta\overline{p}$. Then comparison with Eq. (3-16) suggests choosing

$$\delta\overline{p} = \Lambda\overline{v} - \epsilon\overline{p} \tag{3-31}$$

where the constant ϵ is arbitrary, since the term $\epsilon\overline{p}$ cancels out when substituted into Eq. (3-30). It turns out to be convenient to choose $\epsilon = k$. Then Eq. (3-29) becomes

$$\text{new } \overline{p} = (1 - k)\,\overline{p} + \Lambda\overline{v} \tag{3-32}$$

Recalling the definition of $\overline{v}$, Eqs. (3-31) and (3-32) can be rewritten as

$$\delta\overline{p} = \left[\Lambda M^{-1}\overline{U} - \overline{p} \right] k + \Lambda M^{-1}\overline{B}_\psi \tag{3-33}$$

$$\text{new } \overline{p} = (1 - k)\, \overline{p} + k \Lambda M^{-1} \overline{U} + \Lambda M^{-1} \overline{B}_\psi \qquad (3\text{-}34)$$

If the desired changes in $\overline{R}_f$ and $\dot{\overline{R}}_f$ are sufficiently small, then $|\Lambda M^{-1} \overline{B}_\psi| << |\overline{p}|$ is guaranteed. Therefore, $|\delta \overline{p}| << |\overline{p}|$ is guaranteed if k is sufficiently small, or if $\overline{p}$ is nearly equal to $\Lambda M^{-1} \overline{U}$. The former alternative implies small steps toward optimality, but may be necessary for the first few iterations. Eq.(3-34) shows that, except for the term $\Lambda M^{-1} \overline{B}_\psi$ which is expected to be small, the new $\overline{p}$ is a weighted average of $\Lambda M^{-1} \overline{U}$ and the old $\overline{p}$. Therefore, if $k > 0$ and if $\Lambda M^{-1} \overline{U}$ converges to a limit, $\overline{p}$ converges to the same limit. Call this common limit $\overline{p}_{opt}$. It is evident that $\overline{p}_{opt}$ is identical with the $\overline{p}(t)$ that occurs in the statement of necessary conditions for optimality.

When the trial trajectory becomes sufficiently close to optimum to ensure $|\Lambda M^{-1} \overline{U}| \approx |\overline{p}|$, it is no longer necessary to choose k small. Eq. (3-34) shows that if $\Lambda M^{-1} \overline{U}$ changes little from iteration to iteration, it would be appropriate to choose $k = 1$. This corresponds to Kelly's "Min-H" scheme (Kelley, Kopp, and Moyer, "Successive Approximation Techniques for Trajectory Optimization", in the Proceedings of the IAS Symposium on Vehicle Systems Optimization, Nov., 1961) since the control change jumps in one step to controls that are optimal for the given, non-optimal Lagrange multipliers—which in our case are represented by $\Lambda M^{-1} \overline{U}$ as far as steering is concerned. In the orbit transfer case, the changes of $\Lambda M^{-1} \overline{U}$ are expected to be of the same order as $\delta \overline{p}$, even when optimality is near, so the choice $k = 1$ is not particularly significant except as to order of magnitude. However, Eq. (3-34) does suggest choosing $0 < k < 2$ to make the influence of the initial $\overline{p}(t)$ decline geometrically with successive iterations.

It is of some interest to work out the $r_{opt}(t)$ corresponding to $\overline{p}_{opt} = \Lambda M^{-1} \overline{U}$. For an optimal trajectory,

$$(F/m) \left| \overline{p}_{opt} \right| - (F/c)\, r_{opt} = 0 \qquad (3\text{-}35)$$

at each unconstrained switch time t_s. But for $\overline{B}_\psi = 0$, Eq. (3-24) implies

$$\overline{K}_s^T M^{-1} \overline{U} - 1 = 0 \qquad (3\text{-}36)$$

if the switchtimes are optimal and do not require change. Recalling the definition of $\overline{K}(t)$, Eq. (3-36) becomes

$$o = (F/m)\,\hat{e}^T \Lambda M^{-1}\overline{U} - (F/c)\,(\overline{N}^T - \overline{N}_f^T)\,M^{-1}\overline{U} - 1$$

at switch times. The first term in this equation is (F/m) times $\hat{e}^T\overline{p}_{opt} = |\overline{p}_{opt}|$. Therefore, comparison with Eq. (3-35) suggests defining

$$r(t) = (c/F) + \left[\,\overline{N}(t) - \overline{N}_f\,\right] M^{-1}\overline{U} \tag{3-37}$$

This $r(t)$ obeys the differential equation $\dot{r} = (F/m^2)\,\hat{e}^T\overline{p}$, as may easily be verified. Since it also crosses zero at the proper times, it must give $r_{opt}(t)$ if the right side of the above equation is evaluated for an optimal trajectory.

The initial $\overline{p}(t)$ which starts the iteration procedure is derived from an optimal or near-optimal impulsive trajectory, by a process described in detail in the last section. The necessary conditions for optimality of an impulsive trajectory give the direction of $\overline{p}$ at each impulse, and require its magnitude to be the same at all impulses, but do not determine this magnitude. To speed convergence, this undetermined magnitude should be chosen to make the initial $\overline{p}(t)$ approximate the $\overline{p}_{opt}$ which is the final result of the iteration process. An appropriate choice is

$$|\overline{p}| = m_f/F \text{ at impulses} \tag{3-38}$$

where m_f is the final mass, as computed for an impulsive trajectory. This choice may be derived as follows. Eq. (3-37) gives $r = c/F$ at the last cutoff time, since $\overline{N} = \overline{N}_f$ after this time. If the final cutoff time is unconstrained, Eq. (3-35) then gives

$$|\overline{p}|_{opt} = m_f/F \tag{3-39}$$

at the final cutoff time. If burns are short compared to local Schuler period, $|\overline{p}|_{opt}$ will not differ greatly from this value during any burn, and the choice is justified. If the final cutoff time is constrained, the argument must be modified somewhat, but the result is still approximately correct if the final burn is short enough so that the fractional change in $|\overline{p}|$ during this burn is small.

4. Discussion

A. Storage Requirements

The method derived in the preceding section eliminates the need for control schedule or state variable storage. The quantities which have to be stored are indicated in Eq. (5-1). A component count indicates 85 + 59N where N is the number of burns. For N = 2, there are 203 numbers in storage at the end of the forward integration.

B. Trajectory Smoothness

In addition to the reduced storage requirements, the method of generating the control schedule from $\bar{p}(t_b)$ and $\dot{\bar{p}}(t_b)$ has a more subtle benefit. The benefit stems from the fact that the trial trajectories are determined by a finite number of parameters and are inherently "smooth". Thus, wiggles do not appear in the trajectories and no smoothing is required.

C. Forward Integration Stability

The Λ (t) matrix is computed by integrating the adjoint equations forward from a set of initial conditions. No rapidly expanding exponentials occur in the forward adjoint equations to make accurate numerical integration difficult, since dissipation terms do not occur in the state equations because the orbit transfer is assumed to take place outside the atmosphere. In fact, the adjoint equations and the perturbation state equations are identical (self-adjoint).

D. General Usefulness of the Method

As noted following Eq. (3-2), the control generation technique introduces an unwanted control change caused by evaluating the gravity gradient G on the new trajectory, not on the old trajectory where Λ was computed. The consequent change in G causes an additional change in $\bar{p}$ besides that due to change in the initial conditions $\bar{p}$ and $\dot{\bar{p}}$. Since the unwanted change in $\bar{p}$ results from an error in $\ddot{\bar{p}}$, its effects can be made small by limiting the duration of control generating periods. On a general application, this requirement can be met by dividing the control program into segments. Alternatively, the $\bar{p}$ initial conditions can be compensated for the change in G.

E. Step Size

The derivation of Section 3 is valid in the proximity of the optimum solution where the β -coefficients have the correct signs. To expand the range of validity the appropriate signs for the β-coefficients were incorporated into the programming as shown by Eqs. (5-7) and (5-8). In addition, in order to avoid excessive switching time changes from iteration to iteration, the magnitudes of the β-coefficients have been made program inputs (β') which may be altered at each program restart. This procedure has the additional advantage that beginning and/or end time, or an entire burn may be constrained by setting the appropriate β' equal to zero without any complication of program logic. The computed β -coefficients are outputted to indicate the shape of the switching function.

. The constant k_2 has been introduced into Eq. (5-4) to make it possible to control the size of the step toward rendezvous. Both k and k_2 have been made program inputs which can be altered at each program restart. In addition, it is possible to input a table of values for k_2 and some limits for selecting k_2. Some experimentation has been done with the following automatic method for selecting k_2 based on the largest component in the position miss. A comparison of the ratio of the predicted and actual increments and the limits for selecting k_2 determines whether the lower, same, or higher value in the k_2 - table should be used in the next iteration. However, when using the initiation scheme described in Section 6, it is often possible to set k_2 at unity for all iterations. The selection of k is discussed following Eq. (3-34).

5. Computation Review and Glossary

At the end of the forward integration, the following information has been stored:

$$\bar{R},\ \dot{\bar{R}},\ m,\ \Lambda\ ,\ \dot{\Lambda}\ ,\ \bar{N},\ Q, \qquad \text{at } t_f$$

Λ , $\dot{\Lambda}$, $\bar{p}$, $\dot{\bar{p}}$, and $G\bar{p}$ for each burn begin t_b (5-1)

β and $\bar{K}$ for each switch time t_s

and the following quantities can be produced:

k and k_2

$\bar{U}$ and u

Then the following are computed.

$$\delta \dot{\bar{R}}_f = -(\dot{\bar{R}}_f - \dot{\bar{R}}_f^{\ target}) \tag{5-2}$$

$$\delta \bar{R}_f = -(\bar{R}_f - \bar{R}_f^{\ target}) \tag{5-3}$$

$$\bar{B}\psi = k_2 (\Lambda^T \ \delta\dot{\bar{R}} - \dot{\Lambda}^T \ \delta\bar{R})_f \tag{5-4}$$

$$M = Q_f + \sum_s |\beta'_s| \ \bar{K}_s \bar{K}_s^T \tag{5-5}$$

$$\bar{v} = M^{-1} (\bar{B}\psi + \bar{U}k) \tag{5-6}$$

$$dt_{bi} = |\beta'_{bi}| \ (k - K^T \bar{v}) \tag{5-7}$$

$$dt_{ei} = - |\beta'_{ei}| \ (k - K^T \bar{v}) \tag{5-8}$$

$$t_{bi} = t_{bi\ old} + dt_{bi} \tag{5-9}$$

$$t_{ei} = t_{ei\ old} + dt_{ei}$$

$$\bar{p}_b = (1-k)\,\bar{p}_{old} + \Lambda \bar{v} + \dot{\bar{p}}_{old}\, dt_b \tag{5-10}$$

$$\dot{\bar{p}}_b = (1-k)\,\dot{\bar{p}}_{old} + \dot{\Lambda} \bar{v} + G\bar{p}_{old}\, dt_b$$

The program is now ready to start the forward integration from the initial conditions

$$\bar{R}(t_o) = \bar{R}_o$$

$$\dot{\bar{R}}(t_o) = \dot{\bar{R}}_o$$

$$m(t_o) = m_o$$

$$\begin{bmatrix} \Lambda(t_o) \\ \dot{\Lambda}(t_o) \end{bmatrix} = \begin{bmatrix} I & O \\ O & I \end{bmatrix} \tag{5-11}$$

$$\bar{N}(t_o) = O$$

$$Q(t_o) = O$$

The equations integrated are

$$\ddot{\bar{R}} = \bar{g}(\bar{R}) + SF\hat{e}/m \tag{5-12}$$

$$\dot{m} = SF/c \tag{5-13}$$

$$\ddot{\Lambda} = G\Lambda \tag{5-14}$$

$$\dot{\bar{N}} = FS\hat{e}^T\Lambda \ /m^2 \tag{5-15}$$

$$\dot{Q} = (FS \ \Lambda^T \left[I-\hat{e}\hat{e}^T \right] \Lambda)/m \ |\bar{p}| \tag{5-16}$$

At each t_b the program uses the results of Eq. (5-10) and the current Λ's to compute

$$\bar{b} = \begin{bmatrix} \dot{\Lambda}^T{}_2 \ (t_b) & - \ \Lambda^T{}_2 \ (t_b) \\ - \ \dot{\Lambda}^T{}_1 \ (t_b) & \Lambda^T{}_1 \ (t_b) \end{bmatrix} \begin{bmatrix} \bar{p}\ (t_b) \\ \dot{\bar{p}}\ (t_b) \end{bmatrix} \tag{5-17}$$

where we have introduced Λ_1 and Λ_2 as 3 x 3 submatrices of Λ such that

$$\begin{aligned} \Lambda &= \begin{bmatrix} \Lambda_1 & \Lambda_2 \end{bmatrix} \\ \dot{\Lambda} &= \begin{bmatrix} \dot{\Lambda}_1 & \dot{\Lambda}_2 \end{bmatrix} \end{aligned} \tag{5-18}$$

Then during the burn

$$\bar{p} = \Lambda(t)\ \bar{b} \tag{5-19}$$

$$\hat{e} = \bar{p} / |\bar{p}| \tag{5-20}$$

At each switch time, the program computes

$$\beta_s = (m/F\ |\bar{p}|^{\cdot}\ )_s = (m\ |\bar{p}|\ / F\ \dot{\bar{p}}^{T}\ \bar{p})_s \tag{5-21}$$

$$\bar{K}_s = \left[(\ \Lambda^T \hat{e}\ F/m) + (\bar{N}_f - \bar{N})\ F/c \right]_s \tag{5-22}$$

at the end of the forward integration,

$$\bar{U} = \sum_s \ |\beta_s'|\ \bar{K}_s \tag{5-23}$$

$$u = \sum_s \ |\beta_s'| \tag{5-24}$$

where the prime on the β indicates inputed rather than computed values.

At the end of the forward integration, the results 5-1 are available to begin the next iteration cycle with the constants k and k_2 either determined by an automatic modification scheme or specified directly by the restart program input.

GLOSSARY

	Dimensions	Name/Where Introduced
a	1 x 1	Acceleration magnitude
$\bar{B}_\psi$	6 x 1	Eq. (3-22)
c	1 x 1	Effective exhaust velocity
$\hat{e}$	3 x 1	Steering unit vector
F	1 x 1	Thrust magnitude
$\bar{g}$	3 x 1	Gravity vector
G	3 x 3	Gravity gradient

$\overline{K}$	6 x 1	Eq. (1-11)
k	1 x 1	Eq. (3-12)
M	6 x 6	Eq. (3-20)
m	1 x 1	Vehicle mass
$\overline{N}$	6 x 1	Eq. (1-2)
$\overline{p}$	3 x 1	Eq. (2-2)
Q	6 x 6	Eq. (5-16)
$\overline{q}$	3 x 1	Eq. (2-2)
r	1 x 1	Eq. (2-2)
$\overline{R}$	3 x 1	Position vector

	Dimensions	Name/Where Introduced
S	1 x 1	Switch function/Eq. (1-1)
$\overline{U}$	6 x 1	Eq. (3-19)
u	1 x 1	Eq. (3-21)
$\overline{\nu}$	6 x 1	Eq. (3-12)
$\overline{V}$	3 x 1	Velocity
β	1 x 1	Eq. (3-4)
Λ	3 x 6	Eq. (1-2)

Subscripts

b	Evaluated at t_b where b is an index of burn beginnings
e	Evaluated at t_e where e is an index of burn ends
s	Evaluated at t_s where s is an index of switch times
f	Evaluated at t_f, the final time

6. Initiation Procedure

The complexity of the optimization method suggests the

advantage of carefully selecting the initial trajectory to relieve the program of unnecessary search. This is especially convenient in the orbit transfer problem where the initial trajectory has to be selected with some care anyhow in order to insure that the method converges to the right local optimum. The method presented in this paper is preceded by a preliminary program which uses the impulse burn approximation to make a systematic trajectory search. The output of the program consists of burn times and velocity increment vectors for the minimum fuel trajectory which produces rendezvous. Remaining to be defined is the method for making maximum use of this information in constructing the initial finite thrust trajectory.

The first step in deriving an initial burn program is to replace the impulses with finite width pulses consistent with the specified engine parameters. Let F be the thrust of a constant thrust engine, Isp be the specific impulse, a_o be the initial acceleration, and c be the effective exhaust velocity.

$$c = I_{sp}\, g \tag{6-1}$$

$$-\dot{m}c = F = m_o\, a_o \tag{6-2}$$

$$m(t) = m_o\left(1 - \frac{a_o}{c}\, t\right)$$

$$a = F/m = a_o/(1 - (a_o/c)\, t) \tag{6-3}$$

Integrating Eq. (6-3) and solving the result for t,

$$t = (c/a_o)\left(1 - e^{-\Delta V/c}\right) \tag{6-4}$$

Let ΔV_i be the velocity increment during the ith burn, and Δt_i be the time increment during the ith burn. The ΔV_i's are outputs of the preliminary program.

$$\sum_{i=1}^{n} \Delta t_i = (c/a_o)\left(1 - e^{-\sum_{i=1}^{n} \Delta V_i/c}\right);\ n = 1, 2, 3, 4 \tag{6-5}$$

$$\Delta t_i = \sum_{g=1}^{i} \Delta t_i - \sum_{g=1}^{i-1} \Delta t_i \tag{6-6}$$

The next step in deriving the initial burn program is to compute the centroids of the acceleration vs. time pulses. Taking the moment center at the left end of the pulse, the first moment is

$$Mi = a_{bi} \int_{o}^{\Delta t_i} \frac{t}{1 - (a_{bi}/c)\, t}\, dt = c^2/a_{bi} \left[- (a_{bi}/c)\, \Delta t_i - \ln \left(1 - (a_{bi}/c)\, \Delta t_i\right) \right] = - c\, \Delta t_i + (c/a_{bi})\, \Delta V_i \tag{6-7}$$

where

$$a_{bi} = F/m\, (t_{bi})$$

Since the area of the pulse is ΔV_i

$$\Delta t_{ci} = M_i / \Delta V_i ; \; i = 1, 2, 3, 4 \tag{6-8}$$

Let t_i be the time of the i th impulse, and t_{bi} be the beginning of the finite pulse.

$$t_{bi} = t_i - \Delta t_{ci}$$

$$t_{ei} = t_{bi} + \Delta t_i \tag{6-9}$$

Since the optimum thrust is parallel $\overline{p}$, the initial value of $\overline{p}$, is set parallel to $\overline{\Delta V} / |\overline{\Delta V}|$. $\overline{\Delta V}$ is the velocity increment vector computed by the impulse program. Let J_{12} be the Jacobian transition matrix between points one and two which is available in explicit form for Kepler Arcs.

$$J_{12} = \begin{bmatrix} \frac{\partial X_2}{\partial X_1} & \frac{\partial X_2}{\partial Y_1} & \frac{\partial X_2}{\partial Z_1} & \frac{\partial X_2}{\partial \dot{X}_1} & \frac{\partial X_2}{\partial \dot{Y}_1} & \frac{\partial X_2}{\partial \dot{Z}_1} \\ \frac{\partial Y_2}{\partial X_1} & \frac{\partial Y_2}{\partial Y_1} & \frac{\partial Y_2}{\partial Z_1} & \frac{\partial Y_2}{\partial \dot{X}_1} & \frac{\partial Y_2}{\partial \dot{Y}_1} & \frac{\partial Y_2}{\partial \dot{Z}_1} \\ \frac{\partial Z_2}{\partial X_1} & \frac{\partial Z_2}{\partial Y_1} & \frac{\partial Z_2}{\partial Z_1} & \frac{\partial Z_2}{\partial \dot{X}_1} & \frac{\partial Z_2}{\partial \dot{Y}_1} & \frac{\partial Z_2}{\partial \dot{Z}_1} \\ \frac{\partial \dot{X}_2}{\partial X_1} & \frac{\partial \dot{X}_2}{\partial Y_1} & \frac{\partial \dot{X}_2}{\partial Z_1} & \frac{\partial \dot{X}_2}{\partial \dot{X}_1} & \frac{\partial \dot{X}_2}{\partial \dot{Y}_1} & \frac{\partial \dot{X}_2}{\partial \dot{Z}_1} \\ \frac{\partial \dot{Y}_2}{\partial X_1} & \frac{\partial \dot{Y}_2}{\partial Y_1} & \frac{\partial \dot{Y}_2}{\partial Z_1} & \frac{\partial \dot{Y}_2}{\partial \dot{X}_1} & \frac{\partial \dot{Y}_2}{\partial \dot{Y}_1} & \frac{\partial \dot{Y}_2}{\partial \dot{Z}_1} \\ \frac{\partial \dot{Z}_2}{\partial X_1} & \frac{\partial \dot{Z}_2}{\partial Y_1} & \frac{\partial \dot{Z}_2}{\partial Z_1} & \frac{\partial \dot{Z}_2}{\partial \dot{X}_1} & \frac{\partial \dot{Z}_2}{\partial \dot{Y}_1} & \frac{\partial \dot{Z}_2}{\partial \dot{Z}_1} \end{bmatrix} \tag{6-10}$$

From Eq. (2-7)

$$\overline{p}\,(t) \equiv \frac{\delta J\ (t_f)}{\delta \dot{\overline{R}}\,(t)} = \begin{bmatrix} \frac{\delta J}{\delta \dot{X}} \\ \frac{\delta J}{\delta \dot{Y}} \\ \frac{\delta J}{\delta \dot{Z}} \end{bmatrix} \tag{6-11}$$

$$\dot{\overline{p}}\,(t) \equiv -\frac{\delta J\ (t_f)}{\delta \overline{R}\,(t)} = -\begin{bmatrix} \frac{\delta J}{\delta X} \\ \frac{\delta J}{\delta Y} \\ \frac{\delta J}{\delta Z} \end{bmatrix} \tag{6-12}$$

Therefore,

$$\begin{bmatrix} -\dot{\bar{p}}_2 \\ \\ \bar{p}_2 \end{bmatrix} = J_{21}^T \begin{bmatrix} -\dot{\bar{p}}_1 \\ \\ \bar{p}_1 \end{bmatrix} \qquad (6\text{-}13A)$$

Eq. (6-13A) is equivalent to

$$\begin{bmatrix} \bar{p}_2 \\ \\ \dot{\bar{p}}_2 \end{bmatrix} = J_{12} \begin{bmatrix} \bar{p}_1 \\ \\ \dot{\bar{p}}_1 \end{bmatrix} \qquad (6\text{-}13B)$$

Eq. (6-13B) represents six equations in six unknowns. The values of $\dot{\bar{p}}_1$ and $\dot{\bar{p}}_2$ can be computed by inverting a 3 x 3 matrix. The inversion occurs in solving the three equations, which express $\bar{p}_2$, for $\dot{\bar{p}}_1$. These values of $\dot{\bar{p}}_1$ are substituted into the other three equations to compute $\dot{\bar{p}}_2$.

The preceding procedure determines $\bar{p}(t_i)$ and $\dot{\bar{p}}(t_i)$ which are evaluated at the burn centroids. The next step in the procedure is to determine t_o, $\bar{R}_o$, $\dot{\bar{R}}_o$, t_f, $\bar{R}_f$ target, and $\dot{\bar{R}}_f$ target.

$$t_o = t_{bi} - \Delta t_o$$

$$t_f = t_e \text{ last} + \Delta t_f$$

where Δt_o, and Δt_f, the duration of the initial and final coasts, are inputs. Kepler arc equations are used to compute $\bar{R}_o$ and $\dot{\bar{R}}_o$ at t_o from the given $\bar{R}$ and $\dot{\bar{R}}$ at t_1 of the impulsive trajectory. The interceptor coordinates at the last burn of the impulsive trajectory are assumed to be the target coordinates at the centroid of the last burn. Kepler arc equations are used to compute $\bar{R}_f$ target and $\dot{\bar{R}}_f$ target at t_f.

A modification in the first iteration of the program is required because the $\bar{p}$ and $\dot{\bar{p}}$ vectors are available at the centroid of the burns and not at the burn beginnings. The method starts at t_o and makes the standard forward integration with only the following modifications:

- When thrust is applied between each t_{bi} and t_{ei}, $\hat{e}_i$ is set equal to $\dfrac{\overline{\Delta V}_i}{|\overline{\Delta V}_i|}$ and is held constant.
- The value of the $\begin{bmatrix} \Lambda \\ \dot{\Lambda} \end{bmatrix}$ matrix at t_i (the centroid of the burn period) is stored for each burn period.
- The $\bar{b}_i$ for each burn is computed from

$$\bar{b}_i = \begin{bmatrix} \Lambda(t_i) \\ \\ \dot{\Lambda}(t_i) \end{bmatrix}^{-1} \begin{bmatrix} \bar{p}(t_i) \\ \\ \dot{\bar{p}}(t_i) \end{bmatrix} \tag{6-14}$$

where the inverse 6 x 6 matrix can be evaluated by Schmidt's theorem, i.e.,

$$\begin{bmatrix} \Lambda \\ \\ \dot{\Lambda} \end{bmatrix}^{-1} = \begin{bmatrix} \dot{\Lambda}_2^T & -\Lambda_2^T \\ \\ -\dot{\Lambda}_1^T & \Lambda_1^T \end{bmatrix} \tag{6-15}$$

where

$$\begin{aligned} \Lambda &= \begin{bmatrix} \Lambda_1 & \Lambda_2 \end{bmatrix} \\ \dot{\Lambda} &= \begin{bmatrix} \dot{\Lambda}_1 & \dot{\Lambda}_2 \end{bmatrix} \end{aligned} \tag{6-16}$$

Note: This step requires no additional programming since Eq. (6-14), with $\Lambda(t_{bi})$ and $\bar{p}\,(t_{bi})$, is used during each regular iteration.

Compute $\bar{p}\,(t_{bi})$ and $\dot{\bar{p}}\,(t_{bi})$

$$\bar{p}\,(t_{bi}) = \Lambda\,(t_{bi})\,\bar{b}_i$$

$$\dot{\bar{p}}\,(t_{bi}) = \dot{\Lambda}\,(t_{bi})\,\bar{b}_i \qquad (6\text{-}17)$$

All the necessary information is now available to begin a regular iteration cycle starting at t_o with the forward integration.

ACKNOWLEDGMENT

The research on which this paper is based was performed under AF03(695)-398-Optimal Guidance for Orbital Transfer Investigations.

DYNAMIC PROGRAMMING, INVARIANT IMBEDDING AND QUASILINEARIZATION: COMPARISONS AND INTERCONNECTIONS

R. Bellman and R. Kalaba
The RAND Corporation
Santa Monica, California

1. Introduction

In this paper we shall treat a simple class of variational problems from three different points of view: quasilinearization, dynamic programming, and invariant imbedding. Our aim is to adumbrate the point of view that leads to the various equations associated with each method. Primary emphasis is upon the computational aspects, though the development of effective numerical schemes requires significant analytical advances. The general theme is the computational solution of nonlinear two-point boundary value problems via a direct assault and via conversions into initial value problems.

2. Quasilinearization

Let us consider the problem of minimizing the functional

$$J[u] = \int_0^T \left\{\frac{1}{2}\dot{u}^2 + G(u)\right\}dt, \tag{1}$$

where the function u is subject to the initial condition

$$u(0) = c. \tag{2}$$

The optimizing curve is a solution of the Euler equation

$$\ddot{u} = dG/du = g(u) \tag{3}$$

subject to the initial condition in Eq. (2) and the natural boundary condition

$$\dot{u}(T) = 0. \tag{4}$$

The quasilinearization scheme consists in producing a sequence of approximating functions u_n, n=0,1,2,..., which converge rapidly to the solution of the original problem. This can be done by proceeding in a manner analogous to the finding of roots of a nonlinear equation via the Newton-Raphson method. Assuming that the nth approximation is known, we find the

$(n+1)^{st}$ approximation as the solution of the linear two-point boundary value problem

$$\ddot{u}_{n+1} = g(u_n) + (u_{n+1} - u_n)g'(u_n), \tag{5}$$

$$u_{n+1}(0) = c, \quad \dot{u}_{n+1}(T) = 0. \tag{6}$$

The terms on the right-hand side of Eq. (5) are the first two terms in the power series expansion of the function $g(u_{n+1})$ about the point u_n.

The computational scheme consists in the numerical production of a particular solution and two independent homogeneous solutions of the Eq. (5) on the interval (0,T) and the determination of the constant multiplier of the homogeneous solutions to satisfy the boundary conditions in Eq. (6). Let

$$\begin{cases} \ddot{p} = g(u_n) + (p - u_n)g'(u_n) & (7) \\ p(0) = \dot{p}(0) = 0, & (8) \end{cases}$$

$$\begin{cases} \ddot{h}_1 = g'(u_n)h_1 & (9) \\ h_1(0) = 1, \quad \dot{h}_1(0) = 0, & (10) \end{cases}$$

$$\begin{cases} \ddot{h}_2 = g'(u_n)h_2 & (11) \\ h_2(0) = 0, \quad \dot{h}_2(0) = 1. & (12) \end{cases}$$

The solutions of these initial value problems and their derivatives are readily produced numerically on the interval (0,T). The solution of Eq. (5), subject to the conditions in Eq. (6) is expressible in the form

$$u_{n+1} = p + c_1h_1 + c_2h_2, \tag{13}$$

where c_1 and c_2 are certain constants to be determined from the linear algebraic equations

$$p(0) + c_1h_1(0) + c_2h_2(0) = c \tag{14}$$

$$\dot{p}(T) + c_1\dot{h}_1(T) + c_2\dot{h}_2(T) = 0. \tag{15}$$

We see that

$$c_1 = c \tag{16}$$

and c_2 represents the missing initial value of $\dot{u}_{n+1}$.

Similarly we determine the function u_{n+2} from stored values of the function u_{n+1}. In (1,2,3,4) it is shown that when convergent, the convergence is quadratic; i.e., asymptotically the number of correct digits in each approximation is doubled. In addition we frequently obtain monotone convergence,

$$\dots \geq u_{n+1} \geq u_n \geq u_{n-1} \geq \dots \quad . \tag{17}$$

In the manner sketched large systems of one hundred or more simultaneous nonlinear differential equations subject to boundary values may be resolved.

A method for overcoming the memory problems involved in storing the values of the nth approximation while calculating the $(n+1)^{st}$ is given in (5). Solving the linear algebraic equations for the multipliers can be a major source of difficulty and error. It is possible to select the homogeneous functions with care so as to lighten this task. This is discussed (6). Alternatively we can bypass this problem completely using invariant imbedding or dynamic programming, as we shall see.

There are immediate extensions to problems involving nonlinear boundary conditions, multi-point boundary conditions (6,7), and the equations peculiar to the employment of the Pontryagin maximum principle.

3. Dynamic Programming

Now we shift our point of view and begin the systematic use of functional equation techniques. In place of considering one particular variational process corresponding to particular values of the initial condition c and the initial instant 0, we consider the class of optimal processes corresponding to arbitrary values of c and initial instants a. It is natural to consider the minimal value of the functional

$$K[u] = \int_a^T \left\{\frac{1}{2}\dot{u}^2 + G(u)\right\} dt \tag{18}$$

as a function of the initial condition c and the initial epoch a

$$f(c,a) = \min_u K[u]. \tag{19}$$

We may consider this to be the "cost" of the process. Then employment of the principle of optimality enables us to relate the costs of neighboring processes,

$$f(c,a) = \min_z \left[\left(\frac{1}{2}z^2 + G(c)\right)h + f(c+zh, a+h) + o(h)\right], \tag{20}$$

and in the limit as h tends to zero

$$0 = \min_z \left[\frac{1}{2}z^2 + G(c) + zf_c + f_a\right]. \tag{21}$$

The variable z represents the choice of the slope $\dot{u}$ at the time a, the displacement u being c. The choice of z which minimizes is

$$z_{min}(c,a) = - f_c(c,a), \tag{22}$$

and Eq. (21) becomes the Hamilton-Jacobi partial differential equation

$$- f_a = G(c) - \frac{1}{2} f_c^2, \qquad a < T. \tag{23}$$

In addition the function f(c,a) satisfies the terminal condition

$$f(c,T) = 0. \tag{24}$$

The Eq. (20), together with the condition in (24), furnishes the basis for an effective numerical scheme for determining the cost function f(c,a). In addition, the minimizing choice of z is determined for a suitable grid of values of a and c. This provides the information that is necessary for carrying out the control process as a feedback control process.

The two-point boundary value problem of Section 2 has been converted into an initial value problem. In the event, though, that the state of the system at time a is not a scalar, but is an M-dimensional vector, computational difficulties arise. The cost is then a function of M+1 variables, the M components of c and the initial time a. The analogue of Eq. (20) leads to the consideration of sequences of functions of M variables. If M exceeds two, it is not feasible to store a sufficiently accurate set of values of the cost function f on a grid of points, and various special devices must be employed, such as the use of Lagrange multipliers (8), and various kinds of polynomial approximation (9).

4. Invariant Imbedding

Once again consider the problem of minimizing the functional

$$K[u] = \int_a^T \left\{\frac{1}{2} \dot{u}^2 + G(u)\right\}dt \tag{25}$$

where the function u is subject to the condition

$$u(a) = c. \tag{26}$$

The optimizer is a solution of the Euler equation

$$\ddot{u} = g(u), \tag{27}$$

where

$$dG/du = g(u), \tag{28}$$

and the free end condition

$$\dot{u}(T) = 0, \tag{29}$$

as well as the initial condition in (26).

If we knew the missing value of the derivative at time a, the integration of Eq. (27) would be quite straightforward. Let us show how we may determine this missing initial condition directly via the method of invariant imbedding (10). Early work in this area was done by the astrophysicists V. A. Ambarzumian (11) and S. Chandrasekhar (12); see also Redheffer (13).

We begin by considering the nonlinear two-point boundary value problem for the functions u and v

$$\dot{u} = p(u,v,t), \qquad u(a) = c, \tag{30}$$

$$\dot{v} = q(u,v,t), \qquad v(T) = 0, \tag{31}$$

which is a convenient generalization of the problem posed above. Let us observe that the missing initial value of the function v is a function of both a and c. We denote this by the equation

$$v(a) = r(c,a). \tag{32}$$

Next we focus our attention on the ordinate of the v-curve for the abscissa a+h. On the one hand Eq. (31) shows us that

$$v(a+h) = r(c,a) + q(c,r(c,a),a)h + o(h). \tag{33}$$

On the other hand from Eq. (32) we see that

$$v(a+h) = r(c + p(c,r(c,a),a)h,\ a + h). \tag{34}$$

The right-hand side of Eq. (34) is the value of the v-curve at time a+h corresponding to a value of the u-curve at time a+h of $c + p(c,r(c,a),\ a)h$. Equations (33) and (34) show us that the function r(c,a) satisfies the functional equation

$$r(c+p(c,r(c,a),a)h,a+h) = r(c,a) + q(c,r(c,a),a)h + o(h). \tag{35}$$

In the limit as h tends to zero this equation becomes the first-order quasilinear partial differential equation

$$p(c,r,a)r_c + r_a = q(c,r,a), \qquad a < T. \tag{36}$$

In addition, the function r satisfies the condition

$$r(c,T) = 0, \tag{37}$$

in view of Eq. (31).

Similarly if we denote the unspecified terminal value of u by s(c,a),

$$s(c,a) = u(T), \tag{38}$$

we find that the function s satisfies the equation

$$s(c,a) = s(c+p(c,r(c,a),a)h,\ a+h) + o(h), \tag{39}$$

from which it follows that

$$p(c,r,a)s_c + s_a = 0. \tag{40}$$

In addition

$$s(c,T) = c. \tag{41}$$

These equations were given in Refs. 14 and 15 and discussed from the point of view of the variational principles of mechanics in Refs. 16 and 17. Some computational considerations appear in Ref. 18. They may be employed in several ways.

In the first place a finite difference scheme based on Eq. (35) and condition (37) enables us to calculate the values of r(c,a) for a grid of c-values on the basis of a knowledge of r(c,a+h) on a suitable grid of c-values. In this way the missing initial values of v, v(a) = r(c,a), are determined for a suitable domain of c and a.

Secondly we may base an integration theory for Eqs. (30) and (31) on the determination of the functions r and s. This provides an alternative to the customary Hamilton-Jacobi theory. In fact, if the functions r(c,a) and s(c,a) satisfy Eqs. (36), (37), (40) and (41), then the functions u(t) and v(t) which satisfy the relations

$$v = r(u,t) \tag{42}$$

$$s(u,t) = b = \text{const.} \tag{43}$$

$$u(a) = c \tag{44}$$

are solutions of Eqs. (30) and (31). To see this, differentiate Eq. (43) with respect to t. This yields

$$s_u\dot{u} + s_t = 0. \tag{45}$$

In view of Eq. (40)

$$\dot{u} = p(u,v,a). \tag{46}$$

Next differentiate Eq. (42) with respect to t,

$$\begin{aligned} \dot{v} &= r_u\dot{u} + r_t \\ &= r_u p(u,v,t) + r_t \qquad (47) \\ &= q(u,v,t). \end{aligned}$$

Furthermore, the boundary conditions in Eqs. (30) and (31) are satisfied

$$u(a) = c \tag{48}$$

$$v(T) = 0. \tag{49}$$

The constant b is

$$b = s(u(T), T) = u(T). \tag{50}$$

Though in general we should not expect to be able to determine the functions r and s analytically, various perturbation procedures are feasible, as is customary in analytical mechanics (19,20).

5. Combined Calculations

Many interesting possibilities exist for combining the methods discussed here with one another and with others to produce very efficient computational schemes. Let us merely outline a few.

Suppose we wish to determine the function $r(c,a)$, which represents the unknown initial value of v for the boundary value problem discussed in Section 4. For values of a sufficiently smaller than T appreciable errors may build up in the calculation of r based upon Eqs. (35) and (37). We can use quasilinearization to calculate very accurate solutions of the nonlinear boundary value problem for $a = A$ and a suitable grid of values of c and then continue via invariant imbedding. As a matter of fact a very powerful predictor-corrector method is made available in this fashion. Knowing accurate values of $r(c,a)$ for $a = A$, we can use Eq. (35) to predict values of $r(c,a)$ for $a = A - h$ and then, using these as initial estimates, employ quasilinearization. Alternatively we may employ the invariant imbedding technique advantageously at each step in the quasilinearization procedure to obviate the need for solving linear algebraic equations.

Many computational difficulties can arise during the course of a numerical solution of a general system of linear algebraic equations. No computational scheme which involves the solution of such a system can be considered quite satisfactory. The method of quasilinearization involves the solution of a linear system of algebraic equations for the constants which multiply the solutions of the homogeneous equations. Fortunately this difficulty can be avoided completely through a straightforward use of the method of invariant imbedding.

In passing from the nth to the $(n+1)^{st}$ approximation we have to resolve the linear two-point boundary value problem

$$\dot{u}_{n+1} = v_{n+1}, \tag{51}$$

$$\dot{v}_{n+1} = g'(u_n)u_{n+1} + g(u_n) - u_n g'(u_n), \tag{52}$$

$$u_{n+1}(0) = c, \tag{53}$$

$$v_{n+1}(T) = 0. \tag{54}$$

Let us replace the condition

$$u_{n+1}(0) = c \tag{55}$$

with the condition

$$u_{n+1}(a) = c \tag{56}$$

and then seek the missing initial value of the function v_{n+1} at $t = a$,

$$v_{n+1}(a) = r(c,a). \tag{57}$$

To prepare the way we first specialize our earlier results from the theory of invariant imbedding to the case of linear equations

$$\dot{u} = a_1(t)u + b_1(t)v + c_1(t), \qquad u(a) = c \tag{58}$$

$$\dot{v} = a_2(t)u + b_2(t)v + c_2(t), \qquad v(T) = 0. \tag{59}$$

According to Eq. (36), the function r, which provides the missing initial value of the function $v_{n+1}(t)$ at $t = a$,

$$v_{n+1}(a) = r(c,a), \tag{60}$$

satisfies the partial differential equation

$$(a_1c + b_1r + c_1)r_c + r_a = a_2c + b_2r + c_2. \tag{61}$$

In view of the linearity of the equations in (58) and (59), we know that the function $r(c,a)$ has the form

$$r(c,a) = M(a)c + N(a). \tag{62}$$

Upon substituting in Eq. (61) and equating coefficients, we find that the functions $M(a)$ and $N(a)$ satisfy the ordinary differential equations of Riccati type

$$\frac{dM}{da} = a_2(a) + (b_2(a) - a_1(a))M - b_1M^2 \tag{63}$$

$$\frac{dM}{da} = c_2(a) + b_2(a)N - c_1(a)M - b_1M\,N, \tag{64}$$

In addition these functions satisfy the conditions

$$M(T) = 0 \tag{65}$$

$$N(T) = 0. \tag{66}$$

The missing initial condition is obtained by setting

$$a_1(a) = 0, \quad a_2(a) = g'(u_n(a)) \tag{67}$$

$$b_1(a) = 1, \quad b_2(a) = 0, \tag{68}$$

$$c_1(a) = 0, \quad c_2(a) = g(u_n(a)) - u_n(a)g'(u_n(a)), \tag{69}$$

integrating Eqs. (63) and (64) from a = T to a = 0, and obtaining, numerically, the desired initial condition

$$v_{n+1}(0) = M(0)c + N(0). \tag{70}$$

A more general discussion is given in Refs. 21 and 22. Then the calculation continues as before.

In passing, let us note that the basic Eq. (36) can be obtained directly from our dynamic programming considerations. According to Eq. (22)

$$r(c,a) = - f_c. \tag{71}$$

Upon differentiating Eq. (23) with respect to c we obtain

$$(- f_c)_a = dG/dc + (- f_c)\ (f_c)_c, \tag{72}$$

from which we again conclude that

$$r_a = g(c) - r\ r_c. \tag{73}$$

Recent progress in determining optimal paths through networks can be combined to yield still other algorithms (23).

References

1. Bellman, R., and R. Kalaba, Quasilinearization and Boundary Value Problems, American Elsevier Publishing Co., Inc., N. Y., to appear in 1964.

2. Hestenes, M., "Numerical Methods of Obtaining Solutions of Fixed End Point Problems in the Calculus of Variations," The RAND Corporation, RM-102, August 1949.

3. Kalaba, R., "On Nonlinear Differential Equations, the Maximum Operation and Monotone Convergence," J. of Math. and Mech., v. 8 (1959), pp. 519-574.

4. Kalaba, R., "Some Aspects of Quasilinearization," a chapter in the book Nonlinear Differential Equations and Nonlinear Mechanics, Academic Press, N. Y., 1963.

5. Bellman, R., "Successive Approximations and Computer Storage Problems in Ordinary Differential Equations," Comm. of the ACM, v. 4 (1961), pp. 222-223.

6. Bellman, R., H. Kagiwada, and R. Kalaba, "Orbit Determination as a Multipoint Boundary Value Problem," Proc. Nat. Acad. Sci. USA, v. 48 (1962), pp. 1327-1329.

7. Bellman, R., H. Kagiwada, and R. Kalaba, "Quasilinearization, System Identification and Prediction," The RAND Corporation, RM-3812-ARPA, August 1963.

8. Bellman, R., Adaptive Control Processes, Princeton Univ. Press, Princeton, 1961.

9. Bellman, R., R. Kalaba, and B. Kotkin, "Polynomial Approximation--A New Computational Technique in Dynamic Programming - I: Allocation Processes," Mathematics of Computation, v. 17 (1963), pp. 155-161.

10. Bellman, R., R. Kalaba, and G. M. Wing, "Invariant Imbedding and Mathematical Physics - I: Particle Processes," J. of Mathematical Physics, v. 1 (1960), pp. 280-308.

11. Ambarzumian, V. A., "Diffuse Reflection of Light by a Foggy Medium," Comptes Rendus (Doklady) de l'Académie des Sciences de l'URSS, v. 38 (1943), pp. 229-232.

12. Chandrasekhar, S., Radiative Transfer, Dover Publications, N. Y., 1960.

13. Redheffer, R. "Novel Uses of Functional Equations," J. Rational Mech. and Anal., v. 3 (1954), pp. 271-279.

14. Bellman, R., R. Kalaba, and G. M. Wing, "Invariant Imbedding and the Reduction of Two-point Boundary Value Problems to Initial Value Problems," Proc. Nat. Acad. Sci. USA, v. 46 (1960), pp. 1646-1649.

15. Bellman, R., and R. Kalaba, "On the Fundamental Equations of Invariant Imbedding - I," Proc. Nat. Acad. Sci. USA, v. 47 (1961), pp. 336-338.

16. Bellman, R., and R. Kalaba, "A Note on Hamilton's Equations and Invariant Imbedding," Quart. of App. Math., v. 21 (1963), pp. 166-168.

17. Bellman, R., and R. Kalaba, "Invariant Imbedding and the Integration of Hamilton's Equations," Rendiconti di Palermo, to appear.

18. Bellman, R., R. Kalaba, and B. Kotkin, "On a New Approach to the Computational Solution of Partial Differential Equations," Proc. Nat. Acad. Sci. USA, v. 48 (1962), pp. 1325-1327.

19. Bellman, R., Perturbation Techniques in Mathematics, Physics and Engineering, Holt, Rinehart and Winston, Inc., N. Y., 1964.

20. Sterne, T., An Introduction to Celestial Mechanics, Interscience Publishers, Inc., N. Y., 1960.

21. Bellman, R., and R. Kalaba, "Transport Theory and Invariant Imbedding," Nuclear Reactor Theory, pp. 206-218, Amer. Math. Soc., Providence, 1961.

22. Bellman, R., R. Kalaba, and M. Prestrud, Invariant Imbedding and Radiative Transfer in Slabs of Finite Thickness, American Elsevier Publishing Co., Inc., N. Y., 1963.

23. Kalaba, R., "Graph Theory and Automatic Control," a chapter in Applied Combinatorial Mathematics, John Wiley and Sons, Inc., N. Y., to appear in 1964.

A COMPARISON BETWEEN SOME METHODS FOR COMPUTING OPTIMUM PATHS IN THE PROBLEM OF BOLZA

Frank D. Faulkner, Department of Mathematics and Mechanics, U. S. Naval Postgraduate School, Monterey, California.

A comparison is made between methods for calculating optimum trajectories in the problem of Bolza. For the most part the comparison is between the method of steepest ascent as given by Bryson and Denham (1) and a direct method due to the author, using the differential techniques which G. A. Bliss developed during World War I in ballistics. A second purpose of the paper is to give a modification of Bryson and Denham's method which eliminates one of the minor subproblems and makes it possible to use a trajectory obtained by their method to start the routine for the other method. The reason for this will be given.

Both methods seem to yield reasonably satisfactory results and both have minor problems associated with actual computation, the most recurrent being that of convergence.

Both methods use the adjoint system of differential equations much as used by Bliss; the adjoint system seems imperative for the solution and understanding of all but the simplest problems.

Bryson and Denham's method, henceforth called the BFL method is based on the constructive proof of the fundamental lemma of the calculus of variations. This shows how, if an admissible path is given on which the Euler equations are not satisfied, a better admissible path can be obtained. A modification has been made up to eliminate the trouble of integrating forward and then backward. In the other method only extremals are used. Usually Bliss's differential methods are used to set up a Newton iteration for the constants, though they may also be obtained directly (see (2)). This method will be called the FD method.

The comparisons so far suggest the following conclusions. There are some advantages of the FD method. (1) It converges more rapidly, if it converges. It is a Newton iteration for the roots to a set of equations and tends to converge exponentially once the solution is approached. (2) There is no question of how closely the path approaches an extremal, since only extremals are used. This is often not too important from a practical point of view, since trajectories "near" the optimum are generally "almost" as good. (3) Discontinuous or even unbounded control and constraints on the variables seem to pose no major problem. (4) The optimum correction to a perturbed optimum trajectory involves only a few more iterations. (5) Various identities and relations associated with extremals can be used; for example, if the independent variable does not enter explicitly, the Hamiltonian is constant. (6) There is no arbitrary step size in the solution; they are determined by the Newton-Raphson routine. (7) The method seems more flexible in treating unusual problems. Solutions were obtained for the bang-bang control problem (3), for problems with discontinuous bounded control and further limitations on the energy in rocketry (4), (5), (6), and for problems with impulse solutions; simple allocation problems have also been treated by this method.

There are several advantages to the BFL method. (1) It seems to require less skill or luck in getting started. (2) The integral relations for the corrections are computationally more stable. They involve only first derivatives whereas the other method involves second derivatives with respect to the control variables. (3) It seems easier to get a convergent sequence of paths without interrupting the computation. Another FL method (that is, one based on the fundamental lemma) is due to Kelley (7); it was not investigated at length. It had the desirable feature of simplicity but it converged more slowly, perhaps due to inability of the author to select a sequence of parameters well.

The methods also have their problems and difficulties. In the FD method the parameters are the constants of integration associated with the adjoint system of differential equations. The programmer may have no idea as to the proper range of these. The other method requires only a likely initial path; while even this may be hard to find, the uncertainty seems to be an order less. Usually the FD method must be modified if the strong Legendre condition is not satisfied. The methods based on the fundamental lemma are computationally more stable; in the direct method the control variable is obtained every step from equations which involve second derivatives in the denominator. In the FL methods both forward and backward integration are usually used. This, however, is only a matter of programming; a routine is given which eliminates this. Another problem associated with FL methods is that there is no obvious metric which indicates how much the path differs from an extremal. Finally, no way is seen to extend FL methods to problems involving discontinuous or bounded control generally.

Since FL methods are more likely to converge, but tend to converge more slowly and it is not clear when convergence is attained, it is desirable to get a "good" path using the

FL method, then use it to obtain a set of initial values for the Lagrange multipliers to start a differential routine wherein only extremals are used. A procedure is given for this, together with a measure of the variation of any curve from an extremal. The measure has no obvious significance except that it is zero whenever the curve is an extremal and is positive otherwise.

1. Basic Equations

The equations which govern the system are assumed to have the form

$$\dot{x}^i = f^i , \qquad i = 1,\cdots,n, \tag{1.1}$$

where $f^i = f^i(x,p,t)$, $x = (x^i)$ is an n-dimensional vector $p = (p^\sigma)$ is an m-dimensional vector, and t is a scalar which we may think of as time. The set (x^i) are called state variables and the set (p^σ) are called control variables. The p's are to be chosen as functions of time to effect whatever optimum is desired. Vectors may be written in index notation x^i, in vector notation $\overline{x}$ or in matrix notation (x) or (x^i), whichever suggest the important properties. Partial derivatives will be denoted by subscripts when no error seems likely; for example $f^i_j = \partial f^i/\partial x^j$ and $f^i_\sigma = \partial f^i/\partial p^\sigma$; Latin indices will have the range 1-n and Greek indices will have the range 1-m. It will be assumed that whatever derivatives occur are continuous.

Some familiarity with calculus of variations is assumed. A typical problem is that of going from one specified point to another, from (x_0) to (X) or (X_T) in such a way that the terminal value T of the time is a minimum. The form of the equations involved is the same, independent of the particular problem. The variational equations are

$$\delta\dot{x}^i = f^i_j \delta x^j + f^i_\sigma \delta p^\sigma \tag{1.2}$$

(the summation signs will be omitted if no error seems likely), and the associated adjoint system of equations for the Lagrange multipliers is

$$\dot{\lambda} = - f^j_i \lambda_j . \tag{1.3}$$

The function

$$H = \lambda_i f^i = \overline{\lambda}\cdot\overline{f} \tag{1.4}$$

is called the hamiltonian. The Euler equations

$$H_\sigma = 0 = \lambda_i f^i_\sigma$$

are necessary for an optimum if p lies in an open region. An admissible path is one which begins and ends at the specified initial and terminal points. The fundamental lemma states that if we have an admissible path on which Eq. (1.5) is not satisfied, then we can construct a better admissible path. The principal difficulty is in matching end conditions, in solving a two-, or multi-point boundary problem.

We shall need two fundamental sets for the adjoint system. In the first one, the initial conditions are given: $\overline{\lambda}_j$ or (λ_{ij}) are chosen so that $\lambda_{ij}(0) = \delta_{ij}$ (the Kronecker delta). The other set $\overline{\lambda}^j$ is chosen so that at the terminal time T, or an approximation to it, $\lambda_i^j = \delta_i^j$. We need those with initial values to start integration, but the formulas are neater when the $\overline{\lambda}^j$ are used. For any particular path they are functions of one another, as follows. Let L be the matrix with elements $L_{ij} = \lambda_{ji}(T)$. It is not singular. Let L^{-1} be M, with elements M^{ij}. Then $\overline{\lambda}^i = M^{ij}\overline{\lambda}_j$, as we see from

$$\lambda^i_j(T) = \delta^i_j = M^{ik}\lambda_{jk}(T) = M^{ik}L_{kj} . \tag{1.6}$$

There is also the Green's formula for the variations of the end values of the state variables, as given by Bliss (8),

$$\delta x^i(T) = \int_0^T \overline{\lambda}^i \cdot \overline{f}_\sigma \delta p^\sigma dt \tag{1.7}$$

as a consequence of Eqs. (1.2) and (1.3). The corresponding differentials are

$$dx^i(T) = \delta x^i(T) + \dot{x}^i(T)dT. \tag{1.8}$$

Finally, let us consider a special set of variations; let

$$\delta p^\sigma = \Sigma\, c_i \overline{\lambda}^i \cdot \overline{f}_\sigma . \tag{1.9}$$

Then

$$\delta x^i(T) = \int_0^T c_j \overline{\lambda}^j \cdot \overline{f}_\sigma\ \overline{\lambda}^i \overline{f}_\sigma dt \tag{1.10}$$

which has the form

$$\delta x^i = A^{ij} c_j ; \tag{1.11}$$

The matrix A with elements A^{ij},

$$A^{ij} = \int_0^T \overline{\lambda}^i \cdot \overline{f}_\sigma\ \overline{\lambda}^j \cdot \overline{f}_\sigma dt \tag{1.12}$$

is a positive semi-definite (at least) symmetric matrix, since it is a gramian or a sum of gramian matrices.

Since we will generally integrate forward it will be convenient to have this in terms of $\overline{\lambda}_j$. If we define the matrix α with elements

$$A_{ij} = \int_0^T \overline{\lambda}_i \cdot \overline{f}_\sigma \overline{\lambda}_j \cdot \overline{f}_\sigma dt , \tag{1.13}$$

then, since $\overline{\lambda}_i = L_{ij}\overline{\lambda}^j$,

$$A_{ij} = A^{kl}L_{ki}L_{lj} \quad (\text{or } \alpha = L^* AL). \tag{1.14}$$

We shall be concerned almost entirely with problems wherein A and α have rank n except when the path is an extremal, and on extremals they have rank $n-1$. An extremal is a curve whereon Eq. (1.5) is satisfied. Implicit in the above relations is that there are no corners.

2. Method of the Fundamental Lemma

In this section a variant of the BF method is given which involves only forward integration. The essential of this method is that there are two sets of corrections or variations generated. The first set drives the path toward admissibility and the second is orthogonal to these and drives the path toward an extremal.

Let us consider the minimum time problem as a typical problem. The initial point (x_0^i) and the terminal point (X^i) are specified and we wish to minimize the terminal value T of t. Let us choose a likely path by choosing or generating in some fashion the control variable. Let us compute the trajectory, storing the control variable and a fundamental set of solutions for the adjoint system. Let us calculate also the integrals A_{ij}. We can invert the matrix L and get A^{ij}. If we consider the special variations of Eq. (1.9), then by Eqs. (1.7), (1.8), and (1.12) we get

$$dx^i(T) = A^{ij}c_j + \dot{x}^i(T)dT. \tag{2.1}$$

If we treat differentials as differences, we get

$$X^i - x^i(T) = A^{ij}c_j + \dot{x}^i(T)\Delta T. \tag{2.2}$$

This is a set of n equatons for $n+1$ unknowns $c_1, \cdots, c_n, \Delta T$.

Let us now choose a set of c's to drive the path toward admissibility. Let us examine the n matrices obtained from the n by $n+1$ matrix $(A^{ij}, \dot{x}^i)$ of Eq. (2.2) by omitting the first n columns one at a time. Let us choose the one of these which has the largest determinant. Assume for definiteness that we omit the n'th column. Let us then solve

$$X^i - x^i(T) = A^{i1}c_{11} + A^{i2}c_{21} + \cdots + A^{i\,n-1}c_{n-1\,1} + \dot{x}^i\Delta T . \tag{2.3}$$

If we choose $c_{n1} = 0$ then this set of variations tends to make the resulting path admissible. Now let us choose a second set of variations with $c_{n2} = \epsilon$, satisfying the equations

$$0 = A^{ij}c_{j2} + \dot{x}^i \Delta T_2 \ . \tag{2.4}$$

The first-order effects of this do not change the admissibility of the path. The set $c_{12}, c_{22}, \cdots, c_{n-1\ 2}, \Delta T_2$ are linear in ϵ. If $\Delta T_2/\epsilon$ is positive, choose ϵ negative and vice versa. A minor problem is to choose ϵ well. If it is chosen too large, the corrections overshoot and if it is too small, the sequence creeps toward the desired extremal.

This routine has the advantage that it avoids the alternate forward and backward integration of the original method. This is at the expense of computer storage. It also avoids a term that to the author was puzzling, the quantity in the radical for choosing the step size. The indeterminancy in choosing the step size is inherent in the method unless the operator has some feel for the problem.

Storage of the adjoint variables, for correcting the control variables may be eliminated by using the values of the c's found in one iteration with the solutions to the adjoint generated in the next.

3. Differential Method

In this method only extremals are used. The Euler equation, Eq. (1.5) will be assumed to be satisfied identically on every path considered. Implicitly then, the control variable maximizes H at an interior point. The problem is that the maximization occurs for some unknown solution

$$\bar{\lambda} = C^i \bar{\lambda}_i \tag{3.1}$$

to the adjoint. Now suppose that we have been able to get an estimate of the C's for the desired extremal. It happens that we may choose one C, say C_n, arbitrarily, since the essential equations are homogeneous in the $\bar{\lambda}$'s; we must only be certain that the choice has the right sign.

Now let us consider the effects of changing the C's. Let us change the C's and the control variables, assuming that we can do this leaving x,t fixed. From Eqs. (1.5) and (3.1) we get

$$\bar{\lambda}_i \cdot \bar{f}_\sigma dC^i + \bar{\lambda} \cdot \bar{f}_{\sigma\tau} \delta p^\tau = 0; \tag{3.2}$$

a term involving δx has been omitted from these equations, under the assumption that x,t could be held fixed. We can solve this equation for δp in terms of dC provided the m'th order determinant with elements $\overline{\lambda}\cdot\overline{f}_{\sigma T}$ is not zero, and substitute into Eqs. (1.7) and (1.8) to get n equations of the form

$$dx^i(T) = \sum_1^{n-1} B^i_j dC^j + \dot{x}^i(T)dT \; ; \qquad (3.3)$$

the B^i_j are integrals. This is the basic relation for setting up the Newton-Raphson iteration. We run a trajectory, calculating the integrals B^i_j; we treat differentials as differences; we substitute $X^{i'} - x^i(T)$ for dx^i and solve for ΔC^i, ΔT.

The principal problem is that of convergence. Various problems involving discontinuous control have been solved by this method. A term must be added in the differential formulas for each corner where the value of t is not specified, and corner conditions must be met. It seems to the author that if the path has corners the programmer must anticipate this, since the control variable is discontinuous. Indeed the difficulties in finding the roots of algebraic equations suggest that no method exists for checking the Weierstrass condition generally.

4. Determining a 'Best-fitting' Extremal

The studies have indicated that it is easier to develope a fairly good path with FL methods, but it is not clear how nearly an extremal has been approached. The differential method uses only extremals and tends to converge exponentially when it converges, but it is harder to get a satisfactory approximation for starting. This suggests that we might use an FL method initially, and then use it to determine a 'best-fitting' extremal, to continue with the differential method.

The problem then becomes: how can we get a best-fitting extremal for the path just found? The answer lies in the method of correction for the FL method. Let us consider the matrix A defined by Eq. (1.12). As a gramian or the sum of gramians it is symmetric and positive definite, or at least semi-definite. Hence its eigenvalues are either positive or zero and its eigenvectors are orthogonal, or in case of equal eigenvalues can be chosen so.

Now let us consider Eq. (2.1) for fixed T. We may write it

$$(\delta x)_T = A(c) \qquad (4.1)$$

Generally A has rank n but for extremals it has rank n-1. Let us assume this to be the case in the following.

Then, by Eq. (4.1) we can attain at time T any point in some neighborhood of the endpoint of a curve which is not an extremal, but the endpoint of extremals define an n-1 disc in n-space. We have seen that with an extremal is a solution to the adjoint $\bar{\lambda}$, say $\bar{\lambda}^*$. If E^* is the extremal, embedded in a family (E) of extremals starting from (x_0^i), then for fixed T, $\bar{\lambda}^*(T)$ is normal to the disc defined by the end-points of (E).

Now consider the corrective routine and the matrix A. As the successive iterates approach an extremal A becomes singular. Let $0 \leqq \gamma_1 < \gamma_2 \leqq \cdots \leqq \gamma_n$ be the eigenvalues of A, and assume that $\gamma_1 \ll \gamma_2$. Let $\bar{\lambda}_{A1}, \cdots, \bar{\lambda}_{An}$ be the corresponding eigenvectors of A. It is clear that if we had attained the extremal, so that A were singular, then

$$\bar{\lambda}^*(T) \parallel \bar{\lambda}_{A1} . \tag{4.3}$$

But $\bar{\lambda}^*$ is only determined to within a multiplicative factor. Hence $\bar{\lambda}^*(T)$ is determined as the eigenvector corresponding to the zero eigenvalue of A. We may get $\bar{\lambda}^*(0)$ from the matrix L defined in the first section. Most computing centers have routines for finding the eigenvalues and eigenvectors of a symmetric matrix.

This suggest a measure of approximation to an extremal, either γ_1/γ_2 or γ_1/γ_n, the ratio of the smallest eigenvalue to either the next smallest or to the largest. Unfortunately it seems to have just one important property; it becomes zero when an extremal is attained.

The same procedure works equally well on α. When the curve approaches an extremal, the eigenvector corresponding to the zero eigenvalue gives the starting values for the adjoint. If the path is not an extremal, there seems to be no simple relation among the eigenvalues and eigenvectors of A and α, since the only property of the matrix L is that its determinant is positive.

5. Comments

Considerable computation has been done in an attempt to compare the two methods, without a definite conclusion. Seibel (9) made comparisons mainly in the ship-routing problem wherein convergence is not a serious problem. Usually the time required for determining a course by the FD method was about two-fifths or half that for the BFL method.

Considerable work was done in trying to compare the two methods (10) on the problem of maximum range for a high-speed glider. The problem is on the verge of instability in two ways. First, a slight increase in initial velocity puts it virtually in orbit. Second, the range is apparently extremely sensitive to the value used for the radius of the earth. An increase of about thirty NM (nautical miles) in the value used caused an increase in range from about 39,000 NM to about 54,000 NM. These are reflected in very large values for the Lagrange multipliers, one of them being about 10^{12} times as large as another initially. Discussions suggest that this might be overcome by the adoption of a double-precision routine like that used by Johnson (11) in a related problem. The latest computations actually carried out gave a much better trajectory by the BFL method in the last moments of the trajectory. It does not seem possible, even knowing the initial values of the Lagrange multipliers very closely, to compute the complete trajectory for the desired extremal; it always seems to end in a loop. The ratio of the Lagrange multipliers which are so large initially determines the angle of attack. In the last moment these must both be driven to zero. This could not be done. It might be pointed out that this problem is very stable in another sense. It seems possible to get good open-loop programs and very good closed-loop programs, these leading to ranges quite near the maximum. Different models were used for the atmosphere, but a few computations suggested that this was not a significant factor.

The FD method differs from the so-called method of second variations given by Breakwell, Speyer, and Bryson (12) in that the variations of the state variables were dropped in Eq. (3.2). It seems to the author that the name second-variation given to that method is a misnomer. The coefficients in the linear forms of Eq. (3.2) are the same as the coefficients in the Legendre quadratic form but they are not second variations.

The important thing is that we can calculate differentials associated with extremals. This method has been applied to several problems by the author and his students where no terms appeared corresponding to the second derivatives. McCalla (3) in his thesis treated a low-order bang-bang problem. Faulkner and Ward (5) treat the problem of ballistic missile interception where bounded control and limited energy expenditure were imposed. Professor Bleick and the author treat a launching problem where there is an intermediate period of coasting. In these there are corners at points which are unknown initially; no way is seen to extend the method of the fundamental lemma to these, since the proof assumes that 'two-sided' corrections to the control are allowed. Others have advocated the use of 'slack' variables in posing problems such as these. It is the author's strong opinion that if the problem can be posed without these, its solution is simpler without them.

The author felt perhaps that some of the convergence problems were due to the omission of the terms. This is not always the case, since the two methods coincide when the equations are linear in the state variables and serious convergence problems were encountered in the problem of rendezvous in minimum time, with linearized equations (4).

The FD method also applies to the solution of some allocation problems of the following type. An integral of the form

$$G = \int_0^T f(t,p,q)dt$$

is to be maximized with respect to p and minimized with respect to q, which are probability density functions (13). It is easily posed as a simple linear control problem involving a third order system with limited total input, being unusual in that the solution is of minimax type.

References

(1) Arthur E. Bryson and Walter F. Denham, A steepest-ascent method for solving optimum programming problems, J. Applied Mechanics, p. 247f, June 1962.
(2) Frank D. Faulkner, Determining optimum ship routes, JORSA, 10, No. 6, 799-807, Nov-Dec 1962.
(3) Thomas R. McCalla, Application of the adjoint system of differential equations in the solution of the bang-bang control problem, Thesis, U. S. Naval Postgraduate School, 1961.
(4) Frank D. Faulkner, Direct methods, Ch. 2 in Optimization Techniques, George Leitmann, Editor, Academic Press, New York, 1962.
(5) Frank. D. Faulkner, Optimum interception of a ballistic missile at intermediate range, U. S. Naval Postgraduate School Research Paper No. 29, October, 1961.
(6) W. E. Bleick and F. D. Faulkner, Orbital transfer with minimum fuel, U. S. Naval Postgraduate School Research Paper No. 40, Sept 1963.
(7) R. L. Kelley, Method of gradients, Ch. 6 in Direct Methods, Beorge Leitmann, Editor, Academic Press, New York, 1962
(8) G. A. Bliss, Mathematics for Exterior Ballistics, Chicago, 1944, Chapter IV.
(9) W. E. Seibel, A comparison of two methods for solution of the problem of Bolza, Thesis, U. S. Naval Postgraduate School, 1963.
(10) W. W. McCue and R. C. Good, A comparison between steepest-ascent and differential correction optimization methods in a problem of Bolza, with a method for obtaining starting values for the adjoint variables from a nominal path, Thesis, U. S. Naval Postgraduate School, 1963.
(11) R. G. Johnson, Linear perturbational control for re-entry, presented at joint AIAA-IMS-SIAM-ONR Control Conference,

Monterey, January 1964.
(12) J. V. Breakwell, J. L. Speyer, and A. E. Bryson, Optimization and control of nonlinear systems using the second variation, SIAM J. of Control, No 2, 1963.
(13) Robert H. Bartley, A method for obtaining the solution to some allocation problems, Thesis, U. S. Naval Postgraduate School, (in preparation).

MINIMIZING FUNCTIONALS ON HILBERT SPACE

A. A. Goldstein
The University of Texas
Austin, Texas

This note involves two simple ideas. The first is a generalization of constructive techniques employed by Kantorovich [1] and Altman [2] for the minimization of quadratic functionals on a real Hilbert space H. The extension here is for twice differentiable functionals. Minimizing these functionals on Hilbert space subsumes the problem of minimizing them on a linear variety in Hilbert space, which in turn subsumes certain problems of control theory with linear constraints*. In the related examples considered below, the functionals are not differentiable. They can, however, be uniformly approximated by differentiable functionals. This is the second idea. The first example arises from control theory; the second, from approximation theory in the L_1 metric. In both problems the functional is to be minimized on a closed linear variety. A. V. Balakrishnan [3], motivated also by control theory, extends the gradient method to a class of quadratic-programming problems in Hilbert space, with non-linear constraints.

Let f denote a real-valued function on H, and x_0 an arbitrary point in H. We shall be concerned below with the restriction of f to the set $S = \{x \varepsilon H: f(x) \leqq f(x_0)\}$.

Theorem. Assume f is bounded below. For each x in S, h in H, and for some $\rho_0 > 0$, assume that $f'(x,h)$ exists in the sense of Frechet, $f''(x,h,h)$ exists in the sense of Gateaux, and $|f''(x,h,h)| \leqq \|h\|^2/\rho_0$. Choose δ and ρ_k satisfying $0<\delta \leqq \rho_0$ and $\delta \leqq \rho_k \leqq 2\rho_0 - \delta$. Set $x_{k+1} = x_k - \rho_k f'(x_k, \cdot)$. Then:

*As a result of discussions with A.V. Balakrishnan and E. K. Blum at this conference, I have been encouraged to relax the assumption of linear constraints, and have thereby become convinced of the following. Let H in the theorem be replaced by a closed convex subset of H, say K. We wish to minimize f on K. Let P denote the map which assigns to a point x in H its closest point P(x) in K. Given x_0 in K let $x_{k+1} = P(x_k - \rho_k f'(x_k, \cdot))$ with ρ_k defined as in the theorem below. A theorem, similar to the one below, can be stated for this sequence.

(i) $f'(x_k,\cdot)$ converges to 0 and $f(x_k)$ converges downward to a limit L.

(ii) If S is convex and $f''(x,h,h) \geq \mu\|h\|^2$ for each $x\varepsilon S$, $h\varepsilon H$, and some $\mu \geq 0$, then $L = \inf\{f(x): x\varepsilon H\}$.

(iii) Assume (ii) with S bounded. If z is a weak cluster point for $\{x_k\}$, then $f(z) = L$ and $f'(z,\cdot)=0$. If f has a unique minimizer and either H is finite dimensional or f is the norm on H, then $\{x_k\}$ converges strongly to z.

(iv) Assume (ii) with μ positive. Then $f(z) = L$ for some z in S; x_k converges to z; and z is unique.

Proof. Let $\phi(x_k) = \phi_k = f(x_k,\cdot)$, $f''(\cdot,h,h) = f''[\cdot,h]$, and $J = [\delta,2\rho_0-\delta]$. Assume $x_k\varepsilon S$ and $\|\phi_k\| \neq 0$. Using Taylor's theorem let $\Delta_k(\rho) = f(x_k) - f(x_k - \rho\phi_k) = \rho\|\phi_k\|^2 - \rho^2 f''[x_k - t\rho\phi_k,\phi_k]/2$, $t \varepsilon (0,1)$. The set $\{\rho>0:\Delta_k(\rho)>0\}$ contains some positive interval. Denote by $\hat\rho$ the least positive number ρ for which $\Delta_k(\rho) = 0$, if such exists. If $\hat\rho$ exists and $\rho\leq\hat\rho$, $(x_k-\rho\phi_k) \varepsilon S$. If such $\hat\rho$ does not exist, $(x_k-\rho\phi_k) \varepsilon S$ whenever $\rho>0$. We show that $\rho_k\varepsilon J$ implies $(x_k-\rho_k\phi_k) \varepsilon S$. Assume $\hat\rho$ exists. Then $\Delta_k(\hat\rho) = 0 = \hat\rho\|\phi_k\|^2[1 - \hat\rho f''[x_k-t\hat\rho\phi_k,\phi_k]\|\phi_k\|^{-2}/2]$. Thus $\hat\rho = 2\|\phi_k\|^2/f''[x_k-t\hat\rho\phi_k,\phi_k] \geq 2\rho_0$, since $x_k-t\hat\rho\phi_k\varepsilon S$. Hence if $\rho_k\varepsilon J$, $(x_k-\rho_k\phi_k)\varepsilon S$, and $\Delta_k(\rho_k) \geq \delta[1-(\delta/2\rho_0)]\|\phi_k\|^2>0$. If $\|\phi_k\|^2 \not\to 0$, then for some $\varepsilon>0$, there exists a subsequence $\|\phi_k\|^2 \geq \varepsilon$. Hence $f(x_k)\searrow -\infty$, contradicting that f is bounded below on S. Hence $\|\phi_k\|^2 \to 0$ and $f(x_k)$ converges downward to a limit L. Assume the hypothesis of (ii) and suppose that $L \neq \inf\{f(x): x \varepsilon H\}$. Choose z such that $f(z)<L$. Then $0>f(z) -f(x_k) \geq [\phi_k,z-x_k]$. Since $\|x_{k+1}\|^2-\|x_k\|^2=-2\rho_k[x_k,\phi_k]+\rho_k^2\|\phi_k\|^2$, if $\|x_k\|$ is unbounded, there is a subsequence x_k, such that $-[x_k,\phi_k]>-\|\phi_k\|^2\rho_k/2$. Thus $[\phi_k,z-x_k]>[\phi_k,z]-\|\phi_k\|^2\rho_k/2$. But $\|\phi_k\|\to 0$; consequently, $0>f(z)-L\geq 0$. A similar argument holds when $\|x_k\|$ is bounded; hence $L=\inf\{f(x):x\varepsilon H\}$.

The function f is lower semi-continuous on S if and only if the set $S_K=\{x\varepsilon S: f(x)\leq K\}$ is closed in S for each K. Since f is convex and continuous, S_K is closed and convex, and is thus weakly closed. Hence f is weakly lower semi-continuous. Assuming (iii), S is weakly compact and therefore $f(z) = L$. Clearly $\phi(z) = 0$. Because z is a unique minimizer, z is a weak limit point for $\{x_k\}$; while if H is finite dimensional, x_k converges strongly to z. If f is the norm on H then since $f(x_k) \to f(z)$, x_k converges strongly to z by inspection of $f^2(x_k-z)$.

We now show that if $\mu>0$, the sequence $\{x_k\}$ is Cauchy. Otherwise for some $\varepsilon>0$ and for every $K = 1,2,3,\ldots$, there exists indices k and s, $s>k\geq K$ such that $\|x_s-x_k\|\geq\varepsilon$. Choose K such that $[\phi_k,(x_s-x_k)/\|x_s-x_k\|]>-\mu\varepsilon/4$ for all $s>k\geq K$. Then

$0>f(x_s) - f(x_k) \geq \varepsilon^2\mu/4$, a contradiction. Thus there exists $z=\lim x_k$ minimizing f on H. Finally, $f(x)-f(z)\geq\|x-z\|^2\mu/2$ for all $x\varepsilon H$ and consequently z is unique.

Remarks. 1. The above theorem may be applied to minimize a suitably differentiable function on a closed linear variety in H. With no loss in generality, we may assume the variety to be a closed subspace, say M. If F is the restriction of f to M, the gradient of F may be constructed from the observation that $f'(x,h) = F'(x,h)$ for all x and h in M. Hence $F'(x,\cdot)$ is the projection of $f'(x,\cdot)$ on M.

2. Assume $\{x_k\}$ converges strongly to z. Assume that f has a second Frechet derivative at z and that $f''(z,h,h)\geq\sigma\|h\|^2$ with $\sigma>0$ and $h\varepsilon H$. Then $\{x_k\}$ converges eventually with a speed greater than some geometric progression.

Proof. The bi-linear functional $f''(z,h,g)$ is symmetric ([4,p. 176]); hence the operator $f''(z,\cdot,\cdot)$ is self-adjoint and positive definite. Let λ denote the upper bound for the spectrum of $f''(z,\cdot,\cdot)$. For $\rho\varepsilon J$ define $\beta(\rho) = \max\{|1-\rho\sigma|, |1-\rho\lambda|\} = \|I-\rho f''(z,\cdot,\cdot)\|$. Set $\bar{\beta} = \max\{\beta(\rho): \rho\varepsilon J\}<1$ and $\varepsilon = (1-\bar{\beta})/4\rho_0$. Then $\|x_{k+1}-z\| = \|x_k-z-\rho_k\phi_k\| \leq \|x_k-z-\rho_k f''(z,x_k-z,\cdot)\| + \rho_k\|\phi_k - f''(z,x_k-z,\cdot)\|$. Since f'' exists at z, $|f'(x_k,h)-f'(z,h) - f''(z,x_k-z,h)|<\varepsilon\|h\|\,\|x_k-z\|$, for h and x_k-z in some neighborhood of the origin, say N. Choose K so that $k \geq K$ implies $x_k\varepsilon\ z + N$. Thus $\|\phi_k-f''(z,x_k-z,\cdot)\|\leq\varepsilon\|x_k-z\|$ and $\|x_{k+1} -z\| \leq (\|I-\rho_k f''(z,\cdot,\cdot)\| + \varepsilon\rho_k)\|x_k-z\| \leq (1+\bar{\beta})\|x_k-z\|/2$. Q.E.D. Observe that a choice for $\rho_k\varepsilon J$ would be $2/(\sigma+\lambda)$. This number minimizes the function β.

3. Acceleration of convergence is sometimes possible. Assume the hypothesis of 2) above with $\sigma=\lambda) = 1/\rho_k$, then $\|I-\rho_k f''(z,\cdot,\cdot)\| = 0$. Hence given $\varepsilon>0$, for some K, $k\geq K$ implies $\|x_{k+1}-z\| \leq \varepsilon\ \|x_k-z\|$. The above fact suggests the possibility of accelerating convergence. To fix our ideas, assume $H=E_m$ and f is in C^2 on E_m. The operator $f''(x_k,\cdot,\cdot)$ is then represented by the hessian matrix, say $Q(x_k) = Q_k$, and $Q(x_k) \to Q(z)$. Suppose that K is chosen so large that $k\geq K$ implies that $Q(x_k)$ is non-singular. Let E_k denote a matrix such that $E_k^* Q_kE_k$ is the identity matrix, make the change of variables $x=E_ky$, and put $\rho_k=1$. In practice such a change of variables need only be made infrequently, rather than at each iteration. Limited computational experience indicates that this device can be quite effective.

4. Assume the hypotheses of ii) in the theorem above. Assume $x_k\to z$. If $S\subset S'$ and S' has diameter D, then $f(x_k)$ -

$\|f'(x_k,\cdot)\| D \leq f(z) \leq f(x_k)$.

Proof. By Taylor's theorem $f(z) \geq f(x_k) + f'(x_k, z-x_k)$. Thus $f(z) \geq f(x_k) - \|f'(x_k,\cdot)\| D$. Observe that since $f(x_k) \searrow f(z)$ and $\|f'(x_k,\cdot)\| \to 0$, the above inequalities are useful as a test when computations should terminate.

5. Let $m_k = \sup\{\Delta_k(\rho): 0 \leqq \rho \leqq \infty\}$. If there exists ρ_k' such that $\Delta_k(\rho_k') = m_k$, then $\Delta_k(\rho_k') \geqq \Delta_k(\rho_k)$ and ρ_k' may be used in the theorem above in lieu of ρ_k.

Example.* A problem of space technology is concerned with the system of differential equations,

$$\left.\begin{aligned} \ddot{\xi}_1 - 2\omega\dot{\xi}_2 &= x_i \\ \ddot{\xi}_2 + 2\omega\dot{\xi}_1 - 3\omega^2\xi_2 &= x_2 \end{aligned}\right\} \quad (I)$$

with given initial conditions:

$$\xi_1(0), \dot{\xi}_1(0)\ \xi_2(0) \text{ and } \dot{\xi}_2(0) \qquad (a);$$

and terminal conditions

$$\xi_1(1) = \dot{\xi}_1(1) = \xi_2(1) = \dot{\xi}_2(1) = 0 \qquad (b).$$

Assume that (a) is given such that for some pair of functions $x = (x_1, x_2)$, (I) is satisfied subject to (b). Let N denote the set of such pairs. Let $f(x) = \int_0^1 [x_1^2(t) + x_2^2(t)]^{1/2}$ dt, and $\mu = \inf\{f(x): x \in N\}$. A pair π is sought for which $f(\pi)$ is arbitrarily close to μ. In the physical problem (with certain simplifying assumptions, see [5]) f(x) is the fuel required for a "ferry-vehicle" to achieve a terminal-phase "rendezvous" with a satellite in a fixed time with given initial conditions under a thrust program x.

Assume x_1 and x_2 belong to $L_1(0,1)$, and let $\mathcal{L}_1 = L_1 \oplus L_1$. Define $|x(t)| = [x_1^2(t) + x_2^2(t)]^{1/2}$ and $\|x\|_1 = f(x)$. (This norm is equivalent to the norm on the product topology of

*The interest in this example is enhanced by the fact that the extremals are "impulses" and hence do not belong to N. See Neustadt, [6], Cheney-Goldstein [7] and Goldstein-Seidman [8].

L_1.) Define $L_\infty = L_\infty \oplus L_\infty$ with norm $\|x\|_\infty = \max\{\|x_1\|_\infty, \|x_2\|_\infty\}$ and $[x,y] = \int_0^1 (x_1 y_1 + x_2 y_2) dt$ with $x \varepsilon L_1$ and $y \varepsilon L_\infty$.

Evaluation of the terminal conditions (b) leads to the equations $[x,u^i] = \alpha_i$, $(1 \leq i \leq 4)$. Here u_1^i and u_2^i are simple expressions in circular functions and α_i are constants depending on the initial conditions. These functions are given explicitly in [5]. Let

$$N = \{x \varepsilon L_1 : [x,u^i] = \alpha_i : 1 \leqq i \leqq 4\}.$$

N is a closed linear variety in L_1 and μ is the distance from the origin to N. Let $L_2 = L_2 \oplus L_2$ and define

$$M = \{x \varepsilon L_2 : [x,u^i] = \alpha_i : 1 \leqq i \leqq 4\}.$$

Observe $L_2 \subset L_1$, $M \subset N$ and that M is dense in N. Hence $\mu = \{\inf f(x) : x \varepsilon M\}$.

Choose x_0 in M and let M_0 denote the closed subspace $\{y = x - x_0 : x \varepsilon M\}$. Let $f(y+x_0) = g(y)$. Minimizing f on M is equivalent to minimizing g on M_0, and this latter problem is encompassed by Remark 1, provided that g is suitably differentiable. Clearly g will be suitably differentiable when f is; but f is not; and so we present $f_\delta(x) = \int_0^1 [|x(t)|^2 + \delta^2]^{1/2} dt$ and consider Observation 1.

<u>Observation 1</u>. For each x and h in L_2 the Frechet differential $f_\delta'(x,h)$ and Gateaux differential $f_\delta''[x,h]$ exist, $f_\delta''(x,h) \geq 0$, $f_\delta''(x,h) \leq (1/\delta) \|h\|^2$ and S is convex.

<u>Proof</u>. Let $\phi(x_1(t), x_2(t)) = [x_1^2(t) + x_2^2(t) + \delta^2]^{1/2}$, and verify that the partial derivatives of ϕ with respect to x_1 and x_2 of order γ, $1 \leqq \gamma \leqq 3$, are uniformly bounded over all pairs of $x \varepsilon L_2$. With this in mind one can verify that f_δ is once Frechet differentiable, and that for each x and h in L_2, the Gateaux differential $f''[\cdot,h]$ exists.

We calculate $f_\delta''[x,h] = \int_0^1 [|x(t)|^2 + \delta^2]^{-1/2} [h_1^2(t) + h_2^2(t) - (\alpha(t) h_1(t) + \beta(t) h_2(t))^2] dt$, where $\alpha = x_1/[|x|^2 + \delta^2]^{1/2}$, $\beta = x_2/[|x|^2 + \delta^2]^{1/2}$, and $\alpha^2 + \beta^2 = 1 - \delta^2/[|x|^2 + \delta^2]$. Whence $h_1^2 + h_2^2 - (\alpha h_1 + \beta h_2)^2 = (\delta^2/(|x|^2 + \delta^2))(h_1^2 + h_2^2) + (h_1\beta - h_2\alpha)^2$. Thus $f_\delta''[x,h] \geq 0$, all x and h, and $f_\delta''[x,h] \leqq (1/\delta)\|h\|^2$. Since the function f_δ is convex throughout L_2, the set S is convex.

2. Let $\mu_\delta = \inf\{f_\delta(x) : x \varepsilon M\}$. Given $\varepsilon > 0$, choose $\delta < \varepsilon/3$ and x_δ such that $f_\delta(x_\delta) < \mu_\delta + \varepsilon/3$. Then $f(x_\delta) \leq \mu + \varepsilon$, and x_δ minimizes f with a relative error less than $\sqrt{2}\varepsilon \max(\|u^i\|_\infty / \alpha_i)$.

<u>Proof</u>. $\int_0^1 [|x(t)|^2 + \delta^2]^{1/2} dt \leqq \int_0^1 (|x(t)| + \delta) dt$; hence $f(x) < f_\delta(x) \leqq f(x) + \delta$. Choose z such that $f(z) - \mu < \varepsilon/3$. Then

$f(x_\delta) - \mu < f_\delta(z) + \varepsilon/3 - \mu < f_\delta(z) - f(z) + f(z) - \mu + \varepsilon/3 < \varepsilon$. To bound μ below, use the inequalities $\alpha_i = [x,u^i] \leq \|u^i\|_\infty \cdot \int_0^1(|x_1(t)|+|x_2(t)|)dt \leq \sqrt{2}\ \|u^i\|_\infty f(x)$.

Example. Let (S,μ) denote a positive measure space with $\mu(S) < \infty$. Let N_0 be a subspace of $L_1(S,\mu)$ and z a point not in N_0. A best approximation to z from N_0 is any point x^* satisfying $\|x^* - z\| \leq \|x-z\|$ for all $x \varepsilon N_0$. If N_0 is not finite dimensional x^* does not necessarily exist. even if N_0 is closed. We shall therefore content ourselves with any point in N_0 whose distance from z is within prescribed tolerance of $\inf\{\|x-z\|: x \varepsilon N_0\}$. Let $N = \{x-z: x \varepsilon N_0\}$. Assume $z \varepsilon L_2(S,\mu)$, and $M = \{x-z: x \varepsilon N \cap L_2\}$. Assume M dense in N. Now apply the Theorem to f_δ on M.

Acknowledgments

It is a pleasure to thank A. M. Gleason, B. R. Kripke, and R. T. Rockafellar for helpful criticisms and suggestions. This work was supported by grant AF-AFOSR-62-348, at the Massachusetts Institute of Technology and at the University of Texas. Support was also furnished by research funds of the Boeing Scientific Research Laboratories and the Raytheon Co. The application of the algorithm to the problem of orbital rendezvous was programmed by A. T. Johnson. Several examples were run on the I.B.M. 7090 at the M.I.T. Comp. Ctr. Some of these results are reported in [5].

References

[1] Kantorovich, L. V., Functional Analysis and Applied Mathematics, N.B.S. Report 1509 (out of print) but possibly available from Collins Radio, Cedar Rapids, Iowa. Translated from the Russian by C. D. Benster (Uspekhi Mathematicheskikh Nauk, Vol. III, No. 6), pp. 89-185, 1948. Editor G. E. Forsythe.

[2] Altman, M., The best successive approximation and the method of steepest descent. Approximation Methods in Functional Analysis. California Institute of Technology, p. 37, 1959.

[3] Balakrishnan, A. V., An operator theoretic formulation of a class of control problems and a steepest descent method of solution. Jour. S.I.A.M.Control, Vol. 1, pp. 109-127, 1963.

[4] Graves, L. M., Riemann Integration and Taylor's Theorem in General Analysis. Transactions AMS, Vol. 29, p. 163, 1927.

[5] Goldstein, A. A., Greene, A., and Johnson, A. T., Minimum Fuel in Terminal Rendezvous. To appear in Progress in Astronautics and Aeronautics, Vol.13, Academic Press, N.Y., 1964.

[6] Neustadt, L. W., "Optimization, a Moment Problem, and Non-linear Programming." Pre-print, personal communication.

[7] Cheney, E. W. and Goldstein A.A., Tchebycheff approximation and related extremal problems. D1-82-0293 Boeing Scientific Research Labs, Seattle, Wash.

[8] Goldstein, A. A., and Seidman T., Fuel Optimal Controls, D1-82-0292 Boeing Scientific Research Labs, Seattle, Wash.

Computational Aspects of the Time-Optimal Control Problem

Edward J. Fadden and Elmer G. Gilbert
Instrumentation Engineering Program
The University of Michigan
Ann Arbor, Michigan

1. Introduction

This paper is concerned with the computation of time-optimal controls for systems whose motion can be described by a set of ordinary linear differential equations. The theory of such systems is well developed (6, 12), among other things it being known that the optimal control is expressed explicitly in terms of solutions to the related adjoint differential equations. The principal difficulty is that the initial values for these adjoint equations are not prescribed. Recently, certain iterative procedures have been proposed (Eaton (2) and Neustadt (7, 8)) for computing these initial values. While theory shows that these procedures converge, it has been observed by the authors and others (10, 11) that in applications the number of iterations required to produce initial values of satisfactory accuracy is often unreasonably large.

The purpose of this paper is to examine these convergence difficulties and propose some possible remedies. For simplicity a time-optimal problem of somewhat limited generality is treated; at the end of the paper extensions are indicated. Example problems and computational results are not related to specific physical applications, but merely represent the type of situations one might expect to encounter.

2. The Time Optimal-Control Problem

It is assumed that the linear differential equations of motion can be written in the form

$$\dot{x} = A(t)x + b(t)u, \quad x(0) = x_0, \tag{1}$$

where x is the n - dimensional state vector, u(t) is the scalar control function, A(t) is a continuous n x n matrix, and b(t) is a continuous n-dimensional vector. Admissible control functions are required to be piecewise continuous and limited in magnitude so that $|u(t)| \leq 1$. Given an admissible control function and an initial state x_0, Eq. (1) has a unique solution $x(t)$. The time-optimal control problem which is to be considered is the regulator problem: find the admissible control which makes $x(t) = 0$ in the shortest possible time t. If an optimal control and an optimal time exist, they will be denoted by $u^*(t)$ and t^*.

The theory of this time-minimal problem will now be reviewed briefly. The solution of (1) is given by

$$x(t) = X(t)[x_0 + \int_0^t X^{-1}(\sigma)b(\sigma)u(\sigma)\,d\sigma], \tag{2}$$

where $X(t)$ is the n x n nonsingular matrix function which is a solution of

$$\dot{X} = A(t)X, \quad X(0) = I. \tag{3}$$

Setting $x(t) = 0$ in Eq. (2) gives an equivalent statement of the time-optimal control problem: find the admissible control which makes

$$x_0 = -\int_0^t X^{-1}(\sigma)b(\sigma)u(\sigma)\,d\sigma \tag{4}$$

in the shortest possible time t. The recoverable set,

$$C(t) = \{-\int_0^t X^{-1}(\sigma)b(\sigma)u(\sigma)\,d\sigma \;|\; u(\sigma) \text{ admissible}\}, \tag{5}$$

plays an important role in this statement of the problem. It consists of all those initial states for which the motion (solution of Eq. (1)) can be driven to zero in time t. The following facts are known (6): 1) $C(t)$ is compact, convex, and contains the origin, 2) $\bar{C}(t_1) \subset C(t_2)$, $t_1 < t_2$, 3) if q is interior to $C(t_2)$ there is a $t_1 < t_2$ such that q is an interior point of $C(t_1)$. Result 3) implies that when an optimal control exists, x_0 belongs to the boundary of $C(t^*)$. Thus it is important to consider those controls which yield the boundary points of $C(t)$.

Let p be a boundary point of $C(t)$. Since $C(t)$ is closed and convex, there exists a support hyperplane to $C(t)$ at p.

If $\eta \neq 0$ is a vector normal to the support hyperplane which is directed away from C(t), then

$$(\eta, p) \geq (\eta, q), \quad q \in C(t). \tag{6}$$

Let $u_B(t)$ be a control which produces p, i. e.,

$$p = -\int_0^t X^{-1}(\sigma) b(\sigma) u_B(\sigma)\, d\sigma .$$

Then if u is an admissible control Eq. (6) implies

$$-\int_0^t (\eta, X^{-1}(\sigma) b(\sigma)) u_B(\sigma)\, d\sigma \geq -\int_0^t (\eta, X^{-1}(\sigma) b(\sigma)) u(\sigma)\, d\sigma$$

or

$$-\int_0^t v(\sigma, \eta) u_B(\sigma)\, d\sigma \geq -\int_0^t v(\sigma, \eta) u(\sigma)\, d\sigma , \tag{7}$$

where

$$v(t, \eta) = b'(X^{-1}(t))'\eta. \tag{8}$$

Therefore it is necessary that

$$u_B(\sigma) = -\text{sgn}\, v(\sigma, \eta), \quad 0 < \sigma < t. \tag{9}$$

In order to guarantee that $u_B(t)$ is defined for almost all t, it is assumed that the system (1) is normal, namely $v(t, \eta)$, $\eta \neq 0$, is zero only at isolated points of t. Thus if p is a boundary point of C(t) it is attained by using the control

$$u(t, \eta) = -\text{sgn}\, v(t, \eta) \tag{10}$$

and is given by

$$z(t, \eta) = -\int_0^t X^{-1}(\sigma) b(\sigma) u(\sigma, \eta)\, d\sigma. \tag{11}$$

Conversely it can be shown (2) that $z(t, \eta)$ is always a boundary point of C(t)

The assumption that system (1) is normal has other implications. From the uniqueness of $u(t, \eta)$ and (11) it is clear that all support planes to C(t) are regular, that is they contact C(t) at only one point. It can also be shown (6) that for each point p in the boundary of C(t) the corresponding control is unique (even though the direction of the vector η at p may not be, i. e., C(t) has a "corner" at p). Furthermore, if p is ever in the boundary of $C(t)$, it can only be in the boundary of $C(t)$ for one value of t.

From the foregoing the following conclusions can be drawn. If an optimal control exists, it is unique for almost all t and is given by $u^*(t) = u(t, \eta)$ for some $\eta = \eta^*$. Further (from the last result of the preceding paragraph), if a control of the form $u(t) = u(t, \eta)$ can be found such that the motion of (1) gives $x(\bar{t}) = 0$, then $\bar{t} = t^*$, $\eta = \eta^*$, and the control is optimum. Thus the problem of determining the optimal control reduces simply to the determination of such an η. For simplicity, it is assumed in the sequel that the optimal control exists.

Since $(X^{-1}(t))'\eta$ is a solution of the adjoint differential equation

$$\dot{\xi} = -A'(t)\xi, \quad \xi(0) = \eta , \tag{12}$$

$u(t, \eta)$ is given by

$$u(t, \eta) = -\mathrm{sgn}\,(b'(t)\,\xi(t)) = -\mathrm{sgn}\,(b(t), \xi(t)\,). \tag{13}$$

Therefore it is not necessary to compute the fundamental matrix $X(t)$ in order to search for the time-optimal control. Notice that $u(t, \eta)$ depends only on the direction of η and not on its magnitude.

3. The Computation of Optimal Controls

A great variety of methods for computing time-optimal controls have been proposed. For perspective some of these methods will now be described briefly. Then the techniques on which this paper is based will be reviewed.

The earliest computational methods are based on backward integration of Eq. (1) with $u(t)$ given by Eq. (10) and result in the determination of switching surfaces (1, 6). These methods produce the control law for optimal regulation, but are limited practically to time invariant systems of second or third order. Another approach is to seek η^* by searching through a large number of η values. Even for systems of low order this is often unfeasible because the domain of significant η (those η which produce the great majority of boundary points of $C(t)$) is often very small. Recently, Knudsen (4) has proposed a method of successive approximations whereby $x_0 = z(t, \eta)$ is solved for $t = t^*$ and $\eta = \eta^*$. Although the method works well on an example problem, its derivation is formal, being based on the first order terms in the power series for $z(t, \eta)$, and there is no guarantee that it will converge. Ho (3), has given a quite different method of successive approximations where the terminal time is fixed $(t = T)$ and a quadratic norm of $x(T)$ is minimized. By finding the minimum T for which the minimum norm is zero, the time minimal problem is solved. The iterative procedures treated in this paper have a rigorous basis, may be extended to a wide class of important problems, and have promise of being practical (e. g., they are suitable for hybrid computation). The algorithms which follow are generally derived by using properties of the recoverable set $C(t)$ (2, 7, 8). Similar algorithms may also be derived via well known methods in functional analysis.

Consider the function

$$f(t, \eta) = (\eta, x_0 - z(t, \eta)), \tag{14}$$

where $f(0, \eta) = (\eta, x_0) > 0$. Since Eq. (6) can be written as $(\eta, q) - (\eta, z(t, \eta)) \le 0$, $q \in C(t)$, and x_0 is in $C(t^*)$, $f(t^*, \eta) \le 0$. From Eqs. (8), (10) and (11) it is clear that

$$(\eta, z(t, \eta)) = \int_0^t |v(\sigma, \eta)| \, d\sigma . \tag{15}$$

Therefore $\frac{\partial f}{\partial t} = -|v(t, \eta)| \le 0$ and is zero only at isolated values of t. Thus $T(\eta)$ is uniquely defined by

$$f(T(\eta), \eta) = 0 \tag{16}$$

and $0 < T(\eta) \le t^*$.

Geometrically, $f(t, \eta)$ is proportional to the distance from x_0 to the support hyperplane to $C(t)$ at $z(t, \eta)$. Therefore at $t = T(\eta)$, x_0 is contained in the support hyperplane. Unless $z(T(\eta), \eta) = x_0$, x_0 is outside $C(T)$ (because the support hyperplane is regular) and $T(\eta) < t^*$. When $z(T(\eta), \eta) = x_0$, $\eta = \eta^*$ and $T(\eta) = t^*$. Thus $T(\eta)$ assumes its maximum value t^* if and only if $\eta = \eta^*$.

Neustadt (7, 8) and Eaton (2) have formulated iterative procedures for maximizing $T(\eta)$ which are essentially the same. They involve successive application of the difference equation

$$\eta_{j+1} = \eta_j + k[x_0 - z(T(\eta_j), \eta_j)], \quad j = 0, 1, \ldots ,$$

where the initial trial η_0 must satisfy $(\eta_0, x_0) > 0$. Provided

$k > 0$ is sufficiently small the sequence $\{\eta_j\}$ converges to η^* (2). This equation may be interpreted as an application of the method of steepest ascent to the maximization of $T(\eta)$. A geometric interpretation is shown in Figure 1. Clearly if k is not too large (dashed hyperplane) $f(T(\eta_j), \eta_{j+1}) > 0$. Thus $T(\eta_{j+1}) > T(\eta_j)$.

None of the preceding results depend in an essential way on the magnitude of η. Therefore, it will be assumed hereafter that η has unit Euclidean length ($\|\eta\| = 1$). Thus letting

$$e(t, \eta) = x_0 - z(t, \eta), \tag{17}$$

the difference equation becomes

$$\eta_{j+1} = \|\eta_j + ke(T(\eta_j), \eta_j)\|^{-1} [\eta_j + ke(T(\eta_j), \eta_j)]. \tag{18}$$

4. The Linearized Difference Equation

The choice of k presents a problem. If it is conservatively small, convergence will be very slow. Insight into this problem and others can be gained by linearizing the difference equation at η^*.

For simplicity of notation let

$$\frac{\partial e(T(\eta), \eta)}{\partial \eta} = G(\eta) . \tag{19}$$

Assuming that $G(\eta)$ exists, the linearized difference equation is

$$\delta\eta_{j+1} = \delta\eta_j + kG(\eta^*)\delta\eta_j , \tag{20}$$

where $\delta\eta_j = \eta_j - \eta^*$. In Section 7 the existence of $G(\eta)$ is discussed. Provided $A(t)b(t)$ and $\dot{b}(t)$ satisfy uniform Lipschitz conditions on the interval $[0, t^*]$, $G(\eta)$ fails to exist only on a set of measure zero. Thus from a computational standpoint the existence of $G(\eta)$ does not present any practical problems.

Expanding Eq. (19) yields

$$G(\eta) = \left.\frac{\partial e(t, \eta)}{\partial t}\right|_{t=T(\eta)} \frac{\partial T(\eta)}{\partial \eta} + H(\eta) , \tag{21}$$

where

$$H(\eta) = \left.\frac{\partial e(t, \rho)}{\partial \rho}\right|_{\substack{t=T(\eta)\\ \rho=\eta}} . \tag{22}$$

Neustadt has shown (8) that $\frac{\partial T(\eta)}{\partial \eta}$ is proportional to $e'(T(\eta),\eta)$.

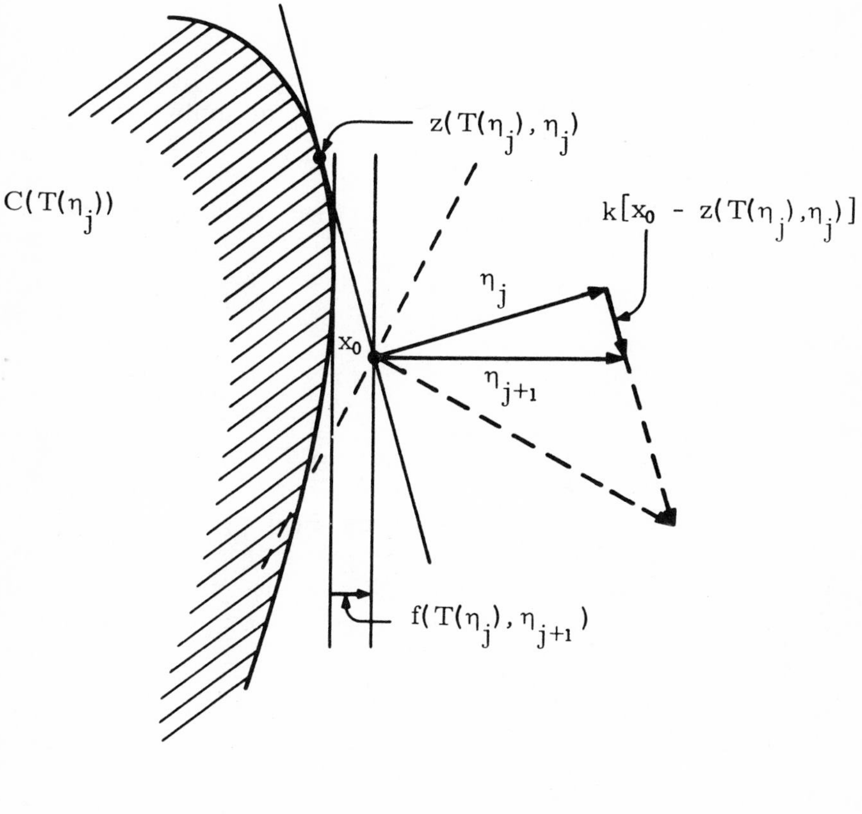

Figure 1. Geometric Interpretation of the Iterative Procedure.

Hence from Eq. (21) it is evident that

$$G(\eta^*) = H(\eta^*). \tag{23}$$

It is also shown in Section 7 that

$$H(\eta) = -2 \sum_{i=1}^{m} \frac{[X^{-1}(t_i)b(t_i)][X^{-1}(t_i)b(t_i)]'}{\left| \frac{\partial}{\partial t}[-X^{-1}(t)b(t),\eta]\Big|_{t=t_i} \right|}, \tag{24}$$

where the t_i, $0 < t_1 < t_2 < \ldots < t_m < T(\eta)$, are the solutions of the equation $(X^{-1}(t)b(t), \eta) = 0$.

In addition to giving $G(\eta^*) = H(\eta^*)$, formula (24) gives the following useful facts:

i) $H(\eta) = H'(\eta)$

ii) $y'H(\eta)y \leq 0$ for all y, i.e., $H(\eta)$ is non-positive definite

iii) $H(\eta)\eta = 0$

iv) rank $H(\eta) \leq n-1$, from iii) it is clear the rank cannot be n

v) rank $H(\eta)$ = number of linearly independent switching vectors, $X^{-1}(t_i)b(t_i)$, $i = 1, 2, \ldots, m$.

A smooth point in the boundary of $C(t)$ is a point, $z(t,\eta)$, at which the direction of η is uniquely determined. For every smooth point where $H(\eta)$ exists, rank $H(\eta) = n - 1$ (note that the converse is also true). Henceforth it is assumed that x_0 is a smooth point of $C(t^*)$, since this is the usual case.

In terms of the above notation the linearized difference Eq. (20) can be written

$$\delta\eta_{j+1} = [I + kH(\eta^*)]\delta\eta_j \,. \tag{25}$$

The solution to this equation is given by

$$\delta\eta_j = [I + kH(\eta^*)]^j \delta\eta_0 \,. \tag{26}$$

If the iterative procedure [Eq. (18)] is to be convergent for all η such that $(\eta_0, x_0) > 0$, it is necessary that these solutions do not diverge. Values of k such that this is so are called stable k. The set of stable k will now be determined.

Because of properties i) and ii), $[I + kH(\eta^*)]$ can be expressed as

$$[I + kH(\eta^*)] = Q(\eta^*)\, \Gamma\, Q'(\eta^*), \tag{27}$$

where: Γ is a diagonal matrix with diagonal elements

$\gamma_i = 1 + k\lambda_i$; λ_i are the (real) eigenvalues of $H(\eta^*)$, and $Q(\eta^*)$ is an orthogonal matrix ($Q^{-1}(\eta^*) = Q'(\eta^*)$) whose columns are eigenvectors of $H(\eta^*)$. The λ_i are ordered so that $0 = \lambda_1 > \lambda_2 \geq \lambda_3 \ldots \geq \lambda_n$. Thus

$$[I + kH(\eta^*)]^j = Q(\eta^*)\,\Gamma\,Q'(\eta^*) \tag{28}$$

and the solutions (26) will not diverge if $|\gamma_i| \leq 1$, $i = 1, \ldots, n$. Consequently the range of stable k is given by

$$0 \leq k \leq k_s = 2|\lambda_n|^{-1}. \tag{29}$$

Since λ_n is often difficult to ascertain, it is helpful to obtain a positive lower bound on k_s. Note that $|\lambda_n| = \|H(\eta^*)\|$ where $\|P\| = \max_{\|x\|=1} \|Px\|$ and $\|x\|$ is the Euclidean length of x.

But

$$\|H(\eta^*)\| = \max_{\|x\|=1} \left\| 2\sum_{i=1}^{m} \frac{[X^{-1}(t_i)b(t_i), x][X^{-1}(t_i)b(t_i)]}{\left|\frac{d}{dt}[-X^{-1}(t)b(t), \eta^*]\Big|_{t=t_i}\right|} \right\|$$

$$\leq 2\sum_{i=1}^{m} \frac{\|X^{-1}(t_i)b(t_i)\|^2}{\left|\frac{d}{dt}[-X^{-1}(t)b(t), \eta^*]\Big|_{t=t_i}\right|}$$

Hence k is stable if

$$0 \leq k \leq k_b = \left[\sum_{i=1}^{m} \frac{\|X^{-1}(t_i)b(t_i)\|^2}{\left|\frac{d}{dt}[-X^{-1}(t)b(t), \eta^*]\Big|_{t=t_i}\right|}\right]^{-1} \leq k_s. \tag{30}$$

In the triple integrator problem, which is discussed in the next section, the difference between k_b and k_s was quite small for the various x_0 considered.

A good choice for k would be $k = \frac{1}{2}k_s$. For this value of k, $\gamma_1 = 1$, $\gamma_n = 0$, and $1 > \gamma_i \geq 0$. $i = 2, 3, \ldots, n-1$. Because x_0 is assumed to be a smooth point of $C(t^*)$, only $\gamma_1 = 1$. The eigenvector corresponding to γ_1 is η^*. Hence the projection of $\delta\eta_j$ on η^* remains unchanged. There is at least one direction (determined by the eigenvector corresponding to γ_n) along which $\delta\eta_0$ will give $\delta\eta_1 = 0$. In other directions the convergence rate usually varies significantly (due to variation in the λ_i's) and may, for $\gamma_{n-1} \cong 1$, be quite slow.

The theory developed in this section will now be used to explain certain aspects of the behavior of the iterative process in an example problem. It also forms the foundation for the modifications of the iterative procedure which are discussed in Section 6.

5. Example Problem

The example problem to be considered is $\dddot{y}(t) = u$. Setting $y = x^1$, $\dot{x}^1 = x^2$, and $\dot{x}^2 = x^3$ gives an equation of the form (1) where

$$A = \begin{bmatrix} 0 & 1 & 0 \\ 0 & 0 & 1 \\ 0 & 0 & 0 \end{bmatrix} \qquad b = \begin{bmatrix} 0 \\ 0 \\ 1 \end{bmatrix} . \tag{31}$$

There are a number of good reasons for choosing this system. First of all, the solution is known for $x_0' = [a \;\; 0 \;\; 0]$. Kulikowski (5) shows that

$$t^* = (32|a|)^{1/3} , \quad \frac{\eta^{2*}}{\eta^{1*}} = \frac{1}{2} t^*, \quad \frac{\eta^{3*}}{\eta^{1*}} = \frac{3}{8} \left(\frac{t^*}{2}\right)^2 , \tag{32}$$

where η^{i*} denotes the ith component of η^*. In addition explicit formulas may easily be derived for other results which follow. The problem exhibits convergence difficulties representative of more complex problems. This would not be the case if the problem were second order. For then η_0 and η^* are coplanar and an appropriate choice for k would give $\eta_1 = \eta^*$. Finally some other results are available on this (10) and a very similar problem (11).

Before looking at some specific iterative computations it is helpful to examine the general behavior of $T(\eta)$. Since η is on the unit sphere, let spherical coordinates ϕ and θ define η as follows:

$$\eta^1 - \eta^{1*} = \sin\phi\cos\theta, \; \eta^2 - \eta^{2*} = \sin\phi\sin\theta, \; \eta^3 - \eta^{3*} = \cos\phi. \tag{33}$$

Figure 2 shows contours of constant $T(\eta)$ for the condition $x_0' = [2 \;\; 0 \;\; 0]$ and $t^* = 4$. These contours are typical of those for all systems in that the set of η vectors for which $\bar{t} \le T(\eta) \le t^*$ is a convex cone. The wedge shaped area bounded by curves I, II, and III (and its reflection in the opposite side of the sphere) defines the set of η vectors such that $u(t, \eta)$ switches sign twice in $[0, t^*]$. It is also the set of η vectors which give rise to smooth points in the boundary of $C(t^*)$. Since the set of all non-smooth points in the boundary of $C(t^*)$ have measure zero, this is the significant set of η for problems

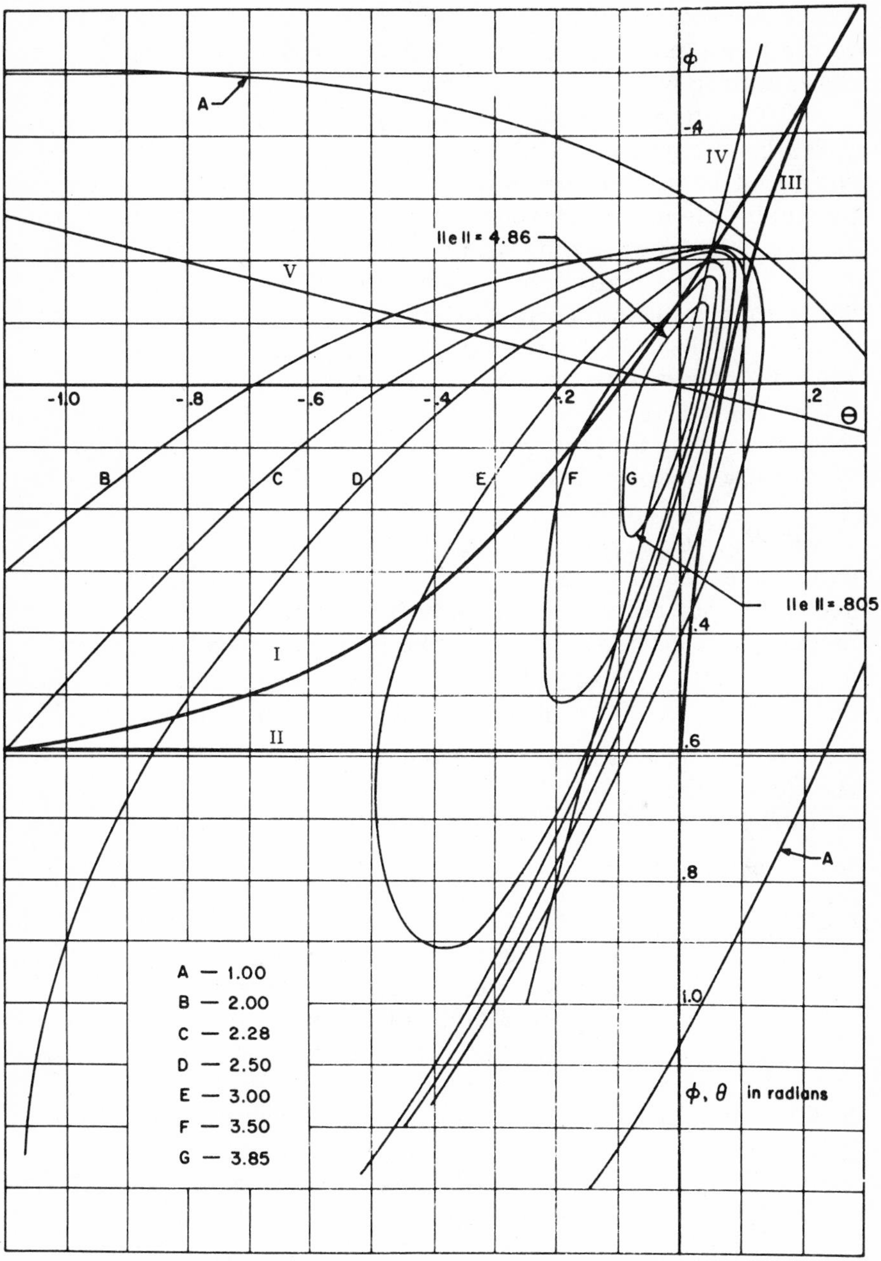

Figure 2. Contours of T(η) on the Unit Sphere.

which have optimal time $t^* = 4$. The limited extent of this set is the principal reason why trial-and-error procedures for determining η^* are ineffective.

The directions of the two eigenvectors of $H(\eta^*)$ are indicated by the straight lines IV and V passing through $\theta = \phi = 0$. Note that in the neighborhood of η^* line IV lies along the pronounced "ridge" exhibited by the function $T(\eta)$. The optimum is generally approached along the ridge.

The eigenvalue corresponding to line IV is $\lambda_2 = -4.94$ while that corresponding to line V is $\lambda_3 = -170.01$. For $k = \frac{1}{2}k_S = 0.00588$, $\gamma_2 = 0.971$ (see previous section). Thus near $\theta = \phi = 0$, convergence along IV is very slow.

The values of $\|e\|$ for two points on the $T(\eta) = 3.85$ contour show that the error is still large, even though $T(\eta)$ is relatively close to t^*.

If $k = \frac{1}{2}k_S$ convergence will be quite slow from the very beginning. On the other hand a much large value of k will cause greater changes in $T(\eta)$ initially, but the process will generally not converge. Hence from a practical standpoint it is desirable to base the iterative procedure on the equation

$$\eta_{j+1} = \|\eta_j + k_j e(T(\eta_j), \eta_j)\|^{-1}[\eta_j + k_j e(T(\eta_j), \eta_j)] \tag{34}$$

Two different methods of choosing k_j were used in the computer work described below:

method (1) $k_j = k_{j-1}, \quad T(\eta_j) \geq T(\eta_{j-1})$
$\quad = \frac{1}{2}k_{j-1}, \quad T(\eta_j) < T(\eta_{j-1})$

method (2) $k_j = m$ where m is chosen such that $T(\eta_{j+1}) - T(\eta_j) > 0$ is the largest obtainable using Eq. (34). To obtain m the iterative procedure $m_{i+1} = m_i + c_i(e(\eta_j), e(\eta_j + m_i e(\eta_j)))$ was used where $m_0 = c_0 = k_{j-1}$ and method (1) was used to determine c_i.

The number of iterations required for $\|e(T(\eta_j), \eta_j)\| < \epsilon$ is given in Tables 1 and 2. (See notes that follow Table 3.) The results are contained in the column headed "Untransformed". For $x_0' = [2\ 0\ 0]$ data is presented for two values of ϵ and several η_0 vectors. One set of data is also presented for $x_0' = [16\ 0\ 0]$. Figure 3 shows $T(\eta)$ and $\|e\|$ versus the number of iterations for $x_0' = [2\ 0\ 0]$ and $\eta_0' = [1\ 0\ 0]$ using method (1). This choice of η_0 corresponds to the point $\phi = 0.6$ and $\theta = -1.1$ on Figure 2. As can be seen, the convergence of $T(\eta)$ to t^* is much faster than that of $\|e\|$ to zero. Similar

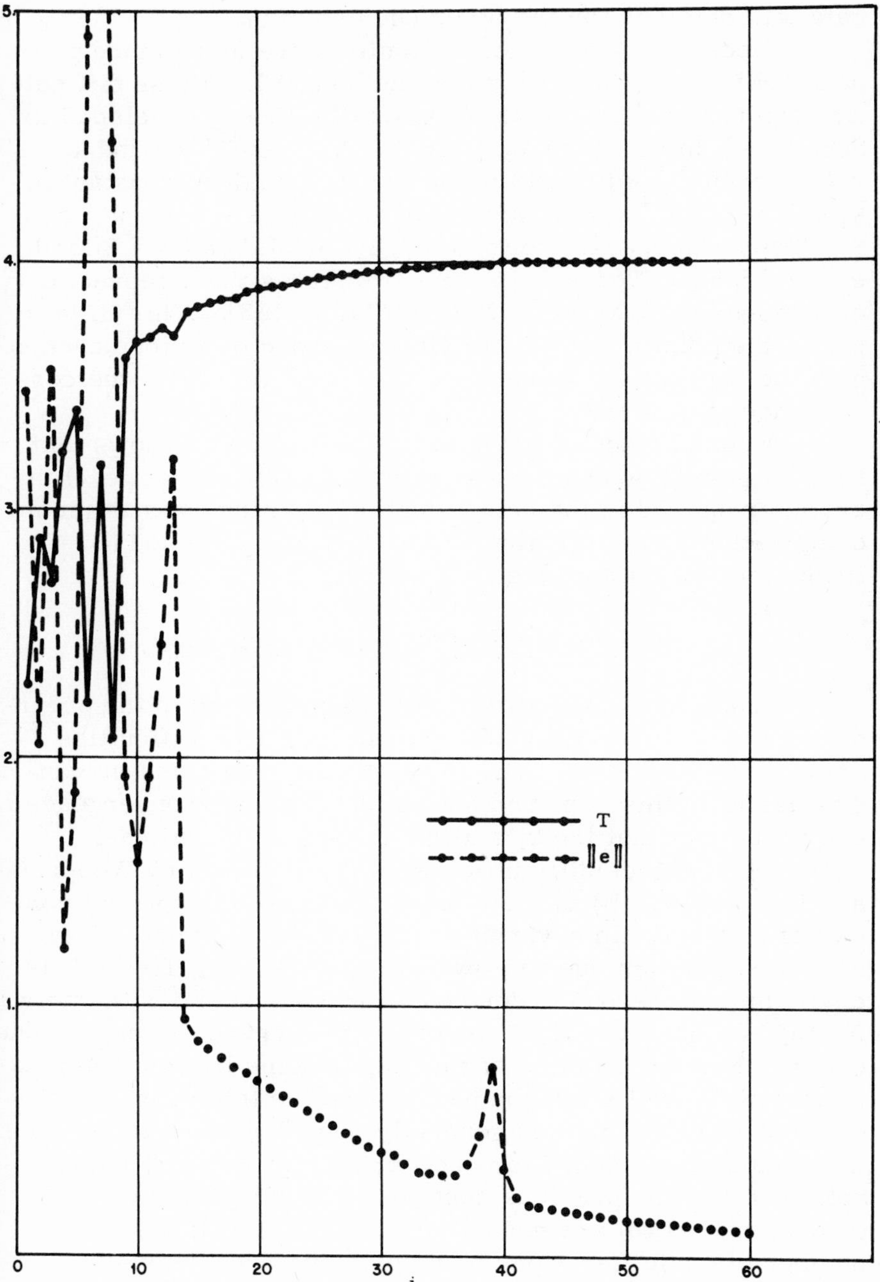

Figure 3. $T(\eta_j)$ and $\|e(T(\eta_j), \eta_j)\|$ for First Run, Table 1 (Untransformed).

data was obtained for the other choices of η_0.

Clearly, convergence difficulties are much more pronounced for $x_0' = [16 \ 0 \ 0]$ (using method (1)). These difficulties can be explained on the basis of the theory developed in Section 4. In this case $\lambda_2 = -16.79$, $\lambda_3 = -2675.85$ and $k_s = 7.48 \times 10^{-4}$. After 218 iterations k_j remained constant at $k_j = 5.84 \times 10^{-4}$. For this value of k_j, $\gamma_1 = -.555$ and $\gamma_2 = 0.9902$. Moreover, for $j = 300$, $T(\eta_j) \cong 7.988$ ($t^* = 8$) and $e_j' = 0.5528 [-.2965 \ -.7476 \ .5943]$ whereas the eigenvector corresponding to λ_2 is $[-.2994 \ -.7701 \ .5633]$. This illustrates the point made earlier; the presence of a ridge causes η^* to be approached along the eigenvector for which the convergence is slowest.

A comparison of the data in Tables 1 and 2 shows that little is gained by choosing k_j by method (2). In fact each iteration required in the determination of k_j involves as much computation as an iteration of Eq. (34) using method (1). Hence method (2) appears impractical.

6. Methods for Improving Convergence

From the computational results presented in the previous section, it is evident that the convergence difficulties arise when $T(\eta_j) \cong t^*$. The linear theory developed in Section 4 is useful in this case and shows that the poor convergence is due to the fact that the λ_i's differ greatly in magnitude.

Convergence difficulties were encountered by Woodrow and Paiewonsky (11) in their investigation of the optimal control of a linear, time-varying, third-order system. They used an algorithm due to Powell for maximizing $T(\eta)$. This algorithm has second order convergence properties (namely, if $T(\eta)$ is a quadratic function of η, convergence occurs in one cycle). For the problem of this paper some limited computations with Powell's method have shown the following. One cycle of Powell's method generally requires about three times the computation needed for one iteration of Eq. (34) using method (2) of the previous section. Three to four cycles (occasionally two) are needed to obtain $\|\epsilon\| < .1$; the total number of basic iterations being on some occasions as low as one half the number shown in the "untransformed" column of Table 1. Small errors in the determination of k_j on each step lead to a significant increase in the number of cycles required.

An alternate approach is presented here. The basic

idea is to use the iterative procedure given by Eq. (34) on a related problem where the matrix corresponding to $H(\eta^*)$ has equal non-zero eigenvalues. Then, if (for η_j in the vicinity of η^*) k_j is chosen as $k_j = \frac{1}{2}k_s$, the convergence will be second-order.

This related problem is set up in the following way. Let

$$y(t) = Px(t) , \tag{35}$$

where P is a non-singular, constant, n x n matrix. This gives the transformed system

$$\dot{y} = PA(t)P^{-1}y + Pb(t)u, \quad y_0 = Px_0 \tag{36}$$

Since P is non-singular, it is clear that the minimal time control for Eq. (36) is the minimal time control for Eq. (1).

The recoverable set for Eq. (36), $C_y(t)$, is related to $C(t)$ by $C_y(t) = PC(t)$. Furthermore, corresponding to $z(t,\eta)$ in the boundary of $C(t)$ is the point

$$w(t, \rho) = Pz(t, \eta) \tag{37}$$

in the boundary of $C_y(t)$, where ρ is the outward normal to a support hyperplane of $C_y(t)$ at $w(t, \rho)$. The points, x, in a support hyperplane to $C(t)$ at $z(t, \eta)$ are defined by $(\eta, x - z(t, \eta)) = 0$ while $(\rho, y - w(t, \rho)) = 0$ defines the points, y, in the corresponding support hyperplane to $C_y(t)$ at $w(t, \rho)$. Since $(\rho, y - w(t, \rho)) = (\rho, Px - Pz(t, \eta)) = (P'\rho, x - z(t, \eta)) = 0$ for all points x in the hyperplane $(\eta, x - z(t, \eta)) = 0$, it is clear that

$$\eta = P'\rho . \tag{38}$$

Applying the iterative procedure to the transformed system gives:

$$\rho_{j+1} = \rho_j + k_j(y_0 - w(T_y(\rho_j), \rho_j)) , \tag{39}$$

where $T_y(\rho_j)$ is defined by $f_y(T_y(\rho_j), \rho_j) = 0$ with

$$f_y(t, \rho_j) = (\rho_j, y_0 - w(t, \rho_j)) . \tag{40}$$

By using Eqs. (35), (37), and (38), $f_y(t, \rho_j)$ can be expressed in terms of x_0, η_j, and $z(t, \eta_j)$ as

$$f_y(t, \rho_j) = (\eta_j, x_0 - z(t, \eta_j)) . \tag{41}$$

But from Eqs. (14) and (41) it is clear that $f_y(t, \rho_j) = f(t, \eta_j)$.

Hence $T_y(\rho_j) = T(\eta_j)$.

Therefore if Eqs. (35), (37), and (38) are used in Eq. (39) one obtains $\eta_{j+1} = \eta_j + k_j P'P[x_0 - z(T(\eta_j), \eta_j)]$. In order to maintain $\|\eta\| = 1$, this becomes

$$\eta_{j+1} = \|\eta_j + k_j P'Pe(T(\eta_j), \eta_j)\|^{-1}[\eta_j + k_j P'Pe(T(\eta_j), \eta_j)]. \quad (42)$$

This difference equation defines a new iterative procedure which is convergent for a suitable choice of k_j because the procedure defined by Eq. (39) is convergent.

The choice of an appropriate transformation P will now be discussed. Linearizing Eq. (42) about $\eta = \eta^*$ yields:

$$\delta\eta_{j+1} = [I + k_j P'PH(\eta^*)]\delta\eta_j \,. \quad (43)$$

Following the suggestion made earlier, P'P is chosen so that the non-zero eigenvalues of $P'PH(\eta^*)$ are all equal. One such choice is

$$P'P = Q(\eta^*)N(\eta^*)\,Q'(\eta^*), \quad (44)$$

where $Q(\eta^*)$ is defined in Section 4, and $N(\eta^*)$ is a diagonal matrix with elements $\nu_1 = 1$, $\nu_i = [\frac{\lambda_n}{\lambda_i}]$, $i = 2, 3, \ldots, n$. As a result of this choice, Eq. (43) becomes

$$\delta\eta_{j+1} = Q(\eta^*)[I + k_j N(\eta^*)\,\Lambda(\eta^*)]Q'(\eta^*)\delta\eta_j \,, \quad (45)$$

where $\Lambda(\eta^*)$ is a diagonal matrix with elements λ_i, $i = 1, 2, \ldots, n$. Obviously $[I + k_j N(\eta^*)\,\Lambda(\eta^*)]$ is diagonal with elements $\gamma_1 = 1$, $\gamma_i = 1 + k_j\lambda_n$, $i = 2, 3, \ldots n$.

Eq. (42) with P'P given by Eq. (44) was used to obtain the results in the columns headed "Transformed" in Tables 1 and 2. The effect of this transformation is evident in Figure 4. In this figure plots of $T(\eta)$ and $\|e\|$ versus the number of iterations show that the number of iterations required in the neighborhood of η^* has been greatly reduced. This was also true for the other η_0's used. The reduction in the number of iterations for a = 16 is particularly impressive.

As it stands, the choice of P'P given by Eq. (44) is not practical since η^* must be known in advance. However, it is possible to take

$$P'P = Q(\eta_j)\,N(\eta_j)\,Q'(\eta_j)\,, \quad (46)$$

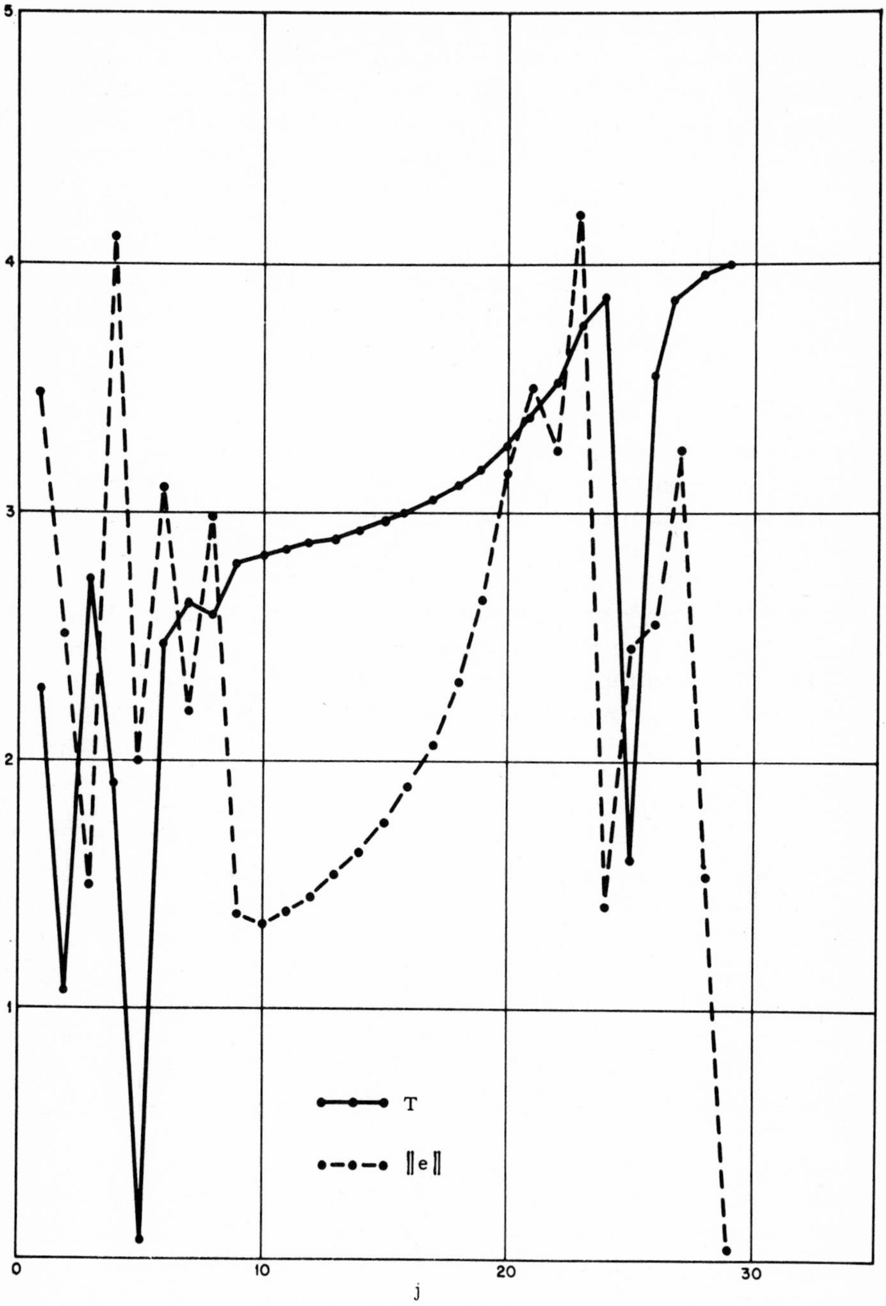

Figure 4. $T(\eta_j)$ and $\| e(T\eta_j), \eta_j) \|$ for First Run, Table 1 (Transformed).

which for η_j in the vicinity of η^* gives $H(\eta_j) \cong H(\eta^*)$. This technique was used to obtain the results in Table 3 (column headed "Transformed"). Whenever less than two switches occured in $(0, T(\eta_j))$, Eq. (34) was used with k_j determined by method (1) of Section 5. However, when two switches occurred, $0 < t_1 < t_2 < T(\eta_j)$, Eq. (42) was used with P'P determined by Eq. (46). The value of k_j used was $k_j = [-\lambda_n(H(\eta_j))]^{-1}$. For η_j sufficiently close to η^* this choice of k_j gives second order convergence. However, away from η^*, this choice of k_j can (and did) cause $T(\eta_{j+1}) < T(\eta_j)$. In order to insure that $T(\eta)$ never decreases, one might decrease k_j by a factor of two and recompute η_{j+1} when, for the initial choice of k_j, $T(\eta_{j+1}) < T(\eta_j)$. How this would affect the number of iterations required is not known.

The results in the column headed "Untransformed" in Table 3 are taken from Table 1. A comparison of the "Transformed" and "Untransformed" columns of Table 3 shows that a significant reduction in the number of iterations has been achieved in every case considered. Figure 5 shows $T(\eta)$ and $\|e\|$ versus the number of iterations (for $x_0' = [2 \;\; 0 \;\; 0]$ and $\eta_0' = [1 \;\; 0 \;\; 0]$). A comparison of Figure 5 with Figure 3 shows a remarkable improvement. Note that the $T(\eta)$ and $\|e\|$ curves are identical for the first seven iterations in these figures. This is due to the fact that $u(t, \eta_j)$ has less than two switches in the interval $(0, T(\eta_j))$ for $j < 7$. In determining η_8, Eq. (42) was used with P'P given by Eq. (46) and $k_7 = [-\lambda_3(H(\eta_7))]^{-1}$. This choice of k_7 caused $T(\eta_8) < T(\eta_7)$. In fact, $u(t, \eta_8)$ had only one switch in the interval $(0, T(\eta_8))$. Thus in determining η_9, Eq. (34) was used with $k_8 = \frac{1}{2}k_7$. Since $u(t, \eta_9)$ had two switches in $(0, T(\eta_9))$, Eq. (46) was again used to determine η_{10} and for this vector the prescribed terminal condition, $\|e\| < 0.1$, was satisfied. It was found that one additional iteration using Eq. (46) was sufficient to cause $\|e\| < 0.01$. This is typical of results obtained for different x_0 vectors.

7. The Derivation of $H(\eta)$

In this section $H(\eta)$ is derived and the question of its existence is discussed briefly.

Since $u(t, \eta)$ is determined by Eqs. (8) and (10), and alternates in sign,

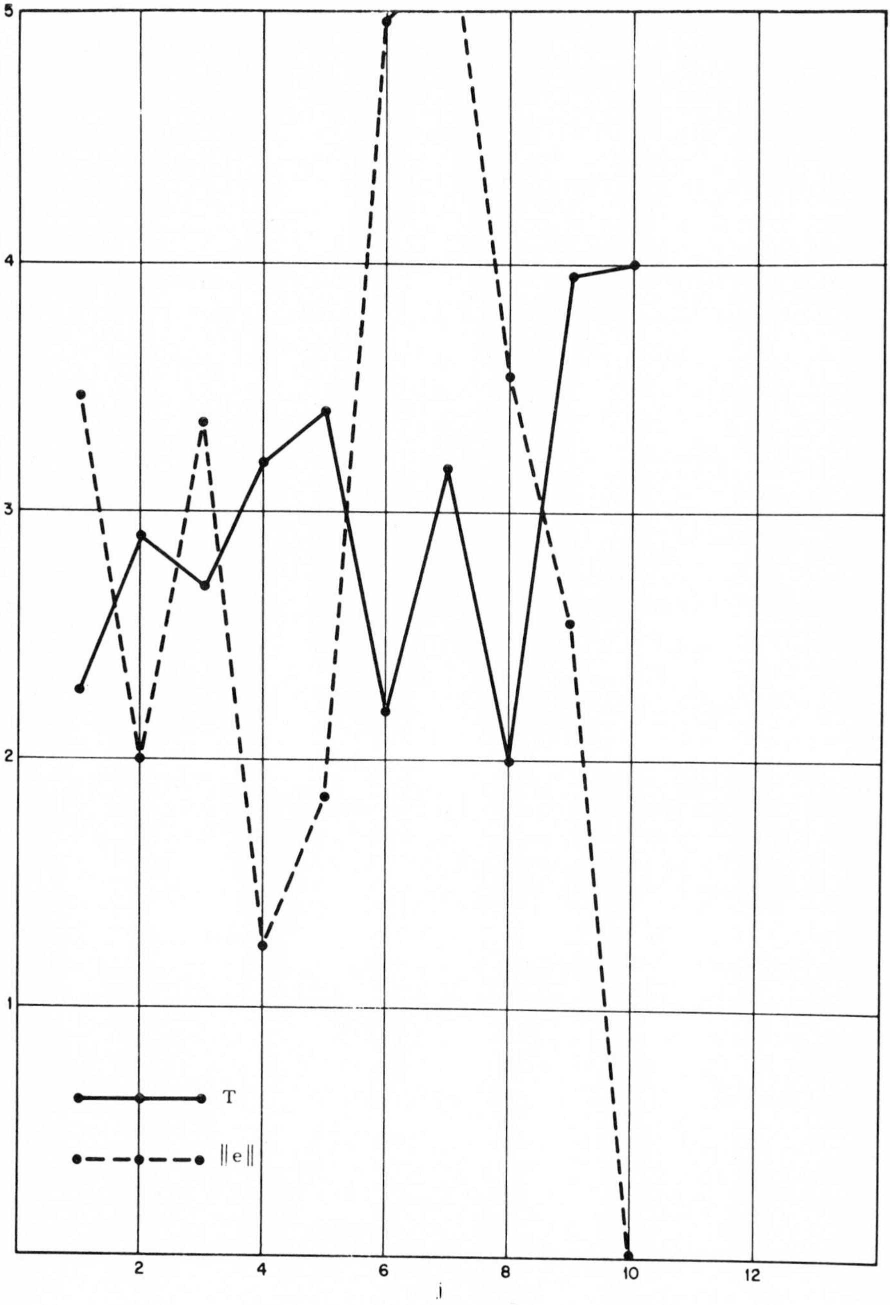

Figure 5. $T(\eta_j)$ and $\|e(T(\eta_j), \eta_j)\|$ for First Run, Table 3 (Transformed).

$$z(T(\eta), \eta) = -\int_0^{T(\eta)} X^{-1}(\sigma) b(\sigma) u(\sigma, \eta) d\sigma$$

$$= -u(0^+, \eta) \sum_{i=0}^{m} (-1)^i \int_{t_i}^{t_{i+1}} X^{-1}(\sigma) b(\sigma) d\sigma \,, \qquad (47)$$

where $t_i = t_i(\eta)$, $i = 1, 2, \ldots, m$, are the solutions of $v(t, \eta) = (X^{-1}(t) b(t), \eta) = 0$; $t_0 = 0$; and $t_{m+1} = T(\eta)$. Assume that $b(t)$ is continuous for all $t \in [0, t^*]$ and that $\left.\frac{\partial v(t, \eta)}{\partial t}\right|_{t=t_i} \neq 0$. Then, since $v(t_i, \eta) = 0$, $i = 1, 2, \ldots, m$,

$$\left.\frac{\partial v(t, \eta)}{\partial t}\right|_{t=t_i} \frac{\partial t_i}{\partial \eta} + \left.\frac{\partial v(t, \eta)}{\partial \eta}\right|_{t=t_i} = 0 \qquad (48)$$

and

$$\frac{\partial t_i}{\partial \eta} = -\left[\left.\frac{\partial v(t, \eta)}{\partial t}\right|_{t=t_i}\right]^{-1} \left[\left.\frac{\partial v(t, \eta)}{\partial \eta}\right|_{t=t_i}\right]$$

$$= \left[\left.\frac{\partial}{\partial t}(-X^{-1}(t) b(t), \eta)\right|_{t=t_i}\right]^{-1} [X^{-1}(t_i) b(t_i)]' \qquad (49)$$

Also assume that $t_1 > 0$ and $t_m < T(\eta)$.

Under the above assumptions it is clear that

$$H(\eta) = \left.\frac{\partial}{\partial \rho}(x_0 - z(t, \rho))\right|_{\substack{t=T(\eta) \\ \rho=\eta}}$$

$$= +u(0^+, \eta) \left\{ \sum_{i=1}^{m-1} (-1)^i \left[X^{-1}(t_{i+1}) b(t_{i+1}) \frac{\partial t_{i+1}}{\partial \eta} - X^{-1}(t_i) b(t_i) \frac{\partial t_i}{\partial \eta} \right] + X^{-1}(t_1) b(t_1) \frac{\partial t_1}{\partial \eta} - (-1)^m X^{-1}(t_m) b(t_m) \frac{\partial t_m}{\partial \eta} \right\}$$

$$= -2u(0^+, \eta) \sum_{i=1}^{m} (-1)^i X^{-1}(t_i) b(t_i) \frac{\partial t_i}{\partial \eta} \,. \qquad (50)$$

Using Eq. (49), Eq. (50) becomes

$$H(\eta) = -2u(0^+, \eta) \sum_{i=1}^{m} (-1)^i \frac{[X^{-1}(t_i)b(t_i)][X^{-1}(t_i)b(t_i)]'}{\frac{\partial}{\partial t}[-X^{-1}(t)b(t), \eta]_{t=t_i}} \tag{51}$$

Now $u(0^+, \eta) = \mathrm{sgn}(-b(0^+), \eta)$ and $\mathrm{sgn}\left[\frac{\partial v(t,\eta)}{\partial t}\Big|_{t=t_1}\right] = -u(0^+, \eta)$. Moreover, since $\frac{\partial v(t,\eta)}{\partial t}\Big|_{t=t_i}$ must alternate in sign as i increases,

$$\frac{\partial v(t,\eta)}{\partial t}\Bigg|_{t=t_i} = u(0^+, \eta)(-1)^i \left|\frac{\partial v(t,\eta)}{\partial t}\Bigg|_{t=t_i}\right| . \tag{52}$$

Using Eqs. (8) and (52), Eq. (51) becomes

$$H(\eta) = -2 \sum_{i=1}^{m} \frac{[X^{-1}(t_i)b(t_i)][X^{-1}(t_i)b(t_i)]'}{\left|\frac{\partial}{\partial t}[-X^{-1}(t)b(t), \eta]_{t=t_i}\right|} ,$$

which is Eq. (24).

The above derivation fails in two cases:

1) Where $v(t, \eta) = 0$ for $t = 0$ or $t = T(\eta)$. In this case m may change when η changes.
2) When $\frac{\partial v(t,\eta)}{\partial t}\Big|_{t=t_i} = 0$ for any i.

It will be shown elsewhere that these cases can only occur for η in a set of measure zero if $A(t)b(t)$ and $b(t)$ satisfy uniform Lipschitz conditions on $[0, t^*]$.

8. Extensions

Under reasonable conditions most of the techniques described above may be extended to the problem where: $\dot{x} = A(t)x + B(t)u + a(t)$; u is a p-dimensional vector in a compact, convex set and x(t) is to intercept a specified target function in minimum time. The line of attack presented in this paper is also useful in treating iterative procedures of a similar type which apply to other optimal control problems (8).

Another area of interest, not mentioned here, is the effect of computer errors on the convergence of the iterative procedures (the computations described above were performed on a digital computer with a high degree of accuracy). Work on computer errors and other algorithms is presently being carried out and will be reported in the future.

This work was sponsored in part under Air Force Contract No. AF33(657-11501).

Bibliography

1. Bushaw, D. W. Optimal Discontinuous Forcing Terms. In "Contributions to the Theory of Nonlinear Oscillations," 4, Princeton Univ. Press, Princeton, N.J., (1958).

2. Eaton, J. H. An Iterative Solution to Time-Optimal Control. J. Math. Anal. and Appl. 5, (1962) pp 329-344.

3. Ho, Y. C. A Successive Approximation Technique for Optimal Control Systems Subject to Input Saturation. J. of Basic Engin., 84, Ser. D. No. 1, (1962) pp 33-40.

4. Knudsen, H. K. An Iterative Procedure for Computing Time-Optimal Controls, presented at the WESCON Conference, 1963.

5. Kulikowski, R. Optimum Processes and Synthesis of Optimum Automatic Control Systems with Non-linear Invariable Elements. In "Proceedings of the International Federation of Automatic Control Congress, Moscow," (1960) p 473.

6. LaSalle, J. P. The Time-Optimal Control Problem. In "Contributions to the Theory of Nonlinear Oscillations," 5, pp 1-24, Princeton Univ. Press, Princeton, N.J., (1960).

7. Neustadt, L. W. Synthesis of Time-Optimal Control Systems. J. Math. Anal. and Appl. 1, (1960) pp 484-492.

8. Neustadt, L. W. On Synthesizing Optimal Controls. Presented at the Second Congress of the International Federation of Automatic Controls, Basel, Switzerland, Sept., 1963.

9. Paiewonsky, B. Time-Optimal Control of Linear Systems with Bounded Controls. In "International Symposium on Nonlinear Differential Equations and Nonlinear Mechanics," Academic Press, New York (1963).

10. Paiewonsky, B. Synthesis of Time-Optimal Control for Linear Systems. A.R.A.P. (Princeton, N.J.) Tech. Memo 62-4 (1962).

11. Paiewonsky, B. and Woodrow, P.J. The Synthesis of Optimal Controls for a Class of Rocket Steering Problems. A.I.A.A. Paper No. 63-224 (1963).

12. Pontryagin, L.S., Boltyanskii, V.G., Gamkrelidze, R. V., and Mishchenko, E.F. "The Mathematical Theory of Optimal Processes," John Wiley and Sons, Inc., New York, 1962.

13. Powell, M.J.D. An Iterative Method for Finding Stationary Values of a Function of Several Variables. The Computer Journal, 5, (1962) pp 147-151.

Notes for Tables

1) The η'_0 is not normalized.
2) The initial condition vector is $x'(0) = [a \;\; 0 \;\; 0]$.
3) The iterative procedure was terminated when $\|e_j\| < \epsilon$.
4) The initial value, k_0, in each case was arbitrarily chosen as $25k_s$. The value of k_j was obtained by method (1).
5) The value of k_j for each major iteration was chosen by method (2). The iterative procedure for determining k_j was terminated when $(e_j, e_{j+1}) < C\|e_j\| \; \|e_{j+1}\|$ or $c_i < C$ where C is a small positive constant $(C = 10^{-4})$.
6) The transformation of coordinates was chosen so as to equalize the non-zero eigenvalues of $H(\eta^*)$.
7) The "Transformed" data was obtained as follows:
   a. For $0 < t_1(\eta_j) < t_2(\eta_j) < T(\eta_j)$, the matrix P'P was chosen to equalize the non-zero eigenvalues of $H(\eta_j)$ and k_j was set equal to $-[\lambda_n(H(\eta_j))]^{-1}$.
   b. For one or zero switching times in $(0, T(\eta_n))$ method (1) was used with $P'P = I$. (See Note 3.)

Table 1

(See Notes 1, 2, 3, 4, 6)

η'_0			Number of Iterations Untrans.	Trans.	ϵ	a
1	0	0	60	29	0.1	2
1	0	0	111	32	0.01	2
1	20	0	67	29	0.1	2
1	20	0	119	33	0.01	2
1	4	8	61	34	0.1	2
1	6	20	69	34	0.1	2
1	-6	-20	56	28	0.1	2
1	0	0	501	47	0.1	16

Table 2

(See Notes 1, 2, 3, 5, 6)

η'_0			Number of Major Iterations Untrans.	Trans.	ϵ	a	Total Number of Iterations Untrans.	Trans.
1	0	0	45	6	0.1	2	503	112
1	0	0	86	7	0.01	2	853	129
1	20	0	6	14	0.1	2	118	297
1	4	8	54	5	0.1	2	887	45
1	6	20	54	7	0.1	2	896	73
1	-6	-20	60	16	0.1	2	752	346
1	0	0	436	12	0.1	16	2811	209

Table 3

(See Notes 1, 2, 3, 7)

η'_0			Number of Iterations Untrans.	Trans.	ϵ	a
1	0	0	60	10	0.1	2
1	0	0	111	11	0.01	2
1	20	0	67	5	0.1	2
1	20	0	119	6	0.01	2
1	4	8	61	10	0.1	2
1	6	20	69	9	0.1	2
1	-6	-20	56	15	0.1	2
1	0	0	501	25	0.1	16

AN ON-LINE IDENTIFICATION SCHEME
for
MULTIVARIABLE NONLINEAR SYSTEMS

by

H. C. Hsieh
Department of Electrical Engineering
Northwestern University
Evanston, Illinois

ABSTRACT

The multivariable nonlinear system considered here is assumed to be characterized by a truncated functional power series. The system is to be identified under normal operating conditions. Least square error criterion is used to estimate the system weighting function matrix and a steepest descent method is employed for solving this problem. A recursive estimation scheme is devised for up-dating its estimation. An "Adjoint Space Approach", which has the advantage of reducing the dimensionality of the identification problem is explored.

I. INTRODUCTION

In the analysis or synthesis of nonlinear systems, just as in the case concerning linear systems, the first problem which one encounters, is how to characterize the systems. One possible way to describe a nonlinear system is by the nonlinear differential equation. This approach has the disadvantage that the equation only gives an implicit relationship between the input and output. Thus, for each different input, the whole problem must be re-solved. It should be noted that the mathematical description of a system, which the system engineers are most interested in, is the one having an explicit input-output relationship.

A new approach for characterizing a dynamic system is through the concept of functional. This representation is logical since a system connecting a value, the present output, to a function, the present and past input, does exhibit the property of a functional. Hence if x(t) is the input to the system, then the output of the system y(t) can be expressed as F(x(t)). If this functional F is continuous, then the relationship between the input and output of such a single variable time invariant nonlinear system can be expressed in terms of a functional power series as

$$y(t) = F(x(t))$$

$$= \lim_{N\to\infty} \left[\int_0^\infty \omega_1(\tau)x(t-\tau)\, d\tau + \int_0^\infty \int_0^\infty \omega_2(\tau_1, \tau_2)x(t-\tau_1)x(t-\tau_2)d\tau_1 d\tau_2 \right.$$

$$+ \ldots + \int_0^\infty \ldots\ldots \int_0^\infty \omega_N(\tau_1, \tau_2, \ldots, \tau_N)x(t-\tau_1)x(t-\tau_2)\ldots x(t-\tau_N)$$

$$\left. d\tau_1 d\tau_2 \ldots d\tau_N \right]$$

where $\omega_N(\tau_1, \tau_2, \ldots, \tau_N)$ is the N-th order weighting function or the N-th order kernel. In fact, this functional power series was studied by Volterra[1] early in the twentieth century and is usually termed as the Volterra series. Frechet[2] also showed that any continuous functional defined on a set of continuous functions over a finite interval can be represented by a functional power series. To consider this approach in a more general form, we actually can invoke the theory in functional analysis concerning analytic functions in a Banach space[3, 4]. It says that an analytic function (or functional) will admit a Taylor series expansion which converges uniformly over certain region.

In this paper, we shall consider a multivariable nonlinear system whose parameters are varying at an unpredicted manner. Thus the system must be identified before any optimal control scheme can be devised. We shall assume that, during the identification period, the system is essentially time-invariant and can be represented by a truncated functional power series. The various order of weighting function matrices will be estimated through the observation of input and output data over a finite time interval by using least-square criterion. We shall devise an updating scheme as more data are available. A computational logarithm based on the steepest descent method will be used. This scheme has been employed extensively by Balakrishnan[4, 5, 6, 7] for solving a class of filtering and control problems. We shall introduce the notion of "Adjoint Space Approach," which will reduce the dimensionality of the problem. This approach was first observed by Balakrishnan[5, 6] and has been explored in more detail by the author[8].

After the system has been identified, the optimal control input can be synthesized by using the generalized quadratic error criterion[7]. This is the actuation phase of the problem. In [7], we have indicated that a steepest descent method also exists. By combining the identification and actuation schemes we have provided one way for solving the adaptive control problem for nonlinear systems.

It should be noted that the approach proposed for solving nonlinear control problems is different from the other existing methods which depends on the linearized versions of the original problems. Here, at the very outset, we include the nonlinear effects into consideration. Of course, the linear problems will always be a simpler and special case of these more general nonlinear problems.

II. DESCRIPTION OF THE MULTIVARIABLE NONLINEAR SYSTEMS

We shall now consider the functional representation of a multivariable nonlinear system. Let $\underline{x}(t)$ be an m-dimensional input vector. If $f_{ki}(x_i(t))$ denote the functional connecting the i-th input component with the k-th output terminal, then the k-th output component will be given by

$$y_k(t) = \sum_{i=1}^{m} F_{ki}(x_i(t)) \triangleq F_k(\underline{x}) \qquad (1)$$

The system configuration is shown in Figure 1.

Let us assume that the parameters of the system vary in an unpredicted manner. However, the rate of variation of these parameters are fairly slow such that the system can be taken as time-invariant over certain finite time interval. Hence the behavior of the system can be adequately represented by a set of time-invariant models. With this assumption, it suffices, from now on, to confine our discussions to a time-invariant nonlinear system.

In order to solve a specific engineering problem, it is necessary to truncate the functional power series at the N-th term for each of the functional F_{ki}. We shall not try to answer the questions such as the convergence of these power series and their common region of convergence. We shall rather adopt the point of view that, by including the higher order terms, these N-th order polynomials will give a better description of the system than just the linear terms. We shall further assume that the system has a finite settling time T_s. Thus the functional representation for $F_{ki}(x_i(t))$ becomes

$$F_{ki}(x_i(t)) = \sum_{j=1}^{N} \int_0^{T_s} \cdots \int_0^{T_s} \omega_{kij}(\tau_1, \tau_2, \ldots, \tau_j)$$

$$x_i(t-\tau_1) \ldots . x_i(t-\tau_j)\, d\tau_1\, d\tau_2 \ldots d\tau_j \qquad (2)$$

In order to put Eqs. (1) and (2) into a better form, it is convenient to define the following quantities:

$$\underline{x}^N(t-\tau_m^N) \triangleq \begin{bmatrix} x_1(t-\tau_1) \\ x_1(t-\tau_1)x_1(t-\tau_2) \\ \vdots \\ x_1(t-\tau_1)x_1(t-\tau_2)\ldots x_1(t-\tau_N) \\ \vdots \\ x_m(t-\tau_1) \\ x_m(t-\tau_1)x_m(t-\tau_2) \\ \vdots \\ x_m(t-\tau_1)x_m(t-\tau_2)\ldots x_m(t-\tau_N) \end{bmatrix} \quad \text{(mNx1 N-th order product input vector)} \quad (3)$$

$$\underline{\omega}^N(\tau_m^N) \triangleq \begin{bmatrix} \omega_{11}(\tau_1) \\ \omega_{12}(\tau_1, \tau_2) \\ \vdots \\ \omega_{1N}(\tau_1, \tau_2, \ldots, \tau_N) \\ \vdots \\ \omega_{m1}(\tau_1) \\ \omega_{m2}(\tau_1, \tau_2) \\ \vdots \\ \omega_{mN}(\tau_1, \tau_2, \ldots, \tau_N) \end{bmatrix} \quad \text{(mNx1 N-th order weighting function vector)} \quad (4)$$

$$\int_o^{T_s^N} \underline{d\left|\tau_m^N\right|} \triangleq \begin{bmatrix} \int_o^{T_s} d\tau_1 & & & & & & & \underline{O} \\ \int_o^{T_s} d\tau_1 & \int_o^{T_s} d\tau_2 & & & & & & \\ & & \ddots & & & & & \\ \int_o^{T_s} d\tau_1 & \int_o^{T_s} d\tau_2 & \cdots & \int_o^{T_s} d\tau_N & & & & \\ & & & & \ddots & & & \\ & & & & \int_o^{T_s} d\tau_1 & & & \\ & & & & \int_o^{T_s} d\tau_1 & \int_o^{T_s} d\tau_2 & & \\ & & & & & & \ddots & \\ \underline{O} & & & & \int_o^{T_s} d\tau_1 & \int_o^{T_s} d\tau_2 & \cdots & \int_o^{T_s} d\tau_N \end{bmatrix}$$

(mNxmN diagonal matrix operator)

Here we have omitted the unnecessary subscript "k" and consider any one of the output components. In terms of these quantities just defined, we have

$$y(t) = \sum_{i=1}^{m} F_i(x_i(t))$$

$$= \int_o^{T_s^N} \underline{x}^{N'} (t-\tau_m^N) \; \underline{d\left|\tau_m^N\right|} \; \underline{\omega}^N (\tau_m^N)$$

$$\triangleq L^N \underline{\omega}^N$$

where the prime is used to denote the transpose of a matrix. This operator L^N is a linear bounded operator which maps the mN-dimensional Hilbert space H_N^{mN}, whose elements have the form given by Eq. (4), into one-dimensional Hilbert space H_1^1. It is obvious that the inner product of this space H_N^{mN} is given by

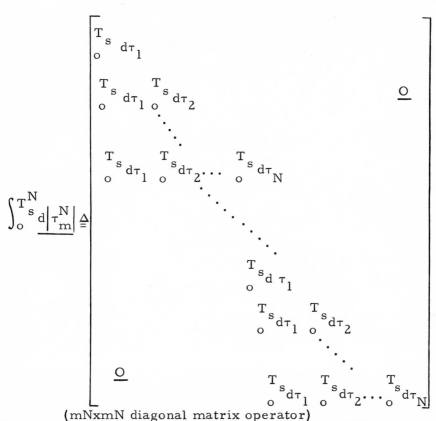

$$[\underline{f}^N, \underline{\omega}^N]_N \triangleq \int_o^{T_s^N} \underline{f}^{N'} (\tau_m^N) \; \underline{d|\tau_m^N|} \; \underline{\omega}^N (\tau_m^N)$$

and every element $\underline{f}^N$ in this space satisfies the condition

$$\|\underline{f}^N\|_N \triangleq \{[\underline{f}^N, \underline{f}^N]_N\}^{1/2} < \infty$$

where $\| \quad \|_N$ denotes the norm.

III. FORMULATION OF THE IDENTIFICATION PROBLEM FOR NONLINEAR SYSTEMS

The basic identification problem to be considered is shown in Fig. 2. The input $\underline{x}(t)$ to the system is assumed to be known exactly. This situation certainly occurs when $\underline{x}(t)$ is the optimal control which has been synthesized from the actuation phase of the adaptive control problem. The observed output $\underline{z}(t)$ is the true output $\underline{y}(t)$ corrupted by additive noise $\underline{n}(t)$. Thus

$$\underline{z}(t) = \underline{y}(t) + \underline{n}(t) \tag{5}$$

where each component of $\underline{y}(t)$ can be expressed in terms of a sum of N-th order polynomials as given by Eq. (1) and (2). Following [6] , the question to be answered now is to find a best estimate of these various order of weighting functions, under certain criterion, based on the input and output data $\underline{x}(t)$ and $\underline{z}(t)$ observed over a finite interval (0, T).

In solving a practical problem, it is quite often that the statistical properties of the noise are not quite known. Under this situation, least square estimation seems to be the most appropriate criterion. Thus, one is trying to find $\underline{W}^N$ such that the following quantity is minimized.

$$I(\underline{W}^N) = \int_o^T \{\underline{y}(t) - \underline{z}(t)\}' \{\underline{y}(t) - \underline{z}(t)\} \, dt$$

where $\underline{W}^N$ denotes the totality of the N-th weighting function vectors. It is observed that the minimization of $I(\underline{W}^N)$ can be performed independently for each component. Thus for any aribirary output component, we have to minimize

$$\begin{aligned} I(\omega^N) &= \int_o^T \{ y(t) - z(t) \}^2 \, dt \\ &= \| y - z \|_1^2 \\ &= \| L^N \underline{\omega}^N - z \|_1^2 \end{aligned} \tag{6}$$

where $\| \quad \|_1$ is the norm of the Hilbert space H_1^1. Let L^{N*} denote the adjoint of the operator L^N. It is then defined by

$$L^{N*} u \triangleq \int_0^T \underline{x}^N (t - \tau_m^N) \; u(t) \, dt$$

It maps H_1^1 space into H_N^{mN}. In the sequel, we shall call the domain of the operator L^N as the solution space, and its range, the adjoint space. Thus the domain of the adjoint operator L^{N*} is the adjoint space and its range, the solution space. Note that in this identification problem, the solution space is the H_N^{mN} space whose dimension is high and whose elements involve functions of multivariables. On the other hand, the adjoint space is the H_1^1 space whose dimension is one and whose elements are just functions of single variable. Thus the adjoint space is much more simpler than the solution space in this case.

IV. SOLUTION OF THE IDENTIFICATION PROBLEM BY THE STEEPEST DESCENT METHOD IN THE ADJOINT SPACE

Let us now expand Eq. (6). We shall have

$$I(\underline{\omega}^N) = [\, L^{N*} L^N \underline{\omega}^N, \underline{\omega}^N \,]_N - 2\, [\, L^{N*} z, \underline{\omega}^N]_N + \| z \|_1^2$$

Since the last term does not contain $\underline{\omega}_N$, then the quantity to be minimized is

$$Q(\underline{\omega}^N) = [\, L^{N*} L^N \underline{\omega}^N, \underline{\omega}^N]_N - 2\, [\, L^{N*} z, \underline{\omega}^N]_N \qquad (7)$$

Here the operator $L^{N*} L_N^N$ is defined explicitly as

$$L^{N*} L^N \underline{\omega}^N \triangleq \int_0^{T_s} \underline{K}_N (s_m^N, \tau_m^N) \, \underline{d|\tau_m^N|} \, \underline{\omega}^N (\tau_m^N)$$

$$0 \leq s_m^N \leq T_s^N \qquad (8)$$

where

$$\underline{K}_N (s_m^N, \tau_m^N) = \int_0^T \underline{x}^N (t - s_m^N) \, \underline{x}^{N'} (t - \tau_m^N) \, dt$$

$$0 \leq s_m^N, \tau_m^N \leq T_s^N$$

We first notice that the operator $L^{N*} L^N$ is self adjoint and, in general, is non-negative definite. Thus the problem involved here is essentially that of minimizing a quadratic functional in Hilbert space H_n^{mN}. It can easily be shown that if there is an optimal $\underline{\omega}^N$ which minimizes Q, it must satisfy the equation [4, 5, 8]

$$L^{N*} L^N \underline{\omega}^N = L^{N*} z \tag{9}$$

The optimal solution will be of the form [4, 8]

$$\underline{\omega}^N = L^{N*} \psi \tag{10}$$

where ψ is in H_1^1 space. If now there is no element in H_N^{mN} which will satisfy Eq. (9), then we can construct a sequence of solution $\underline{\omega}_n^N$, in the form of $L^{N*} \psi_n$, such that

$$\lim Q(\underline{\omega}_n^N) = \operatorname{Inf} Q(\underline{\omega}^N)$$

The proof of this conclusion can be found in the original paper by Balakrishnan[4].

In the identification problem considered, the input and output records are available only in the form of numerical data and we want to identify the system on-line with its normal operation. Under these conditions, the most effective way for solving the problem will be devising a convenient computational algorithm to process the available data directly. Thus we resort to the steepest descent method.

Since the quantity to be minimized as given by Eq. (7) is a quadratic functional in Hilbert space, the computational procedure based on the steepest descent method initiated in [4] can be easily derived[6, 8, 9]. It is given by the following equations:

$$\underline{\omega}_n^N = \underline{\omega}_{n-1}^N + \epsilon_{n-1} \underline{v}_{n-1}^N \tag{11}$$

where

$$\underline{v}_{n-1}^N = L^{N*} L^N \underline{\omega}_{n-1}^N - L^{N*} z \text{ (gradient)}$$

$$\epsilon_{n-1} = - \frac{\| \underline{v}_{n-1}^N \|_N^2}{[L^{N*} L^N \underline{v}_{n-1}^N, \underline{v}_{n-1}^N]_N}$$

It should be noted that the operator $L^{N*} L^N$ considered is such that

$$0 \leqq [L^{N*} L^N \underline{h}^N]_N \leqq M \| \underline{h}^N \|_N^2$$

where $\underline{h}^N$ is any element in H_N^{mN} and $M > 0$. Thus there may not be an optimal element in H_N^{mN} which will satisfy Eq. (9). However, we can show that the steepest descent method always gives us the desired answer[4, 8]. This means that if the solution is in H_n^{mN}, then

$$\underline{\omega}_n^N \longrightarrow \underline{\omega}^N$$

In other words, the sequence converges strongly. On the other hand, if there is no element in H_N^{mN} which will satisfy Eq. (9), then we shall have

$$\left\| L^{N*} L^N \underline{\omega}_n^N - L^{N*} z \right\| \longrightarrow o$$

and it implies that

$$Q(\underline{\omega}_n^N) \longrightarrow \text{Inf } Q(\underline{\omega}^N)$$

Since we know that $\underline{\omega}_n^N$ can always be chosen as

$$\underline{\omega}_n^N = L^{N*} \quad \psi_n$$

for some ψ_n in H_1^1, then

$$\begin{aligned} \underline{v}_{n-1}^N &= L^{N*} L^N L^{N*} \psi_{n-1} - L^{N*} z \\ &= L^{N*} (L^N L^{N*} \psi_{n-1} - z) \\ &= L^{N*} r_{n-1} \end{aligned}$$

where r_{n-1} is in H_1^1. Thus the computational algorithm in this H_1^1 space, or the adjoint space, is

$$\psi_n = \psi_{n-1} + \epsilon_{n-1} r_{n-1} \tag{12}$$

where

$$r_{n-1} = L^N L^{N*} \psi_{n-1} - z \qquad \text{(gradient)}$$

$$\epsilon_{n-1} = - \frac{[L^N L^{N*} r_{n-1}, r_{n-1}]_1}{[L^N L^{N*} r_{n-1}, L^N L^{N*} r_{n-1}]_1}$$

Here the operator $L^N L^{N*}$ is defined explicitly as

$$L^N L^{N*} \psi = \int_o^T K^a(t_1, t_2) \psi(t_2) dt_2 \qquad o \leq t_1 \leq T \tag{13}$$

with

$$K^a(t_1, t_2) = \int_o^{T_s^N} \underline{x}^{N'}(t_1 - \tau_m^N) \, \underline{d|\tau_m^N|} \, \underline{x}^N(t_2 - \tau_m^N)$$

It is evident now, by comparing Eqs. (11) and (12), that a great reduction of the dimensionality of the problem is obtained by carrying out the iteration scheme in the adjoint space, the H_1^a space. Thus it results in a great saving of computational time. We shall call this approach for solving the problem as the "adjoint Space Approach."[8] Once we obtain the solution ψ in the adjoint space, the optimal system weighting function vector is then given by

$$\hat{\underline{\omega}}^N = \int_o^T \underline{x}^N (t - \tau_m^N) \psi(t)\, dt \qquad o \leqq \tau_m^N \leqq T_s^N$$

It should be noted that, in treating any least square error problem, we always have the choice of either solving the problem in the solution space or the adjoint space. Of course we would always choose that one of smaller dimensionality and less complexity. In Eq. (8), the kernel $\underline{K}_N$ in the solution space is an mNx mN matrix whose elements involve functions of multivariables. On the other hand, in Eq. (13), the kernel K^a in the adjoint space is just a scalar function of two variables. Thus, in this identification problem for nonlinear systems, the "Adjoint Space Approach" should always be used even if the systems are single variable.

V. RECURSIVE ESTIMATION OF SYSTEM WEIGHTING FUNCTION MATRICES FOR GROWING DATA

When a system has to be identified on-line with its normal operation, it is quite desirable that we can up-date the estimation of its system weighting function matrix as more input-output data are obtained. Clearly, the longer the input-output record, in conforming with the assumption of time invariant model during this period, the better would be the filtering of noise. Let us assume now that the observation interval has been increased from (0, T) to (0, T+ΔT). Thus we have to minimize the quantity

$$I_1 (\underline{\omega}^N) = \int_o^{T+\Delta T} \{y(t) - z(t)\}^2\, dt$$

$$= \int_o^T \{y_1(t) - z_1(t)\}^2\, dt + \int_T^{T+\Delta T} \{\Delta y(t) - \Delta z(t)\}^2 dt$$

$$= \| y_1 - z_1 \|_1^2 + \| \Delta y - \Delta z \|_2^2 \qquad (14)$$

Here $\| \;\|_2$ denotes that the integration interval for the norm of this H_2^1 space is of (T, T+ΔT).

Suppose now that $\hat{\underline{\omega}}_1^N$ is the optimal estimate of the system weighting function vector for the data over the interval (0, T). Then either

$$L_1^{N*} L_1^N \underline{\omega}_1^N - L_1^{N*} z_1 = 0$$

or

$$\left\| L_1^{N*} L_1^N \underline{\omega}_1^N - L_1^{N*} z_1 \right\|_N < \epsilon \tag{15}$$

where ϵ is some small positive number. To provide the clarity to the problem, we have used appropriate subscripts for the operators to signify their particular integration intervals used. We shall do so whenever there are necessary. Let $\underline{\omega}^N$ now be the new estimate to incorporate with the newly available data Δy and Δz. Then it can certainly be expressed as

$$\underline{\omega}^N = \hat{\underline{\omega}}_1^N + \Delta \underline{\omega}^N \tag{16}$$

Here $\Delta\underline{\omega}^N$ is the incremental correction for the system weighting function vector such that the new estimate will be optimal over the interval $(0, T+\Delta T)$. Hence the identification problem is reduced to the solution of optimum estimate for $\Delta\underline{\omega}^N$.

Let us now substitute Eq. (16) into Eq. (14) and then expand the resultant expression. We shall have

$$I_1(\Delta\underline{\omega}^N) = \left\| L_1^N(\hat{\underline{\omega}}_1^N + \Delta\underline{\omega}^N) - z_1 \right\|_1^2 + \left\| L_2^N(\hat{\underline{\omega}}_1^N + \Delta\underline{\omega}^N) - \Delta z \right\|_2^2$$

$$= \left\| L_1^N \hat{\underline{\omega}}_1^N - z_1 + L_1^N \Delta\underline{\omega}^N \right\|_1^2 + \left\| L_2^N \hat{\underline{\omega}}_1^N - \Delta z + L_2^N \Delta\underline{\omega}^N \right\|_2^2$$

$$= \left\| L_1^N \hat{\underline{\omega}}_1^N - z_1 \right\|_1^2 + 2\left[L_1^N \hat{\underline{\omega}}_1^N - z_1, L_1^N \Delta\underline{\omega}^N \right]_1 + \left\| L_1^N \Delta\underline{\omega}^N \right\|_1^2$$

$$+ \left\| L_2^N \hat{\underline{\omega}}_1^N - \Delta z \right\|_2^2 + 2\left[L_2^N \hat{\underline{\omega}}_1^N - \Delta z, L_2^N \Delta\underline{\omega}^N \right]_2 + \left\| L_2^N \Delta\underline{\omega}^N \right\|_2^2$$

Now

$$\left[L_1^N \hat{\underline{\omega}}_1^N - z_1, L_1^N \Delta\underline{\omega}^N \right]_1 = \left[L_1^{N*} L_1^N \hat{\underline{\omega}}_1^N - L^{N*} z_1, \Delta\underline{\omega}^N \right]_N$$

$$\leqq \left\| L_1^{N*} L_1^N \hat{\underline{\omega}}_1^N - L^{N*} z_1 \right\|_N \left\| \Delta\underline{\omega}^N \right\|_N$$

Thus by using Eq. (15), we know that this term can be neglected. Hence we only have to minimize the quantity

$$Q_1(\Delta\underline{\omega}^N) = \left\| L_1^N \Delta\underline{\omega}^N \right\|_1^2 + \left\| L_2^N \Delta\underline{\omega}^N \right\|_2^2 + 2\left[L_2^N \hat{\underline{\omega}}_1^N - \Delta z, L_2^N \Delta\underline{\omega}^N \right]_2$$

$$= \left[R\Delta\underline{\omega}^N, \Delta\underline{\omega}^N \right]_N - 2\left[L_2^{N*} g, \Delta\underline{\omega}^N \right]_N \tag{17}$$

where

$$R = L_1^{N*} L_1^N + L_2^{N*} L_2^N$$

$$g = \Delta z - L_2^N \hat{\underline{\omega}}_1^N$$

It is evident that the Adjoint Space Approach is also preferable in solving this problem. To do this, let us first notice that the optimal $\underline{\omega}^N$ must be of the form

$$\begin{aligned}
\hat{\underline{\omega}}^N &= L^{N*} \hat{\psi} \\
&= \int_o^{T+\Delta T} \underline{x}^N (t - \tau_m^N) \hat{\psi}(t)\, dt \\
&= \int_o^T \underline{x}^N (t - \tau_m^N) \hat{\psi}_1(t)\, dt + \int_T^{T+\Delta T} \underline{x}^N (t - \tau_m^N) \Delta\hat{\psi}(t)\, dt \\
&= L_1^{N*} \hat{\psi}_1 + L_2^{N*} \Delta\hat{\psi} \\
&= \hat{\underline{\omega}}_1^N + \Delta\hat{\underline{\omega}}^N \qquad 0 \leq \tau_m^N \leq T_s^N
\end{aligned} \tag{18}$$

Hence we know that Eq. (17) can be rewritten in the form

$$\begin{aligned}
Q_1(\Delta\psi) &= [R L_2^{N*} \Delta\psi, L_2^{N*} \Delta\psi]_N - 2[L_2^{N*} g, L_2^{N*} \Delta\psi]_N \\
&= [L_2^N R L_2^{N*} \Delta\psi, \Delta\psi]_2 - 2[L_2^N L_2^{N*} g, \Delta\psi]_2 \qquad (19) \\
&= [R_2 \Delta\psi, \Delta\psi]_2 - 2[g_2, \Delta\psi]_2
\end{aligned}$$

where

$$\begin{aligned}
R_2 &= L_2^N L_1^{N*} L_1^N L_2^{N*} + L_2^N L_2^{N*} L_2^N L_2^{N*} \\
&= R_a + R_b \\
g_2 &= L_2^N L_2^{N*} (\Delta z - L_2^N L_1^{N*} \hat{\psi}_1)
\end{aligned}$$

Here the kernel for the operators $L_1^N L_2^{N*}$ and $L_2^N L_1^{N*}$ are respectively

$$K_{12}^a(t_1, t_2) = \int_o^{T_s^N} \underline{x}^{N'} (t_1 - \tau_m^N)\, d|\underline{\tau_m^N}|\, \underline{x}^N (t_2 - \tau_m^N)$$

$$0 \leq t_1 \leq T$$

$$T \leq t_2 \leq T + \Delta T$$

$$K_{21}^{a}(t_3, t_1) = \int_{o}^{T_s^N} \underline{x}^{N'}(t_3 - \tau_m^N) d\underline{|\tau_m^N|} \underline{x}^N(t_1 - \tau_m^N)$$

$0 \leqq t_1 \leqq T$

$T \leqq t_3 \leqq T + \Delta T$

Hence the kernel for the operator R_a is

$$K_a^a(t_3, t_2) = \int_o^T K_{21}^a(t_3, t_1) K_{12}^a(t_1, t_2)\, dt_1$$

$T \leqq t_2, t_3 \leqq T + \Delta T$

The kernel for the operator $L_2^N L_2^{N*}$ is

$$K_{22}^a(t_1, t_2) = \int_o^{T_s^N} \underline{x}^{N'}(t_1 - \tau_m^N)\, d\underline{|\tau_m^N|}\, \underline{x}^N(t_2 - \tau_m^N)$$

$T \leqq t_1, t_2 \leqq T + \Delta T$

Hence, the kernel for the operator R_b is

$$K_b^a(t_3, t_2) = \int_T^{T+\Delta T} K_{22}^a(t_3, t_1) K_{22}^a(t_1, t_2)\, dt_1$$

$0 \leqq t_2, t_3 \leqq T + \Delta T$

Finally the kernel for R_2 is

$$K_2^a(t_3, t_2) = K_a^a(t_3, t_2) + K_b^a(t_3, t_2)$$

The steepest descent method can now be used to minimize $Q_1(\Delta\psi)$. The computational algorithm is obviously given by

$$\Delta\psi_n = \Delta\psi_{n-1} + \epsilon_{n-1} p_{n-1}$$

where

$$p_{n-1} = R_2\, \Delta\psi_{n-1} - g_2 \qquad (20)$$

$$\epsilon_{n-1} = - \frac{\| p_{n-1} \|_2^2}{[R_2\, p_{n-1}, p_{n-1}]_2}$$

We thus have seen another application of Adjoint Space Approach for simplifying problems. Since the function $\Delta\psi$ is defined in the interval $(T, T+\Delta T)$ only and is a scalar function, a great saving of the computational time can thus be achieved. Once the optimum $\Delta\psi$ is determined, the new best estimate $\hat{\underline{\omega}}^N$ is obtained by using Eq. (18).

VI. RECURSIVE ESTIMATION OF SYSTEM WEIGHTING FUNCTION MATRIX FOR FIXED DATA LENGHT

In carrying out the identification scheme, we have to make the assumption that the system parameters do not change appreciably during the identification period and then the system can be taken essentially as time-invariant. Thus over the entire operation, it can be adequately represented by a sequence of such time-invariant models. It is evident then that, in estimating the system weighting function vector, the data of the remote past should be discarded since they will convey the wrong information about the current system model. Thus, we are required to maintain an optimal usable data length for the estimation problem. When the new data are avilable, we may have to delete some of the old data in order to conform our assumption of time invariant property for the system over this optimal interval.

The recursive estimation scheme for the system weighting function vector to incorporate with the adding of new data has been presented in the last section. It suffices now to devise a similar acheme to re-evaluate the system weighting function vector after a portion of the past data has been deleted. Thus the new estimate will be optimal over a shorter time interval. By executing these two schemes consecutively, we shall be able to up-date our optimal estimation about the system weighting function vector over a floating fixed interval.

Let us assume again that the original optimization interval is of (0. T). It is now required to optimize the quantity.

$$I_2(\underline{\omega}^N) = \int_{\Delta T}^{T} \{y(t) - z(t)\}^2 \, dt$$

This equation can be rewritten as

$$\begin{aligned} I_2(\underline{\omega}^N) &= \int_{o}^{T} \{y_1(t) - z_1(t)\}^2 \, dt \\ &\quad - \int_{o}^{\Delta T} \{\Delta y_{-1}(t) - \Delta z_{-1}(t)\}^2 \, dt \\ &= \left\| L_1 \underline{\omega}^N - z_1 \right\|_1^2 - \left\| L_{-1} \underline{\omega}^N - \Delta z_{-1} \right\|_{-1}^2 \qquad (21) \end{aligned}$$

It is obvious that Eq. (21) is analogous to Eq. (14). If we define the new estimate as

$$\underline{\omega}^N = L_1^* \hat{\psi}_1 - L_{-1}^* \Delta\psi$$

then the problem is reduced to the minimization of

$$Q_2(\Delta\psi) = [\, R_{-1}\Delta\psi, \Delta\psi\,]_{-1} - 2[\, g_{-1}, \Delta\psi\,]_{-1} \qquad (22)$$

where

$$R_{-1} = L_{-1}L_1^* L_1 L_{-1}^* - L_{-1}L_{-1}^* L_{-1} L_{-1}^*$$
$$= \overline{R}_a - \overline{R}_b$$
$$g_{-1} = L_{-1}L_{-1}^* (\Delta z_{-1} - L_{-1}L_1^* \hat{\psi}_1)$$

The kernels of all these operators involved here are defined in the same way as those in the previous section if we replace the interval (T, T+ΔT) by the interval (0, ΔT). The steepest descent method can now be used to minimize Eq. (22).

REFERENCES

1. Volterra, V., "Theory of Functional and of Integral and Introgro-Differential Equations," (Book), Balcki and Sons, Ltd., London England, 1930.
2. Frechet, M., "Sur les Junctionelles Continnos," Annales de Ecole Normale, No. 3, Vol. 27, May, 1910.
3. Hille, E., and Philipe, R.S., "Functional Analysis and Semigroups," American Mathematical Society colloquimm Publications, Vol. 31, 1957.
4. Balakrishnan, A.V., "A General Theory of Nonlinear Estimation Problem in Control Systems," Presented at the Symposium on Mathematical Problems in Control systems, Washington D.C., Nov., 1961.
5. Balakrishnan, A.V., "An Operator Theoretic Formulation of a Class of Control Problems and a Steepest Descent Method of Solution," J. SIAM on Control, Sereis A, Vol. 1, No. 2, 1963, pp. 109-127.
6. Balakrishnan, A.V., "Determination of Nonlinear Systems from Input-Output Data," Proceedings of the Princeton Conference on Identification Problems in Communication and Control, March, 1963.
7. Balakrishnan, A.V., and Hsieh, H.C., "Function Space Methods in Control System Optimization," Proceedings of the Optimum System Synthesis Conference, Wright-Patterson Air Force Base, Ohio, Feb., 1963.

References cont' d

8. Hsieh, H. C., "Least Square Estimation of Linear and Nonlinear Weighting Function Matrices," to be published in the Information and Control, March, 1964.

9. Kantarovich, L. V., "Functional Analysis and Applied Mathematics," Usp. Mat. Nank, Vol. 3, 1948. English translation, National Bureau of Standard, Report No. 1509, 1953.

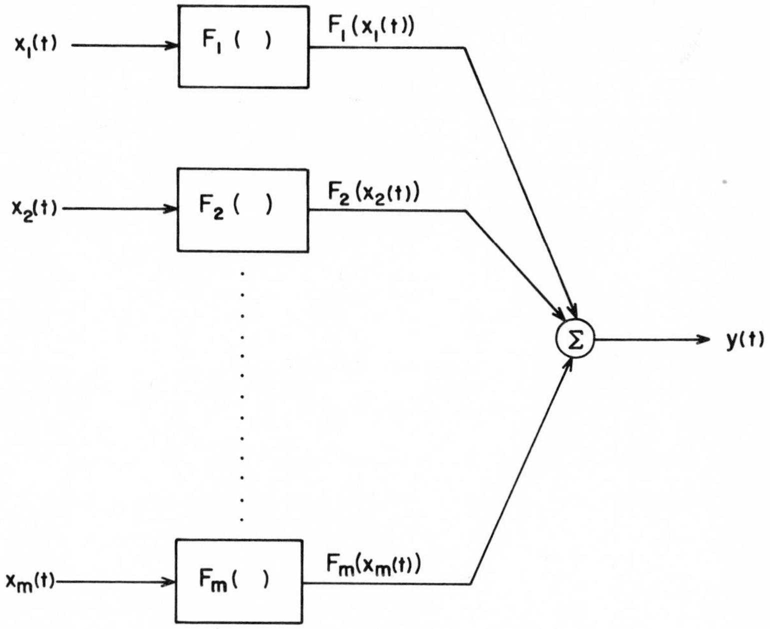

CONFIGURATION OF GENERAL MULTIVARIABLE NONLINEAR SYSTEMS (WITH ONLY ONE OUTPUT COMPONENT SHOWN)

FIGURE I

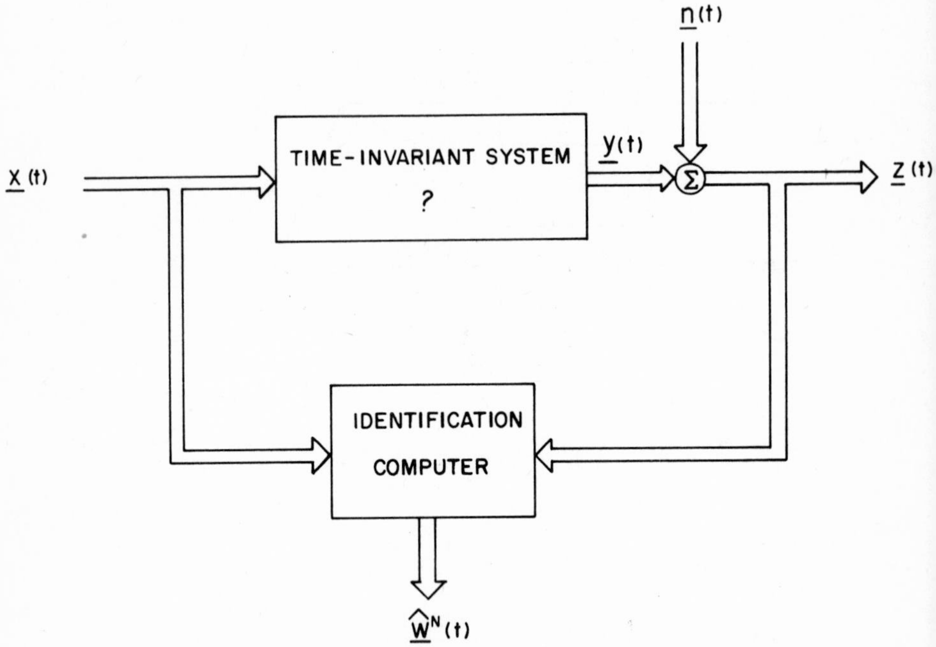

IDENTIFICATION OF SYSTEM WEIGHTING FUNCTION MATRIX

FIGURE 2

METHOD OF CONVEX ASCENT

Hubert Halkin

Bell Telephone Laboratories

Introduction

In this paper we describe a computational procedure for the solution of a class of nonlinear optimal control problems. This computational procedure is directly inspired by the results obtained previously by the author in the study of the necessary condition for optimal control of nonlinear systems, see (1).

The problem considered is the following. The evolution of a system is described by the vector differential equation

$$\dot{x} = f(x,u,t) \tag{0.1}$$

where x is the state vector, u is the control vector, t is the time. The class F of all admissible control functions* is the set of all time functions taking their values in a given set Ω. We are given an initial time t_a and an initial state x_a. We are given also a final time t_b and a set E of final states. We assume that the set E is an oriented straight line. The question is then to find a control

*We shall use Corinthian script $\mathcal{u}$, $\mathcal{v}$, $\mathcal{w}$, etc., to denote functions in the class F. It is understood that the function $\mathcal{u}$ is the function whose value at the time t is u(t), similarly the function $\mathcal{v}$ is the function whose value at the time t is v(t), etc. We shall reserve the symbols u, v, w, etc., to denote points in the set Ω.

function in F such that the corresponding solution** of (0.1) from $x = x_a$ at $t = t_a$ intersects the set E at $t = t_b$ as far as possible in the positive direction.

A complete description of the preceding problem requires also some auxiliary conditions concerning the function f and the class F. These auxiliary conditions will be given in Section 1.

The Method of Convex Ascent is based upon some properties of certain sets called sets of reachable events. These sets will be defined precisely in Section 3 and their properties will be given in Section 4. We shall give in this introduction a first and elementary description of these concepts.

The set H is the set of all states which can be reached at the time $t = t_b$ from the state $x = x_a$ at the time $t = t_a$ if we integrate the system (0.1) for all possible control functions u in the class F.† If $H \cap E = \emptyset$, i.e., if the sets H and E have no point in common, the problem has obviously no solution. If $H \cap E \neq \emptyset$, i.e., if the sets H and E have some point in common, then the problem has some feasible solution. Moreover, if $H \cap E$ contains a point B which is the

---

**By solution of

$$\dot{x} = f(x,u,t)$$

corresponding to the control function v we mean the solution of the differential equation

$$\dot{x} = f(x,v(t),t)$$

†For every t with $t_a \leq t$ we could define H(t) as the set of all states which could be reached at the time t from the state $x = x_a$ at the time t_a. We have then $H = H(t_b)$. The set

$$\{(x,t) : x \in H(t),\ t \geq t_a\}$$

which is called the set of reachable events from (x_a, t_a) plays a fundamental role in optimal control. A very important question is the following: given an x is it always possible to find a t such that $x \in \text{int}\, H(t)$. This problem has been considered by Kalman in the linear case. Some interesting results have been obtained recently by Falb.

farthest in the positive direction along E then the problem has an optimal solution. We shall assume that this is the case and our task will be to determine a control function leading to this point B. It is not difficult to see that B belongs to $E \cap \partial H$, i.e., the intersection of E and ∂H, the boundary of H.

Let ν be a control function in F. We shall write $x(t_b;\nu)$ to denote the state obtained at $t = t_b$ after integration of the system (0.1) from $x = x_a$ at $t = t_a$ with the control function of ν. We shall now analyze under which conditions this control function ν is the optimal control function we are looking for. The first condition is obviously

$$x(t_b;\nu) \in E \tag{0.2}$$

and the second condition is

$$x(t_b;\nu) \in \partial H \tag{0.3}$$

It is easy to verify the first condition but not the second condition since, in general, we do not know the set ∂H and since the determination of the set ∂H would be equivalent to the solution of the problem under consideration.

The preceding difficulty is turned in the following manner: we replace the differential equation (0.1) by another differential equation

$$\dot{x} = f(x,u,t;\nu) \tag{0.4}$$

called the ν approximate differential equation.‡ The definition of the ν approximate differential equation will be given explicitly in Section 2. At this stage the reader needs only to know that the equation (0.4) is a certain linearization, with respect to the state variable but not necessarily with respect to the control variable, of the equation (0.1). The linearization has no effects on the trajectory corresponding

‡It is important to understand clearly the logical structure of the function $f(x,u,t;\nu)$ in the framework of our previous notations. The first three arguments of f are points in respective spaces but the fourth argument ν is a function in the class F. In other words f is a function of its three first arguments and a functional of its fourth argument.

to the control function ν, i.e., if we integrate the equation (0.4) from the state $x = x_a$ at $t = t_a$ with the control function ν we obtain a trajectory identical to the trajectory obtained by integrating the equation (0.1) from the state $x = x_a$ at $t = t_a$ with the control function ν.

We write $x(t_b;u,\nu)$ to denote the state obtained at the time t_b after integration of the system (0.4) from $x = x_a$ at $t = t_a$ with the control function u.[‡] To the ν approximate differential equation we associate the set $\tilde{H}(\nu)$ defined as the set of all points $x(t_b;u,\nu)$ for all u in F. The ν approximate differential equation has been defined in such a way that the set $\tilde{H}(\nu)$ has the following properties:

1. The set $\tilde{H}(\nu)$ is relatively easy to determine[+] numerically. In particular we can prove that the set $\tilde{H}(\nu)$ is always convex.
2. If $x(t_b;\nu) \in \partial H$ then we must have $x(t_b;\nu) \in \partial\tilde{H}(\nu)$. In other words the set $\tilde{H}(\nu)$ is a certain approximation of the set H and this approximation is good

---

‡ In accordance with the preceding remark what we call solution of the ν-approximate differential equation

$$\dot{x} = f(x,u,t;\nu)$$

with the control function u, is in fact the solution of the differential equation

$$\dot{x} = f(x,u(t),t;\nu)$$

+ Here we use the simple words "we determine numerically a set $\tilde{H}(\nu)$" to mean "we obtain numerically some useful informations on the set $\tilde{H}(\nu)$". In the case of a convex set these informations could consist of a sufficiently dense subset of $\partial\tilde{H}(\nu)$, the boundary of $\tilde{H}(\nu)$. We should even mention that it is rarely necessary to determine the totality of the set $\tilde{H}(\nu)$. In Section 5 we shall describe precisely which subset of $\tilde{H}(\nu)$ should be determined in practice.

enough to allow us to replace the necessary condition $x(t_b;\nu) \in \partial H$ by the necessary condition $x(t_b;\nu) \in \partial\tilde{H}(\nu)$.*

This very fortunate situation suggests the following procedure for verifying that a control function ν is optimal for the problem under consideration:

1. Verify that $x(t_b;\nu) \in E$
2. Compute $\tilde{H}(\nu)$
3. Verify that $x(t_b;\nu) \in \partial\tilde{H}(\nu)$

This simple verification procedure is not yet very useful for selecting the optimal control function. We shall now introduce an iterative scheme based upon the preceding verification procedure. We choose a control function ν_1 in the class F. We compute $x(t_b;\nu_1)$ and analyze $\tilde{H}(\nu_1)$. In general ν_1 will be neither feasible, i.e., we will have $x(t_b;\nu_1) \notin E$, nor optimal, i.e., we will have $x(t_b;\nu_1) \notin \partial\tilde{H}(\nu_1)$. Hence in general we have to choose another control function ν_2 in F. Instead of choosing ν_2 at random we take advantage of the experience gained with ν_1. We assume that the ν_1 approximate differential equation is the exact differential equation.

---

*Someone could perhaps think that the condition $x(t_b;\nu) \in \partial\tilde{H}(\nu)$ is trivially weak. This is not the case: we have proved in (1) that the condition $x(t_b;\nu) \in \partial H(\nu)$ is at least as strong as Pontryagin's Maximum Principle, i.e., at least as strong as the conditions of Euler-Lagrange, Weierstrass-Erdmann, Clebsch-Legendre and the Weierstrass-E Test of the classical calculus of variations.

From $\tilde{H}(\nu_1)$ we determine easily[#] the optimal control $\hat{\nu}_1$ for this approximate problem, and then we let $\nu_2 = \hat{\nu}_1$. The same procedure is then repeated up to the moment where $x(t_b;\nu_n)$ is "close enough" to the boundary of $\tilde{H}(\nu_n)$.

These are the guiding ideas behind the Method of Convex Ascent. In fact, the Method of Convex Ascent is slightly more sophisticated than the crude procedure described in this introduction. In particular some refinements are added to the preceding scheme which insure a stable computational procedure. See Section 6.

At this point the reader can understand easily why the words "Convex Ascent" have been chosen to describe this method: in general $x(t_b;\nu_1)$ is not on the boundary of the convex set $\tilde{H}(\nu_1)$ as it should be if ν_1 would be optimal.

[#]The reader should make an act of faith at this particular point of the introduction. We shall describe in Section 5 a procedure to determine $\tilde{H}(\nu_1)$. The reader who is familiar with the optimal solution of control problems for systems described by linear differential equation of the type

$$x = A(t)x + \varphi(u,t)$$

(which includes as a particular case the differential equations of the types

$$\dot{x} = A(t)x + B(t)u + f(t)$$

$$\dot{x} = A(t)x + B(t)u$$

$$\dot{x} = Ax + Bu + C$$

and

$$\dot{x} = Ax + Bu \qquad)$$

will realize immediately that in such a case the determination of $\tilde{H}(\nu_1)$ is equivalent to the determination of H, i.e., equivalent to the very solution of the problem itself. The computational aspects of linear control theory have been studied with great success by Neustadt and Paiewonsky.

The iterative procedure consists in choosing a sequence $\nu_2, \nu_3, \ldots$ of control functions in F such that the sequence $x(t_b;\nu_2), x(t_b;\nu_3), \ldots$ ascends in the proper direction toward the boundaries of the convex sets $\tilde{H}(\nu_2), \tilde{H}(\nu_3), \ldots$.

At the end of this introduction we want to make some comments on a very important characteristic of the Method of Convex Ascent: no inversion of matrices is needed. This result is achieved very simply by performing the computations in the comoving space along the trial trajectory, see Section 2. The difference between this approach and the conventional approach can be compared with the difference, for an astronomer studying the movements of the planets of the sun, between using a sun centered coordinate system and using an earth centered coordinate system.

The Method of Convex Ascent has been applied to the sounding rocket problem, called also the Goddard Problem. The Goddard problem is singular in the sense of the Calculus of Variations⊥ and no computational solution has been successfully applied to this problem before.△ The Method of Convex Ascent can easily handle the Goddard problem.

Finally we want to mention that many specific "tricks" described in this paper could be applied, as separate units, to improve certain aspects of the methods of gradient and steepest descent or of Neustadt's method for linear problems. Along these lines we mentioned above the advantages of carrying out certain computations in the comoving space along a trajectory. Another trick is to compute a priori (and again in the comoving space along a trajectory) the sensitivity directions for the adjoint variables. In the case of Goddard

---

⊥Very crudely speaking a singular problem of the calculus of variations is a problem where there exist arcs, called singular arcs, along which the necessary conditions are trivially satisfied, i.e., the necessary conditions are satisfied but they are not strong enough to give enough useful information on the local choice of the control variable. For an illuminating discussion of singular problems in control theory and their relation to some classical problems in analysis, see the work of Hermes.

△Of course, some simplified versions of the Goddard problem, e.g., neglecting drag, etc., have been solved completely before. See the works of Leitmann and Miele for instance.

Problem we have experienced that such technique gives directly the range of sensitivity for the most critical adjoint variable. The computational advantages are tremendous: instead of trying to locate the right p between $-\infty$ and $+\infty$ we were able to restrict a priori our search to the interval between 1.0345 and 1.0355!

In the development of the Method of Convex Ascent we took full advantages of theoretical results obtained by Bellman, Bushaw, LaSalle, McShane, Neustadt and Pontryagin and of the computational experiences gained by Bryson, Kelley and Paiewonsky.

Section 1. Statement of the Problem

In this section we shall give a precise formulation to the problem described in the introduction.

We assume that we are given the following elements:

(i) An initial time $t_a \in T$, where T is the real line with elements t.

(ii) A final time $t_b \in T$

(iii) An initial state $x_a \in X$, where X, called the state space, is the euclidean n-dimensional space with elements $x = (x^1,\dots,x^n)$

(iv) A set E of terminal states defined as follows:

$$E = \{x : x^i = x^i_b \text{ for } i = 1,\dots,n-1;\ x^n \in R\} \qquad (1.1)$$

where R is the real line. In other words E is a line parallel to the x^n axis and determined by its projections $x^1_b, x^2_b,\dots,x^{n-1}_b$ on the other (n-1) first axis.

(v) A set

$$\Omega \subset U \qquad (1.2)$$

where U, called the control space, is the euclidean r-dimensional space with elements $u = (u^1,\dots,u^r)$.

(vi) An n-dimensional vector valued function

$$f(x,u,t) = (f^1(x,u,t),\ f^2(x,u,t),\dots,f^n(x,u,t)) \qquad (1.3)$$

defined on an open subset Q of X×U×T such that f(x,u,t) and $f_x(x,u,t)$ are defined, measurable* with respect to u and t, uniformly equicontinuous with respect to x, and uniformly bounded for all (x,u,t) in a compact subset of Q.

(vii) The class F of all bounded measurable r-dimensional vector valued functions

$$\mathcal{U} = \{(u(t),t) : t \in [t_a,t_b]\} \tag{1.4}$$

satisfying the condition

$$u(t) \in \Omega \quad \text{for all } t \in [t_a,t_b] \tag{1.5}$$

We shall denote by

$$x(\mathcal{U}) = \{(x(t;\mathcal{U}),t) : t \in [t_a,t_b]\} \tag{1.6}$$

whenever it exists, an absolutely continuous function defined and a.e. differentiable over $[t_a,t_b]$ such that

(i) $x(t_a;\mathcal{U}) = x_a$ (1.7)

(ii) $\dot{x}(t;\mathcal{U}) = f(x(t;\mathcal{U}),u(t),t)$ a.e. $t \in [t_a,t_b]$ (1.8)

(iii) $(x(t;\mathcal{U}),u(t),t) \in Q$ for all $t \in [t_a,t_b]$ (1.9)

---

*The words "measure", "measurable", "almost everywhere" (abbreviated a.e.), etc., have very precise definitions which can be found in any good book on measure theory. See Halmos' book for instance. In this paper we consider Lebesgue's measure only. The reader who knows the elements of measure theory is requested to skip the remainder of this footnote. To the reader who does not know the elements of measure theory we can say that:

1. Virtually all functions encountered in Physics (continuous, piecewise continuous, etc.) are measurable. Indeed it is necessary to know measure theory in order to imagine functions which are not measurable.

2. The sets consisting of a finite number of points or a countably infinite number of points have zero measure.

3. A relation holds a.e. on $[t_a,t_b]$ if it holds for all points of $[t_a,t_b]$ with the exception of a set of measure zero.

Let F* be the subset of F consisting of all those elements u in F for which $x(u)$ exists. It is a trivial matter, see (1), to prove that $x(u)$ is unique for each u in F*.

Given all these data the problem is to find a function ν in F* such that

$$(\alpha)\ x(t_b;\nu) \in E \tag{1.10}$$

(β) for any $u \in F^*$ such that

$$x(t_b;u) \in E \tag{1.11}$$

shall hold the relation

$$x^n(t_b;u) \leq x^n(t_b;\nu) \tag{1.12}$$

The function ν satisfying the conditions (α) and (β) shall be called an optimal control function and the corresponding function $x(\nu)$ shall be called an optimal trajectory.

Section 2. Comoving Coordinate Space Along a Given Trajectory

For any $\nu \in F^*$ we define an n×n matrix $D(t;\nu)$ as follows:

$$D(t;\nu) = \left.\frac{\partial f(x,v(t),t)}{\partial x}\right|_{x=x(t;\nu)} \qquad t \in [t_a,t_b] \tag{2.1}$$

From our assumptions we know that $D(t;\nu)$ is bounded and measurable over $[t_a,t_b]$.

Let $G(t;\nu)$ be an n×n matrix, continuous with respect to t, defined over $[t_a,t_b]$, satisfying the matrix differential equation

$$\dot{G}(t;\nu) = -G(t;\nu)D(t;\nu) \quad \text{a.e. } t \in [t_a,t_b] \tag{2.2}$$

and such that

$$G(t_b;\nu) = I \tag{2.3}$$

where I is the identity n×n matrix. It is a trivial matter, see (1), to prove that $G(t;\nu)$ and $G^{-1}(t;\nu)$ exist, are unique and bounded over $[t_a,t_b]$.

We shall now introduce a euclidean n-dimensional space $Y(\nu)$ with elements $y = (y^1, \ldots, y^n)$ by the mapping

$$\varphi(\nu) : X\times[t_a, t_b] \rightarrow Y(\nu)\times[t_a, t_b] \tag{2.4}$$

where

$$(y, t) = \varphi(x, t; \nu) \tag{2.5}$$

is defined by

$$y = G(t;\nu)(x - x(t;\nu)) \tag{2.6}$$

Under the mapping $\varphi(\nu)$ the trajectory

$$\mathcal{x}(u) = \{(x(t;u), t) : t \in [t_a, t_b]\} \text{ with } u \in F^* \tag{2.7}$$

will be transformed into the trajectory

$$\mathcal{y}(u,\nu) = \{(y(t;u,\nu), t) : t \in [t_a, t_b]\} \tag{2.8}$$

defined by the relation

$$y(t;u,\nu) = G(t;\nu)(x(t;u) - x(t;\nu)) \text{ for all } t \in [t_a, t_b] \tag{2.9}$$

It is a trivial matter, see (1), to verify that for every ν and u in F* the function $\mathcal{y}(u,\nu)$ exists, is unique and continuous. The space $Y(\nu)$ is called the comoving space along the trajectory $\mathcal{x}(\nu)$.

Let us now define in the space $Y(\nu)$ the relative ν approximate trajectory corresponding to the control function u:

$$\overset{+}{\mathcal{y}}(u,\nu) = \{(y(t;u,\nu), t) : t \in [t_a, t_b]\} \tag{2.10}$$

by the relation

$$\overset{+}{y}(t;u,\nu) = \int_{t_a}^{t} G(\tau;\nu)(f(x(\tau;\nu), u(\tau), \tau) - f(x(\tau;\nu), v(\tau), \tau))d\tau$$

$$\text{for all } t \in [t_a, t_b] \tag{2.11}$$

It is a trivial matter, see (1), to verify that for every $\nu \in F^*$ and every $u \in F$ the function $\overset{+}{y}(u,\nu)$ exists, is unique and continuous.

Let us now define in the space X the ν approximate trajectory corresponding to the control u

$$\tilde{x}(u,\nu) = \{(\tilde{x}(t;u,\nu),t) : t \in [t_a,t_b]\} \tag{2.12}$$

by the relation

$$\tilde{x}(t;u,\nu) = x(t;\nu) + G^{-1}(t;\nu)\overset{+}{y}(t;u,\nu) \text{ for all } t \in [t_a,t_b] \tag{2.13}$$

It is a trivial matter, see (1), to verify that for every $\nu \in F^*$ and every $u \in F$ the function $\tilde{x}(u,\nu)$ exists, is unique and continuous.

Some algebraic manipulations

At this point it is convenient to write down some relations which will be very useful in the rest of the paper. No new concept, definition or theorem is introduced in this paragraph. We shall only perform some algebraic manipulations on the relations introduced at the beginning of Section 2.

From the relations 2.2 and 2.3 defining $G(t;\nu)$ we obtain easily the corresponding relations for $G^{-1}(t;\nu)$:

$$\dot{G}^{-1}(t;\nu) = D(t;\nu)G^{-1}(t;\nu) \text{ a.e. } t \in [t_a,t_b] \tag{2.14}$$

$$G^{-1}(t_b;\nu) = I \tag{2.15}$$

The relation 2.15 is indeed obvious from 2.3. An immediate way to check 2.14 is to verify, from 2.2 and 2.14, that we have

$$(G(t;\nu)G^{-1}(t;\nu))^{\cdot} = 0 \text{ for a.e. } t \in [t_a,t_b] \tag{2.16}$$

Indeed

$$(G(t;\nu)G^{-1}(t;\nu))^{\cdot} = \dot{G}(t;\nu)G^{-1}(t;\nu)+G(t;\nu)\dot{G}^{-1}(t;\nu)$$
$$= -G(t;\nu)D(t;\nu)G^{-1}(t;\nu)+G(t;\nu)D(t;\nu)G^{-1}(t;\nu)$$
$$= 0$$

The definition of $y(u,\nu)$, given by (2.11), could equivalently be given by

(i) $\overset{+}{y}(t;u,\nu)$ is continuous and a.e. differentiable over $[t_a,t_b]$ (2.17)

(ii) $\overset{+}{y}(t_a;u,\nu) = 0$ (2.18)

(iii) $\dot{\overset{+}{y}}(t;u,\nu) = G(t;\nu)(f(x(t;\nu),u(t),t)-f(x(t;\nu),v(t),t))$ for a.e. $t \in [t_a,t_b]$ (2.19)

We see immediately that for all $\nu \in F^*$ we have

$$\overset{+}{y}(t;\nu,\nu) = 0 \text{ for all } t \in [t_a,t_b] \tag{2.20}$$

From the relation (2.13) we have

$$\overset{+}{y}(t;u,\nu) = G(t;\nu)(\tilde{x}(t;u,\nu)-x(t;\nu)) \tag{2.21}$$

It is now easy to obtain the differential equation for $\tilde{x}(u,\nu)$. Indeed from 2.13 we have

$$\dot{\tilde{x}}(t;u,\nu) = \dot{x}(t;\nu) + \dot{G}^{-1}(t;\nu)y(t;u,\nu)$$
$$+ G^{-1}(t;\nu)\dot{\overset{+}{y}}(t;u,\nu) \text{ for a.e. } t \in [t_a,t_b] \tag{2.22}$$

Replacing $\dot{x}(t;\nu)$, $\dot{G}^{-1}(t;\nu)$, $\overset{+}{y}(t;u,\nu)$ and $\dot{\overset{+}{y}}(t;u,\nu)$ by the by the expressions 1.8, 2.14, 2.21 and 2.19 we obtain

$$\begin{aligned}\dot{\tilde{x}}(t;u,\nu) = {} & f(x(t;\nu),v(t),t) \\ & + D(t;\nu)G^{-1}(t;\nu)G(t;\nu)(\tilde{x}(t;u,\nu)-x(t;\nu)) \\ & + G^{-1}(t;\nu)G(t;\nu)(f(x(t;\nu),u(t),t)-f(x(t;\nu),v(t),t))\end{aligned}$$

i.e.,

$$\dot{\tilde{x}}(t;u,\nu) = f(x(t;\nu),u(t),t)+D(t;\nu)(\tilde{x}(t;u,\nu)-x(t;\nu))$$
$$\text{a.e. } t \in [t_a,t_b] \tag{2.23}$$

The equation (2.23) is the ν-approximate differential equation

$$\dot{x} = f(x,u,t;\nu)$$

if we define $f(x,u,t;\nu)$ by the relation

$$f(x,u,t;\nu) = f(x(t;\nu),u,t) + D(t;\nu)(x-x(t;\nu)) \tag{2.24}$$

From the relation 2.9 we have

$$x(t;u) = x(t;\nu) + G^{-1}(t;\nu)y(t;u,\nu) \tag{2.25}$$

It is now easy to obtain the differential equation for $y(u,\nu)$. Indeed from (2.9) we have

$$\dot{y}(t;u,\nu) = \dot{G}(t;\nu)x(t;u)-x(t;\nu))$$
$$+ G(t;\nu)(\dot{x}(t;u)-\dot{x}(t;\nu)) \text{ for a.e. } t \in [t_a,t_b]$$

Replacing $\dot{G}(t;\nu)$, $\dot{x}(t;u)$ and $\dot{x}(t;\nu)$ by the expressions 2.2 1.8 we obtain

$$\dot{y}(t;u,\nu) = -G(t;\nu)D(t;\nu)(x(t;u)-x(t;\nu))$$
$$+G(t;\nu)(f(x(t;u),u(t),t)-f(x(t;\nu),v(t),t))$$

Replacing now $x(t;u)$ by the expression 2.25 we have finally

$$\dot{y}(t;u,\nu) = G(t;\nu)(f(x(t;\nu)+G^{-1}(t;\nu)y(t;u,\nu),u(t),t)$$
$$-f(x(t;\nu),v(t),t))$$
$$-G(t;\nu)D(t;\nu)G^{-1}(t;\nu)y(t;u,\nu) \text{ for a.e. } t \in [t_a,t_b] \tag{2.26}$$

Section 3. Reachable Sets

We shall define the sets H, H(v), $\overset{+}{H}(v)$ and $\tilde{H}(v)$ as follows:

$$H = \{x(t_b;u) : u \in F^*\} \tag{3.1}$$

$$H(\nu) = \{y(t_b;u,\nu) : u \in F^*\} \text{ for all } \nu \in F^* \tag{3.2}$$

$$\overset{+}{H}(\nu) = \{\overset{+}{y}(t_b;u,\nu) : u \in F\} \text{ for all } \nu \in F^* \tag{3.3}$$

$$\tilde{H}(\nu) = \{\tilde{x}(t_b;u,\nu) : u \in F\} \text{ for all } \nu \in F^* \tag{3.4}$$

It is a trivial matter to verify that for every $\nu \in F^*$

$$H(\nu) = \{\alpha - x(t_b;\nu) : \alpha \in H\} \tag{3.5}$$

$$\overset{+}{H}(\nu) = \{\alpha - x(t_b;\nu) : \alpha \in \tilde{H}(\nu)\} \tag{3.6}$$

The study of these sets and particularly of their boundaries will be made in the next section.

For a linear system we have

$$x(u) = \tilde{x}(u,\nu) \tag{3.7}$$

and

$$y(u,\nu) = \overset{+}{y}(u,\nu) \tag{3.8}$$

Hence, for a linear system, we have

$$H = \tilde{H}(\nu) \tag{3.9}$$

and

$$H(\nu) = \overset{+}{H}(\nu) \tag{3.10}$$

Theorem III of Section 4 which states some topological relationships between H and $\tilde{H}(\nu)$ is, of course, trivially true when $H = \tilde{H}(\nu)$, for instance in the case of a linear system.

Section 4. Necessary Condition for the Optimal Control of Nonlinear Systems

In this section we give a series of seven theorems. These seven theorems constitute the theoretical foundation of the subsequent sections. The proofs of Theorems I, II, IV, V and VI are trivial. The proof of Theorem VII is easy. The proof of Theorem III is rather long. All these proofs are given in (1) and will not be repeated here.

Theorem I If an element ν of F^* is optimal then the point $x = x(t_b;\nu)$ is a boundary point of the set H.

Theorem II If the point $x = x(t_b;\nu)$ is a boundary point of the set H then y=0 is a boundary point of the set $H(\nu)$.

Theorem III If the point y=0 is a boundary point of the set $H(\nu)$ then y=0 is a boundary point of the set $\overset{+}{H}(\nu)$.

Theorem IV If the point y=0 is a boundary point of the set $\overset{+}{H}(\nu)$ then $x = x(t_b;\nu)$ is a boundary point of the set $\tilde{H}(\nu)$.

Theorem V If the point $x = x(t_b;\nu)$ is a boundary point of the set H then the point $x = x(t_b;\nu)$ is a boundary point of the set $\tilde{H}(\nu)$.

Theorem VI If an element ν of F^* is optimal then the point $x = x(t_b;\nu)$ is a boundary point of the set $\tilde{H}(\nu)$.

Theorem VII The sets $\overset{+}{H}(\nu)$ and $\tilde{H}(\nu)$ are convex.

Comments on the logical structure of the previous theorems

In Theorem I we associate two different notions: the concept of optimality for the particular optimal control problem under consideration and a topological property of the set H, which set depends only on the given system with initial conditions but not on any particular optimal control problem.

In Theorems II, III and IV we give a series of implications concerning certain properties of the sets H, $\tilde{H}(\nu)$, $H(\nu)$ and $\overset{+}{H}(\nu)$.

In Theorem V we give the combined result of all the implications contained in Theorems II, III and IV.

In Theorem VI we use Theorem I as an intermediary in order to obtain from the topological results of Theorem V the necessary condition for an optimal solution of the particular optimal control problem under consideration.

Theorem V is the most important result in the theory of optimal control for nonlinear systems. This theorem depends only on the given system with initial condition but not on any particular optimal control problem. Hence, when a particular optimal control problem is given, we need only to verify that Theorem I is valid in order to derive from Theorem V the appropriate necessary conditions for an optimal control. The verification of Theorem I is particularly simple in the case of the fundamental optimal control problem considered in this paper but could also be easily done for a large class of different optimal control problems.

Section 5. Optimal Solution for the ν-Approximate Differential Equation

As we have indicated in the introduction the Method of Convex Ascent is an iterative procedure on the control functions. In other words it is a rule for determining a control function ν_{m+1} from the knowledge of a control function ν_m in such a way that the trajectory $x(\nu_k)$ tends to a feasible optimal trajectory as k tends to infinity. A first step toward the determination of the control function ν_{m+1} is to find the control function $\hat{\nu}_m$ which is the optimal solution for the problem associated with the ν_m approximate differential equation

$$x = f(x,u,t;\nu_m) \tag{5.1}$$

which was briefly described in the introduction and precisely defined in Section 2. In this section we shall be concerned with the determination of $\hat{\nu}_m$.

The problem is the following: given a control function ν_m in F* find a control function $\hat{\nu}_m$ in F such that

$$(\alpha) \quad x(t_b;\hat{\nu}_m,\nu_m) \in E \tag{5.2}$$

(β) for all u in F such that

$$x(t_b;u,\nu_m) \in E \tag{5.3}$$

shall hold the relation

$$\tilde{x}^n(t_b;u,\nu_m) \leq \tilde{x}^n(t_b;\hat{\nu}_m,\nu_m) \tag{5.4}$$

Let us now express the same problem in the comoving space around the trajectory $x(\nu_m)$. We have first to define $E(\nu_m)$, the set E seen relatively to the end of the trajectory $x(\nu_m)$, by the relation

$$E(\nu_m) = \{x - x(t_b;\nu_m) : x \in E\} \tag{5.5}$$

The preceding problem can then be formulated as follows: given a control function ν_m in F* find a control function $\hat{\nu}_m$ in F such that

(α) $\overset{+}{y}(t_b;\hat{\nu}_m,\nu_m) \in E(\nu_m)$ (5.6)

(β) for all u in F such that

$$\overset{+}{y}(t_b;u,\nu_m) \in E(\nu_m) \tag{5.7}$$

shall hold the relation

$$\overset{+}{y}{}^n(t_b;u,\nu_m) \leq \overset{+}{y}{}^n(t_b;\hat{\nu}_m,\nu_m) \tag{5.8}$$

This last version of the problem is particularly convenient since the functions $\overset{+}{y}(u,\nu_m)$ can be obtained by the simple quadratures:

$$\overset{+}{y}(t;u,\nu_m) =$$

$$\int_{t_a}^{t} G(\tau;\nu_m)(f(x(\tau;\nu_m),v_m(\tau),\tau) - f(x(\tau;\nu_m),u(\tau),\tau))d\tau \tag{5.9}$$

The simplicity of relation 5.9 is no accident: the whole purpose of introducing the space $Y(\nu_m)$ and the ν_m approximate differential equation is to obtain that relation

5.9. The theoretical utility of relation 5.9 has been exhibited in the previous section and the computational utility of relation 5.9 will be seen here.

Using the concept of reachable sets and the convexity of the set $\overset{+}{H}(\nu_m)$ the preceding problem can be equivalently formulated as follows: given a control function ν_m in F* find a control function $\hat{\nu}_m$ in F such that

$$\overset{+}{y}(t_b;\hat{\nu}_m,\nu_m) \in E(\nu_m) \cap \partial\overset{+}{H}(\nu_m) \tag{5.10}$$

We have now the following proposition, whose proof is given in (1):

Proposition 5.1. If $\overset{+}{y}(t_b;u,\nu_m) \in \partial\overset{+}{H}(\nu_m)$ and if $\Phi(u,\nu_m)$ is a nonzero outward normal to a supporting hyperplane of the convex set $\overset{+}{H}(\nu_m)$ at the boundary point $\overset{+}{y}(t_b;u,\nu_m)$ then for all ν in F we have

$$\langle \Phi(u,\nu_m) \mid G(t;\nu_m)(f(x(t;\nu_m),u(t),t) - f(x(t;\nu_m),v(t),t))\rangle \geq 0$$

$$\text{for a.e. } t \in [t_a,t_b] \tag{5.11}$$

Proposition 5.1 gives an easy rule to find for every supporting hyperplane of $\overset{+}{H}(v_m)$ a point of contact $\overset{+}{y}(t_b;u,\nu_m)$ and the corresponding control function u leading to this point of contact. In order to determine the point $E(\nu_m) \cap \partial\overset{+}{H}(\nu_m)$ we apply standard techniques of "calculus" gradient method and convex programming. Interesting results along these lines have been obtained by Neustadt and Paiewonsky.

Important Remark

The techniques of "calculus" gradient method and convex programming are iterative on the normals to the supporting hyperplanes. In other words it is a rule to find a sequence of normals $\Phi_1,\Phi_2,\Phi_3,\ldots$ which converges to the normal Φ to a supporting hyperplane of $\overset{+}{H}(\nu_m)$ at $E(\nu_m) \cap \partial\overset{+}{H}(\nu_m)$. This iterative search for the normal Φ can be greatly improved if we can restrict our search to a relatively small set determined a priori.

This a priori determination of a smaller set of normals can be done particularly easily in the case of a differential equation linear in the control variables: let $\mathcal{F}(t)$ be the set of all vector $\Phi(t)$ normal to the linear manifold:

$$\{G(t;\nu_m)(f(x(t;\nu_m),v_m(t),t) - f(x(t;\nu_m),u,t)) : u \in \Omega\} \tag{5.12}$$

and such that

$$\Phi^n(t) \geq 0 \tag{5.13}$$

More precisely

$$\mathcal{F}(t) = \{\Phi(t) : \Phi^n(t) \geq 0,$$

$$\langle G(t;\nu_m)(f(x(t;\nu_m),\nu_m(t),t)-f(x(t;\nu_m),u,t)) \mid \Phi(t)\rangle = 0$$

for some $u \in \Omega$ such that

$$\mid G(t;\nu_m)(f(x(t;\nu_m),\nu_m(t),t)-f(x(t;\nu_m),u,t)) \mid \neq 0\} \tag{5.14}$$

It is not difficult to prove that the search of the normal Φ can be restricted to the closure $\overline{C}$ of the cone

$$C = \{\Phi(t) : \Phi(t) \in \mathcal{F}(t) \quad \text{for some } t \in [t_a,t_b]\} \tag{5.15}$$

A fortiori the search of the normal Φ can be restricted to the convex hull of $\overline{C}$.

In general we shall obtain useful informations on the domain of sensitivity for the vector Φ by direct inspection of the sets (5.12).

In the case of Goddard Problem we have experienced that the a priori determination of the range of sensitivity of the vector Φ is very useful. The computational advantages are tremendous in that case: instead of trying to locate the right value of the most critical component of the vector Φ between $-\infty$ and $+\infty$ we were able to restrict <u>a priori</u> our search to the interval between 1.0345 and 1.0355!

Section 6. Optimal Gain of the Iterative Computational Procedure

In the preceding section we have been concerned with the problem: given ν_m find $\hat{\nu}_m$ which is the optimal control function associated with the ν_m approximate differential equation. In that section we have given a procedure to determine $\hat{\nu}_m$ and the corresponding vector $\overset{+}{y}(t_b;\hat{\nu}_m,\nu_m)$. If the ν_m approximate differential equation would be the true basic differential equation then the vector $y(t_b;\hat{\nu}_m,\nu_m)$ would represent the distance between the end of the trajectory $x(\nu_m)$ and the end of the optimal trajectory we are looking for. In fact the vector $\overset{+}{y}(t_b;\hat{\nu}_m,\nu_m)$ is only an approximation of that distance.

Let us introduce a deflection index $Q(\nu,\nu_m)$ to characterize the quality of the ν_m approximate solution corresponding to the control ν

$$Q(\nu,\nu_m) = \frac{|\tilde{x}(t_b;\nu,\nu_m) - x(t_b;\nu)|}{|\tilde{x}(t_b;\nu,\nu_m) - x(t_b;\nu_m)|} \tag{6.1}$$

or equivalently

$$Q(\nu,\nu_m) = \frac{|\overset{+}{y}(t_b;\nu,\nu_m) - y(t_b;\nu,\nu_m)|}{|\overset{+}{y}(t_b;\nu,\nu_m)|} \tag{6.2}$$

If $Q(\hat{\nu}_m,\nu_m)$ is "small" this means that the ν_m approximation of the trajectory corresponding to the control function $\hat{\nu}_m$ is good enough, we let

$$\nu_{m+1} = \hat{\nu}_m \tag{6.3}$$

and proceed to the next iterative step. If $Q(\hat{\nu}_m,\nu_m)$ is "large" this means that the ν_m approximation of the trajectory corresponding to the control function $\hat{\nu}_m$ is not good enough and we have to select an appropriate control function ν_{m+1} "between" ν_m and $\hat{\nu}_m$ in such a way that $Q(\nu_{m+1},\nu_m)$ is "small".

We shall now precise what we mean by a "small" or "large" $Q(\hat{\nu}_{m+1},\nu_m)$ and by a control function ν_{m+1} "between" ν_m and $\hat{\nu}_m$. We have found convenient to consider that a deflection index is small when it is less than 0.5 and large otherwise. When

$$Q(\hat{\nu}_m,\nu_m) > \frac{1}{2} \tag{6.4}$$

we construct ν_{m+1} according to the following rules.

For any n-dimensional vector p of length 1 and any non-negative number ρ we consider the functions

$$\alpha(t) = G(t;\nu_m)(f(x(t;\nu_m),\hat{v}_m(t),t) - f(x(t;\nu_m),v_m(t),t)) \tag{6.5}$$

$$B(t,p) = \frac{\langle p \mid \alpha(t) \rangle}{\mid \alpha(t) \mid} \tag{6.6}$$

$$\gamma(t,p,\rho) = \min \{1,\max\{0,\rho B(t,p)\}\} \tag{6.7}$$

and the control function $\nu_{m,p,\rho}$, which could namely be a generalized function,** such that

$$\begin{aligned} f(x(t;\nu_m),v_{m,p,\rho}(t),t) = &+ \gamma(t,p,\rho)f(x(t;\nu_m),\hat{v}_m(t),t) \\ &+ (1-\gamma(t,p,\rho))f(x(t;\nu_m),v_m(t),t) \end{aligned} \tag{6.8}$$

**See the papers of Warga for instance.

For each ρ we determine* the vector $\overline{p}$ such that

$$\overset{+}{y}(t_b;\nu_{m,\overline{p},\rho},\nu_m) = \alpha\overset{+}{y}(t_b;\hat{\nu}_m,\nu_m)$$

$$\text{for some positive } \alpha \tag{6.9}$$

We write

$$\nu_{m,\rho} = \nu_{m,\overline{p},\rho} \tag{6.10}$$

The deflection index

$$Q(\nu_{m,\rho},\nu_m) \tag{6.11}$$

is a continuous function of ρ and

$$\lim_{\rho \to 0} Q(\nu_{m,\rho},\nu_m) = 0 \tag{6.12}$$

hence it is possible to choose a $\overline{\rho}$ such that

$$Q(\nu_{m,\overline{\rho}},\nu_m) \leq \frac{1}{2} \tag{6.13}$$

We write then

$$\nu_{m+1} = \nu_{m,\overline{\rho}}$$

and proceed to the next iterative step.

The preceding procedure of determination of ν_{m+1} can be visualized in the following terms: ν_{m+1} is a control function "between" ν_m and $\hat{\nu}_m$ such that ν_{m+1} is near $\hat{\nu}_m$ for those instant of time t for which the change from $v_m(t)$ to $\hat{v}_m(t)$ would lead to a relatively large change of the terminal point in the desired direction and such that ν_{m+1} is near ν_m for

---

*This determination is performed iteratively by a search procedure similar to the procedure described in Section 5 for the determination of $\hat{\nu}_m$.

those instant of time t for which the change from $v_m(t)$ to $\hat{v}_m(t)$ would lead to a relatively small change of the terminal point in the desired direction.

In a future paper we hope to prove the convergence of the Method of Convex Ascent for a large class of problems.

Section 7. Application of the Method of Convex Ascent to the Goddard Problem

We have considered the following version of the Goddard Problem: we are given a sounding rocket whose thrust can be chosen arbitrarily between zero and a given maximum value; we are also given initial altitude, mass and velocity and terminal altitude and velocity; the problem is to find an admissible thrust history such that the rocket starting from the initial conditions satisfies the terminal conditions and maximizes the terminal mass.* We have chosen the altitude as independent variable.+

The equations describing the motion of the rocket are then

$$\begin{aligned} \frac{dv}{dh} &= -\frac{g(h)}{v} - \frac{D(h,v)}{mv} + \frac{cu}{mv} \\ \frac{dm}{dh} &= -\frac{u}{v} \end{aligned} \qquad (7.1)$$

where v is the vertical velocity, h is the altitude, g(h) is the gravity, D(h,v) is the drag, m is the mass, c is the exhaust velocity, u is the control variable representing the rate of mass flow.

---

*This is one among many different versions of the Goddard Problem. These different versions are not always strictly equivalent. We have chosen this particular version of the Goddard Problem because it exhibits in a simple manner the most interesting features common to the various other versions.

+This choice of the altitude as independent variable leads to some analytical difficulties when the velocity is zero, see equation (7.1). In this section we assume that the velocity is bounded away from zero.

The application of the Method of Convex Ascent was particularly easy: we guessed an initial control function, we computed the corresponding trajectory and the corresponding adjoint matrix along that trajectory. The solution of the resulting linearized problem was straightforward since we had only two state variables. Following the procedure indicated in Section 6 we obtained a new control function which we used as the next guess, etc.

Experimentally we found that the Method of Convex Ascent converged very fast even if the initial guess of the control function was very far from the optimal control function. We have adopted the following rule to decide when to stop the iterative process: when the expected increase in the terminal mass is less than 10^{-7} times the current value of the terminal mass. In all cases treated this precision was achieved after at most 10 iterations. The program was completely automatic, i.e., there was no outside intervention between two successive iterations. The total computing time, on an IBM 7094, was at most 15 seconds and sometimes as small as 5 seconds when the initial guess of the control function was particularly good.

The same program was used for different types of drag law and gravity law by changing appropriate subroutines. We have considered three different cases:

Case I

$$g(h) = g_o, \quad D(h,v) = 0$$

where g_o is a constant

Case II

$$g(h) = \frac{g_o h_o^2}{(h+h_o)^2}, \quad D(h,v) = D_o e^{-kh} v^2$$

where g_o, h_o, D_o and k are constant

Case III

$$g(h) = \frac{g_o h_o^2}{(h+h_o)^2}, \quad D(h,v) = D_o e^{-kh} v^2(1 + \alpha \sin \beta h)$$

where g_o, h_o, D_o, k, α and β are constant.

In order to describe the results let us denote by M a maximum thrust subarc, by V a variable thrust subarc and by C a coasting or zero thrust subarc.

In Case I we have obtained optimal control functions of the type MC (with the possible special cases M or C).

In Case II we have obtained optimal control functions of the types MVC, MVM, CVC or CVM (with all the possible special cases corresponding to the absence of one or two of the subarcs in the previous types, for instance MV, MC, VC, M, V, C, etc.).

In Case III we have obtained optimal control functions of all possible types with all possible number of subarcs by appropriate choices of the constants α and β.

The results of Cases I and II are in complete agreement with the results obtained previously by the various authors who have studied the Goddard Problem. However we must stress here the fundamental difference between our approach and the earlier papers devoted to the Goddard Problem. In our approach we do not assume or study beforehand the structure of the optimal solution: this structure is known only by inspection of the final result. In the earlier papers devoted to the Goddard Problem the main emphasis was placed on the preliminary study of the structure of the optimal solution and the synthesis of the optimal solution, whenever considered, was obtained by trial and error in a few particular cases. It is difficult to imagine how the classical approach could possibly lead to a synthesis of the optimal solution in a situation similar to Case III. The drag law considered in Case III belongs of course to the realm of pure fantasy but it gives a clear idea of the power and of the flexibility of the proposed method.

In a future paper, devoted entirely to the Goddard Problem, we shall give a more detailed account of the results contained in this section.

Acknowledgments

This paper owes much to many interesting conversations with Dr. A. G. Lubowe.

I am also very grateful to Professor C. A. Desoer, and to Drs. F. T. Geyling and D. v. Z. Wadsworth for some valuable comments on this paper.

REFERENCES

(1) Halkin, H., On the Necessary Condition for Optimal Contral of Nonlinear Systems, Journal d'Analyse Mathématique, Vol. 12, 1963. (Also Technical Report No. 116, June 13, 1963, Department of Mathematics, Stanford University.)

(2) Bellman, R., Glicksberg, I. and Gross, O., On the 'Bang-Bang' Control Problems, Quarterly of Applied Mathematics, Vol. 14, 1956, pp. 11-18.

(3) Bryson, A. E. and Denham, W. F., A Steepest-Ascent Method for Solving Optimum Programming Problems, Technical Report BR-1303, 10 August 1961, Raytheon Company.

(4) Bushaw, D., Dynamical Polysystems and Optimization, Technical Report 63-10, April 1963, RIAS. (To appear in Vol. 2, n. 3 of Contributions to Differential Equations.)

(5) Falb, P. L., Infinite Dimensional Control Problems I: On the closure of the set of attainable states for linear systems, to appear in J. Math. An. and Appl.

(6) Flügge-Lotz, I. and Halkin, H., Pontryagin's Maximum Principle and Optimal Control, Technical Report 130, September 1961, Department of Engineering Mechanics, Stanford University.

(7) Halkin, H., Trajectoires Optimales, Engineering Dissertation, Université de Liège, 1960.

(8) Halkin, H., Nondegenerate variational problems and the principle of optimal evolution, Proceedings of the Symposium on Vehicle Systems Optimization, Institute for the Aerospace Sciences, New York, 1962, pp. 43-44.

(9) Halkin, H., Lyapounov's theorem on the range of a vector measure and Pontryagin's maximum principle, Arch. Rational Mech. Anal., Vol. 10, 1962, pp. 296-304.

(10) Halkin, H., The principle of optimal evolution, in "Nonlinear differential equations and nonlinear mechanics", New York, 1963, pp. 284-302.

(11) Hermes, H., Controllability and the Singular Problem, Technical Report SR0520-60, October 1963, Martin Co.

(12) Kalman, R. E., On the General Theory of Control Systems, Proceedings of the First IFAC Congress, Moscow, 1960.

(13) Kelley, H. J., Method of Gradient. In "Optimization Techniques", G. Leitmann ed., Academic Press, New York, 1963.

(14) LaSalle, J. P., Time Optimal Control Systems, Proc. Nat. Acad. Sci. Wash. 45 (1959) 573.

(15) Leitmann, G., An Elementary Derivation of the Optimal Control Conditions, XII International Astronautical Congress, Washington, D.C., 1961.

(16) McShane, E. J., On multipliers for Lagrange problems, Amer. J. Math., Vol. 61, 1939, pp. 809-819.

(17) Miele, A., A Survey of the Problem of Optimizing Flight Paths of Aircraft and Missiles, Technical Report No. 27, Boeing Scientific Research Laboratories, July 1960.

(18) Neustadt, L. W., The existence of optimal controls in the absence of convexity conditions, J. Math. An. and Appl. 7, 110-117, (1963).

(19) Paiewonsky, B. and Woodrow, P. J., The Synthesis of Optimal Controls for a Class of Rocket Steering Problems, to appear.

(20) Pontryagin, L. S., Boltyanskii, V. G., Gamkrelidze, R. V. and Mishchenko, E. F., The mathematical theory of optimal processes, English Translation, L. W. Neustadt ed., Interscience, New York, 1962.

(21) Warga, J., Relaxed Variational Problems, Journal of Mathematical Analysis and Applications, Vol. 4, No. 1, 1962, pp. 111-128.

A great number of papers have been devoted to the theory of optimal control and its applications to engineering problems. For a complete bibliography of the early papers see:

(22) Fuller, A. T., Bibliography of optimum nonlinear control of determinate and stochastic-definite systems, J. Electronics and Control, Vol. 13, 1962, pp. 589-611.

(23) Higgins, T. J., A Résumé of the basic literature of state-space techniques in automatic control theory, JACC, 1962.

Many recent papers consider other interesting problems in the field of optimal control. See for instance:

(24) Antosiewicz, H. A., Linear Control Systems, Archive Rational Mechanics and Analysis, Vol. 12, 1963, pp. 313-324.

(25) Aoki, M., Minimal effort control systems with an upper bound of the control time, IEEE Transactions on Automatic Control, No. 1, 1963, pp. 60-61.

(26) Athans, M., Falb, P. L., and Lacoss, R. T., Time-, Fuel-, and Energy-Optimal Control of Nonlinear Norm-Invariant Systems. IEEE Transactions on Automatic Control, July 1963, No. 3, pp. 196-201.

(27) Flügge-Lotz, I. and Marbach, R., The Optimal Control of Some Altitude Control Systems for Different Performance Criteria. ASME Journal of Basic Engineering, Series D, Vol. 85, 1963, pp. 165-176.

(28) Stoleru, L. G., A quantitative model of growth of the Algerian Economy, Technical Report 124, September 13, 1963, Institute for Mathematical Studies in the Social Sciences, Stanford University.

STUDY OF AN ALGORITHM FOR DYNAMIC OPTIMIZATION

R. Perret
Faculté des Sciences, Grenoble, France

R. Rouxel
Battelle Memorial Institute, Geneva, Switzerland

I. INTRODUCTION

In this paper is presented a rather pragmatic approach to the optimization problem in a particular class of problems. This approach may be considered as a "hill-climbing" method applied to dynamic systems. We shall describe essentially the method used and the principal results that have been obtained. The structure of the studied system is shown in Fig. 1. In such a system, the cost function can be measured only through a stable transfer function $1/F(s)$ ($F(s)$ is a polynomial of degree n) and a pure delay $e^{-T_r s}$.

The acting variable $x(t)$ is made up of a series of ramps of positive or negative slope (plus or minus K). The switching between the two types of action is caused by the sign ϵ of a function $C(t)$ which is linearly dependent on the first and second derivatives of $h(t)$.

$$p_1 h'(t) + p_2 h''(t) - \Delta = C(t) \tag{1}$$

p_1 and p_2 are positive coefficients. Δ is a positive or negative coefficient.

Such a system has the advantage of not superimposing a test signal on the main acting signal, and under these conditions, of rapidly converging towards the optimum, defined by the minimum of $f(x)$. In fact, the sign of the function $C(t)$ determines at each instant whether the behavior of the system is favorable or not.

The sign $\epsilon(\epsilon = \pm 1)$ is determined by the following strategy.

a) When $C(t)$ changes from a negative to a positive value, $\epsilon(t)$ changes polarity (natural switching). Then, while $C(t)$ is positive, $\epsilon(t)$ takes alternatively positive and negative values of unit amplitude with period W (forced commutations).

b) While $C(t)$ is negative, ϵ does not change.

II. AUTOSTABILITY

We shall show first of all that the system cannot diverge. If

$$F(s) = \sum_{i=0}^{n} a_i s^i \qquad \text{with } a_o = 1$$

$$\frac{dx}{dt} = \epsilon K$$

The solution $h(t)$ can be expressed as a function of the action $x(t)$ by means of the reduced variables:

$$H = \frac{h}{2K^2 a_1^2} \qquad X = \frac{x}{K a_1}$$

We get

$$H = \frac{X^2}{2} - \epsilon X + 1 - \frac{a_2}{a_1^2} + \sum_{i=0}^{n} \lambda_i e^{-\epsilon \alpha_i X} \tag{2}$$

from which:

$$H'_X = X - \epsilon - \epsilon \sum_{i=0}^{n} \lambda_i \alpha_i e^{-\epsilon \alpha_i X} \tag{3}$$

$$H''_{X^2} = 1 + \sum_{i=0}^{n} \lambda_i \alpha_i^2 e^{-\epsilon \alpha_i X} \tag{4}$$

Consider the expression

$$p_1 h'(t) + p_2 h''(t) - \Delta =$$

$$p_1 \epsilon 2K^2 a_1 H'_X + p_2 2K^2 H''_{X^2} - \Delta =$$

$$\epsilon P_1 H'_X + P_2 H''_{X^2} - \Delta$$

Putting

$$P_1 = 2K^2 a_1 p_1 \qquad P_2 = 2K^2 p_2$$

$$C = \epsilon P_1 [X - \epsilon - \epsilon \sum_{i=0}^{n} \lambda_i \alpha_i e^{-\epsilon \alpha_i X}] +$$

$$P_2 [1 + \sum_{i=0}^{n} \lambda_i \alpha_i^2 e^{-\epsilon \alpha_i X}] - \Delta \tag{5}$$

If ϵX tends to infinity $(t \to \infty)$, this expression is equivalent to

$$P_1 \epsilon X - P_1 + P_2 - \Delta$$

This expression is positive since the coefficients P_1 and P_2 are positive (a_1 is positive since $1/F(s)$ represents a stable transfer function). Where $P_1 = 0$, Δ must be limited to P_2. The most unfavorable condition possible is when the expression C remains positive whatever the switching. Under these conditions, the system is subjected to a triangular periodic waveform of period W at its input. The function $h(t)$ describes an amplitude-limited unit cycle since the system is inherently stable. The presence of a pure lag $(e^{-\tau_r s})$ does not change the foregoing.

This property of autostabilization seems to us to be fundamental for the systems studied, justifying afterwards the adopted switching criterion. It should be noticed that this property implies that the acting modes used (ramps in this case) are not chosen independently of the switching criterion.

One more important fact can be deduced from the foregoing. The study of the stability may be limited to the study of the limit cycles.

III. DYNAMIC TRAJECTORY

We have limited the study to that of a system of the first order $F(s) = \dfrac{1}{\tau s + 1}$ in series with a pure time-lag of $(e^{-\tau_r s})$ whose equivalent value, following the component X, equals $R = \tau_r/\tau$. It is convenient for the study to assume that the lag occurs in the switching device.

In this case, Eqs. (2) and (5) can be written:

$$H(X) = \frac{(\epsilon X)^2}{2} - \epsilon X + 1 + \lambda e^{-\epsilon X} \tag{6}$$

$$C(X) = \epsilon P_1 [X - \epsilon - \epsilon \lambda e^{-\epsilon X}] + P_2 [1 + \lambda e^{-\epsilon X}] - \Delta \tag{7}$$

Fig. 2 shows the network of curves $H(X)$ drawn for $\epsilon = -1$. They have the following properties:

a) They tend towards diminishing values of X if $\epsilon = -1$;
they tend towards increasing values of X if $\epsilon = +1$.

b) The initial value of H determines the value of (λ). The particular curve (λ) $(\lambda = 0)$, which is a parabola, divides the surface into two zones where the initial conditions give to λ a positive or negative value.

c) When the absolute value of X becomes very large, the curves are asymptotic to (λ).

d) Switching action (change of sign of ϵ) makes the point representing the dynamic state of the system pass from one network of curves to the other.

e) Symmetric curves correspond to opposite values of ϵ.

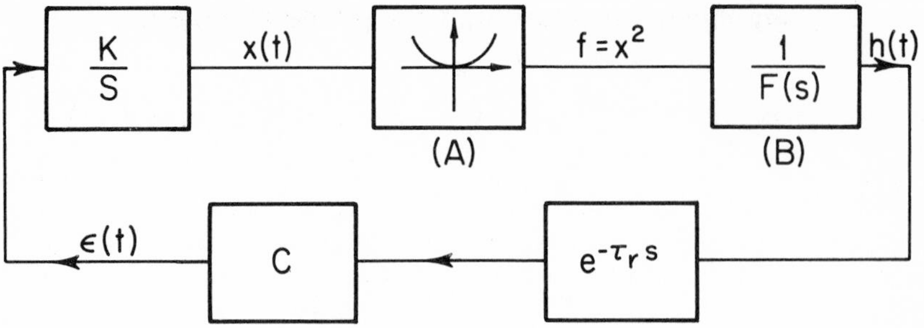
K
S
x(t)
f = x²
1
F(s)
h(t)
(A)
(B)
ε(t)
C
e^{-τ_r s}

Fig. 1

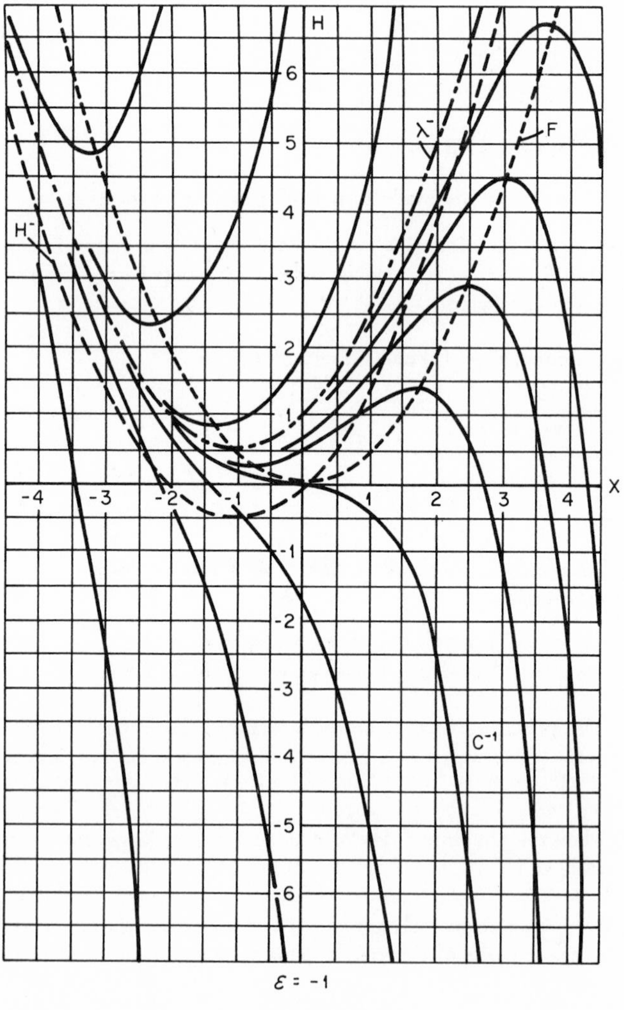
H
6
5
4
3
2
1
-1
-2
-3
-4
-5
-6
X
-4
-3
-2
-1
1
2
3
4
λ⁻
F
H⁻
C⁻¹
ε = -1

Fig. 2

IV. NATURAL SWITCHING

In the same plane $H(X)$, the points where $C(X) = 0$ can be traced. Eliminating (λ) between Eqs. (6) and (7), we get symmetrical parabolas:

$$H_c = \frac{(\epsilon X_c)^2}{2} - \epsilon X_c \frac{P_2}{P_2 - P_1} + \frac{\Delta}{P_2 - P_1} \tag{8}$$

The switching effectively takes place at an abscissa X_e such that $X_e - X_c = \epsilon R$. In fact, the function C is detected after a lag R. The effective switching points are obtained by noticing that the points on the abscissa X_e and X_c satisfy the relationships:

$$H_e = \frac{X_e^2}{2} - \epsilon X_e + 1 + \lambda e^{-\epsilon X_e} \tag{9}$$

$$\epsilon P_1 [X_c - \epsilon - \epsilon \lambda e^{-\epsilon X_c}] + P_2 [1 + \lambda e^{-\epsilon X_c}] - \Delta = 0$$

$$X_e - X_c = \epsilon R \tag{10}$$

The effective switching points then obtained are two parabolic equations:

$$H_e = \frac{(\epsilon X_e)^2}{2} - \epsilon X_e \left(1 + \frac{P_1 e^{-R}}{P_2 - P_1}\right) + 1 - \left[1 - \frac{\Delta + P_1 R}{P_2 - P_1}\right] e^{-R} \tag{11}$$

It should be noticed that for the switching:

a) the two parabolas obtained are symmetrical,

b) natural effective switching is only produced on the H_e if the condition $C = 0$ has previously been effectively realized on the considered trajectory. Otherwise, the curve H_e can be crossed without switching occurring,

c) the described switching mechanism can only be used if the forced switching period W is greater than the lag R. In fact, where there is a lag, realization of the switching condition $(C = 0)$ produces a natural switching. If this latter is not produced after an interval W $(W < R)$, a forced switching intervenes and alters the proper working of the system. Hence, the condition $W > R$ must be imposed to avoid false switching,

d) the two parabolas (H_c) divide the surface into four regions: (I), (II), (III), (IV) [Fig. 3.4]. In zone (I), C is negative and no switching can occur: any movement in this zone must necessarily cut a switching parabola. In zone (II), C is positive. Hence, periodic forced switching occurs. Such behavior must always lead finally to crossing a switching parabola. Under these conditions, the final regime must always be established, at least partially in zones (III) and (IV) in the form of limit cycles which will be studied below. These zones are dispersed differently according to the value of the ratio P_2/P_1. When Δ is positive, Figs. 3, 4, 5 and 6 show how the switching parabola H_c is disposed with the direction for which switching is produced.

V. TIME-LAG COMPENSATION

Eq. (11) suggests the possibility of a negative switching threshold compensating for a lag. If the relationships of Eq. (12) are produced, the effective switching curve (H_e) becomes the same as the curve (H_c) for switching with neither threshold nor lag ($\Delta = R = 0$).

$$P_1 = 0 \qquad 1 - \left(1 - \frac{\Delta}{P_2}\right) e^{-R} = 0 \tag{12}$$

This point favors a switching criterion which only brings in the second derivative. That the condition $W > R$ must still be fulfilled, however, does not make the possibility any the less remarkable.

VI. FREE OSCILLATIONS

It is convenient to study these oscillations in the $H(X)$ plane. They are represented by a closed limit cycle, formed from two branches of curves which belong to the networks of curves and have the following properties:

a) They necessarily comprise increasing and decreasing parts; hence they cut at least twice the points where $H_X' = 0$; i.e., the parabola $H = X^2/2$.

b) If C is negative at one point of a limit cycle, the next switching is natural.

c) If C is positive at one point, the next switching is forced unless the curve H_c has previously been crossed, in which case, it is natural.

In these conditions, three main types of limit cycles are produced:

a) NF type cycles where forced and natural switching alternate

b) NN type cycles where all switching is natural

c) FF type cycles where all switching is forced. These three types will be considered successively. (Figs. 7, 8, 9, 10, 11, 12).

VII. NF CYCLES

Calling X_M and X_m the abscissa of the end of the cycle, λ_0 and λ_1 the values of (λ) corresponding to the two trajectories which comprise the limit cycle, the following relationships are obtained:

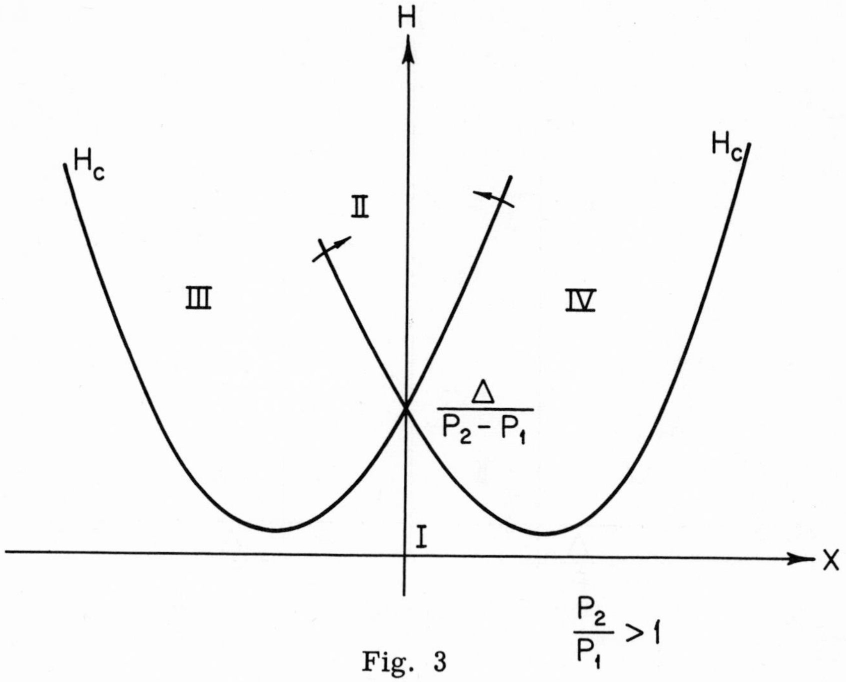
H
H_c
H_c
II
III
IV
$\frac{\Delta}{P_2 - P_1}$
I
X
$\frac{P_2}{P_1} > 1$

Fig. 3

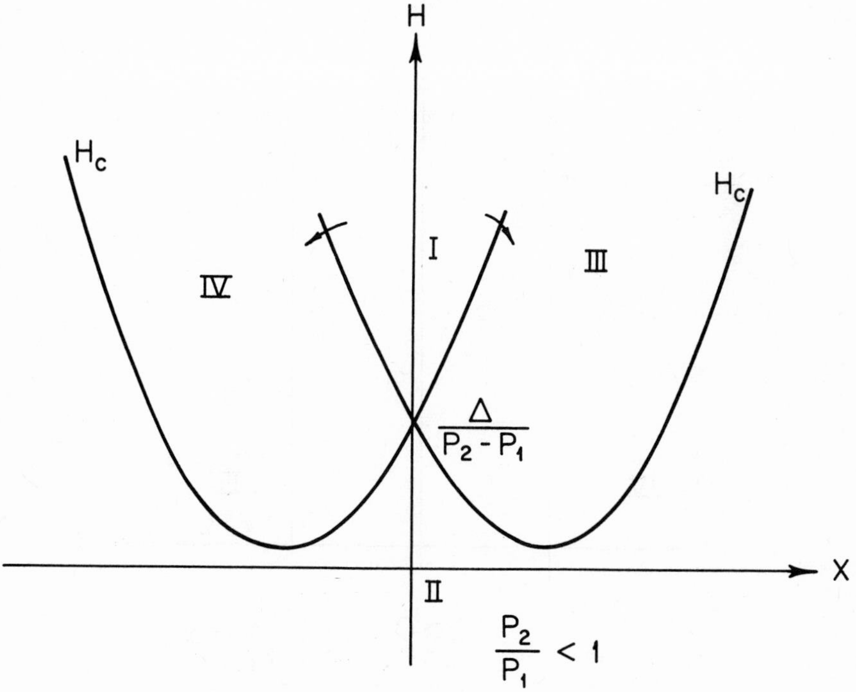
H
H_c
H_c
I
IV
III
$\frac{\Delta}{P_2 - P_1}$
X
II
$\frac{P_2}{P_1} < 1$

Fig. 4

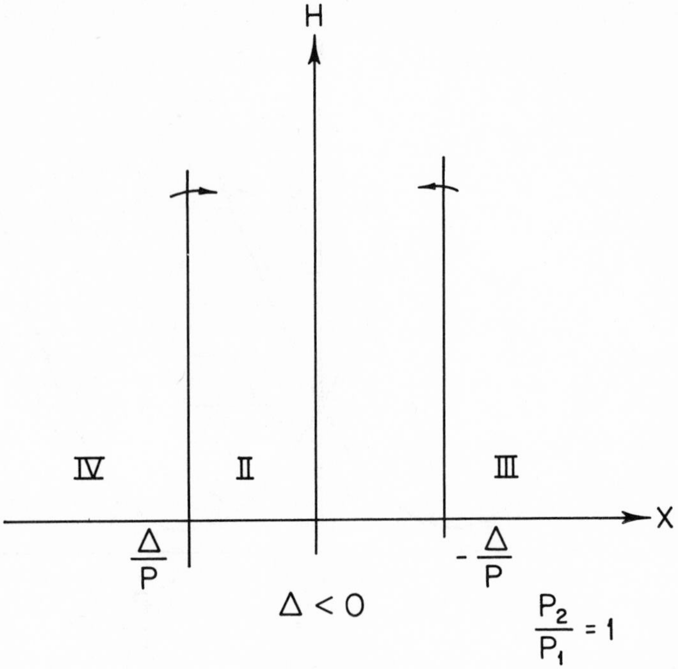

Fig. 5

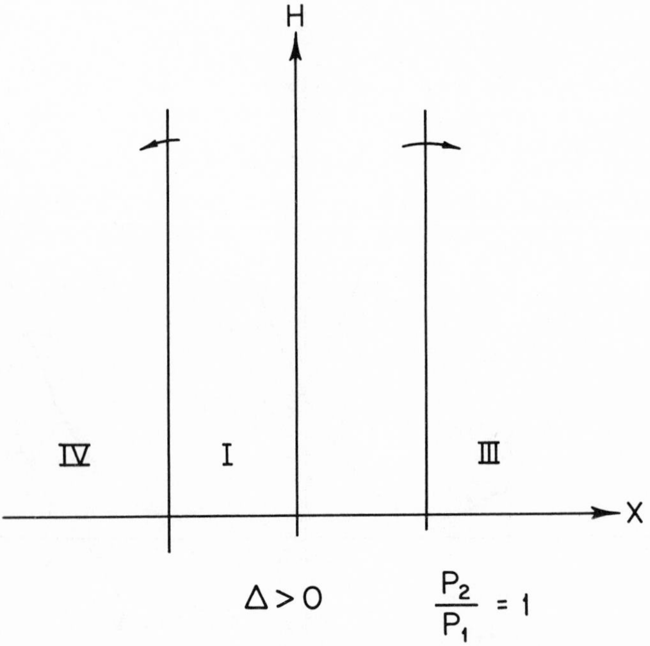

Fig. 6

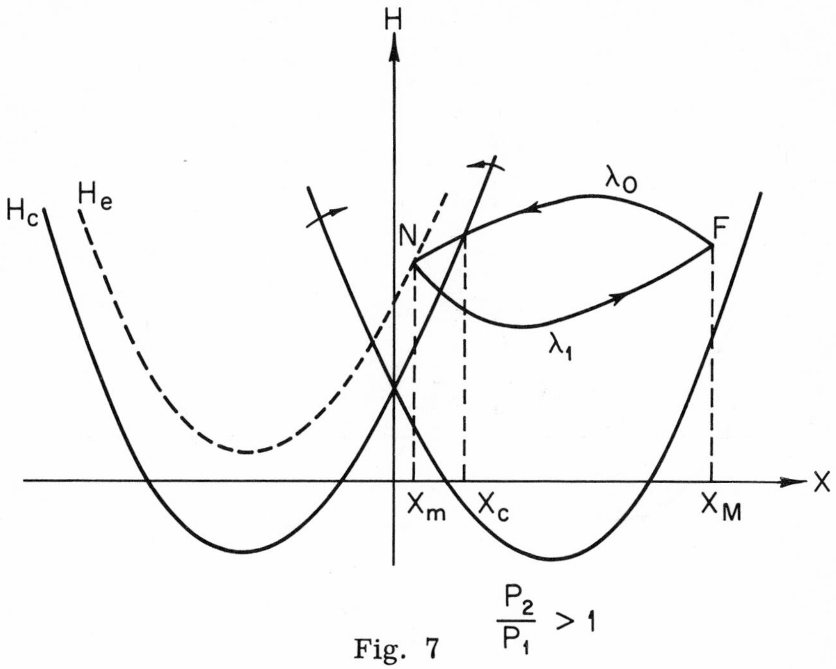
H
H_c
H_e
N
λ_0
F
λ_1
X
X_m
X_c
X_M
$\frac{P_2}{P_1} > 1$

Fig. 7

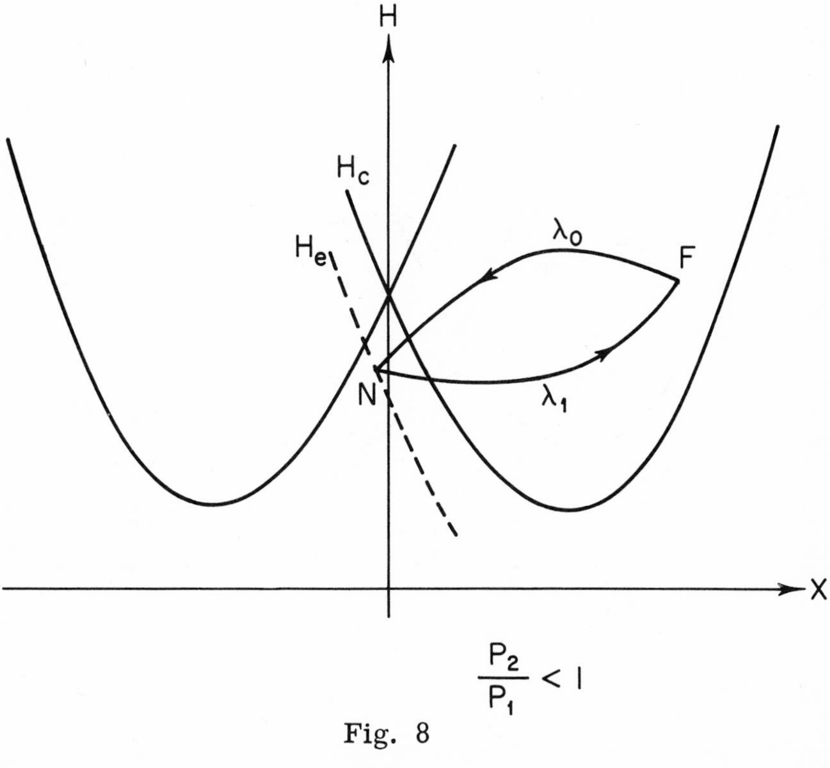
H
H_c
H_e
λ_0
F
N
λ_1
X
$\frac{P_2}{P_1} < 1$

Fig. 8

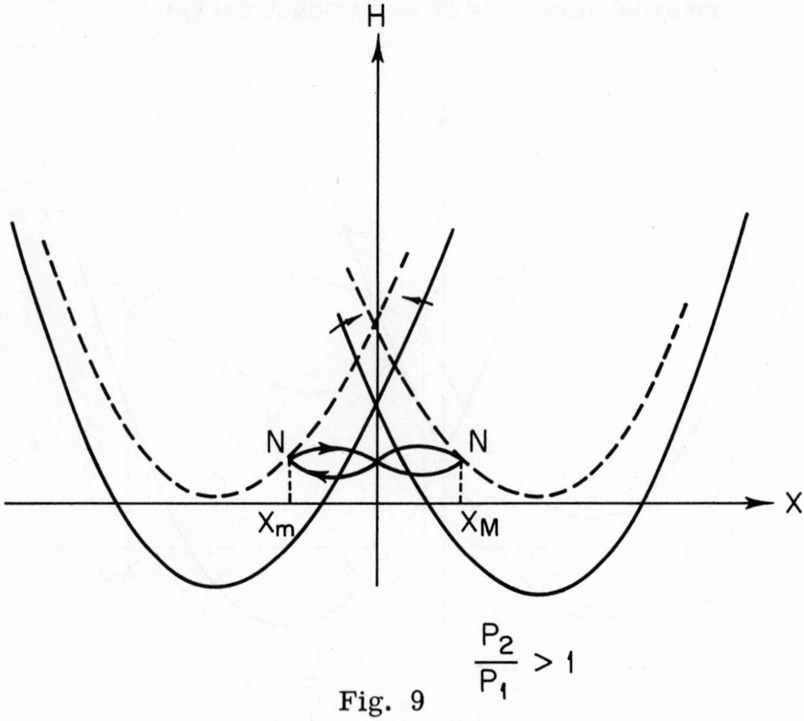

Fig. 9

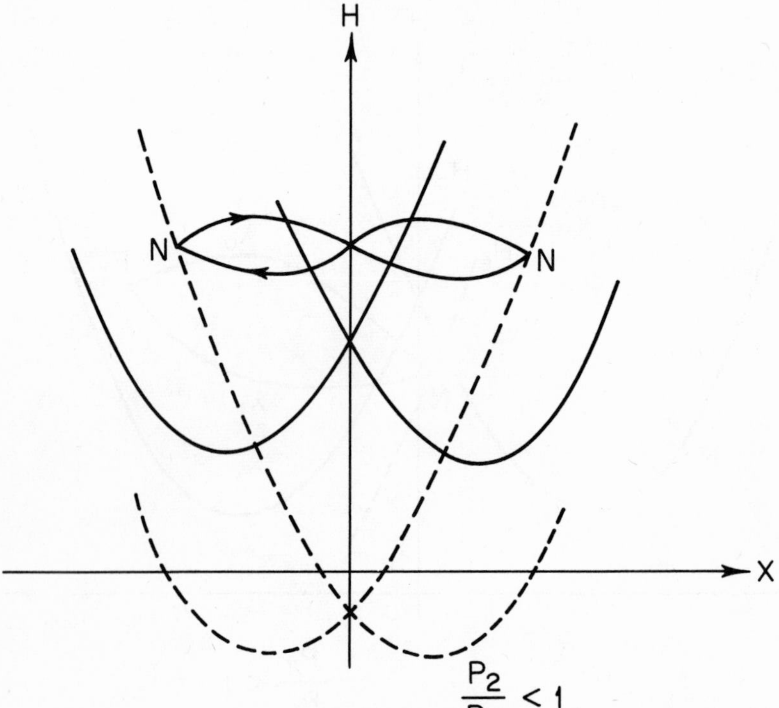

Fig. 10

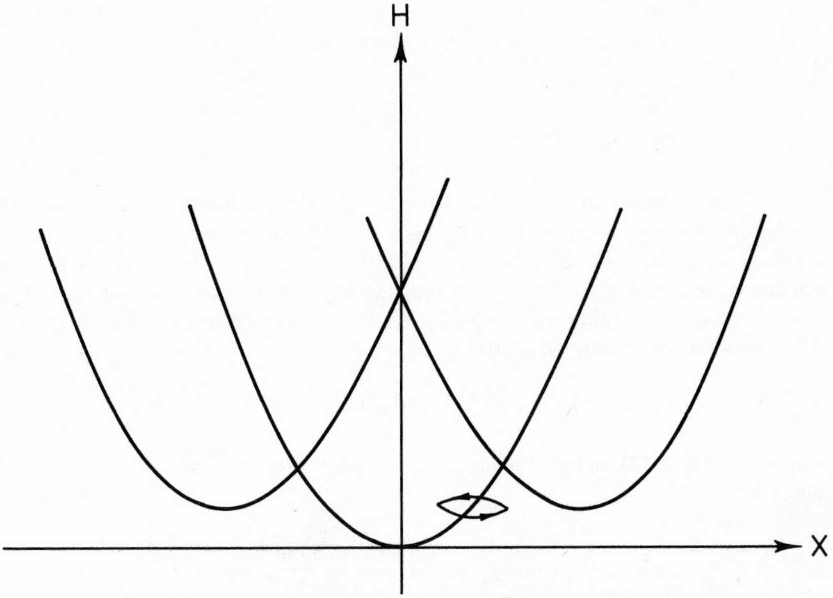

Fig. 11 $\frac{P_2}{P_1} < 1$

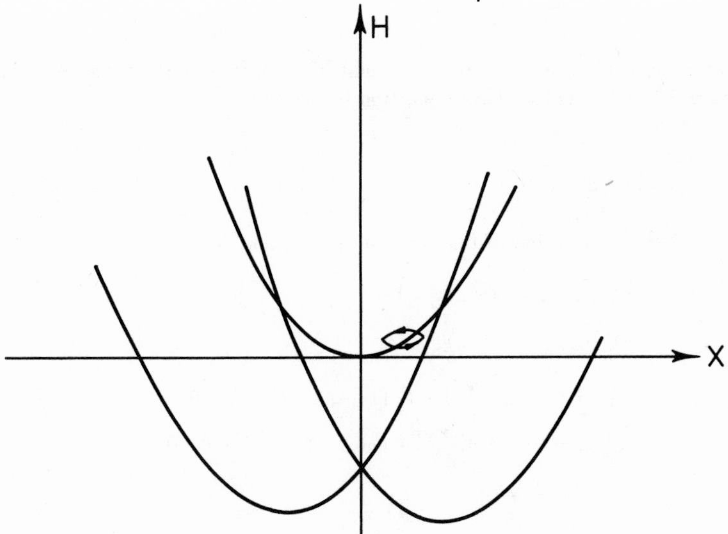

Fig. 12 $\frac{P_2}{P_1} > 1$

$$
\begin{aligned}
&2X_m = \lambda_1 e^{-X_m} - \lambda e^{X_m} \\
&2X_M = \lambda_1 e^{-X_M} - \lambda_0 e^{X_M} \\
&-P_1[X_c + 1 + \lambda_0 e^{+X_c}] + P_2[1 + \lambda_0 e^{X_c}] - \Delta = 0 \\
&X_c - X_m = R \\
&X_M - X_m = W
\end{aligned}
\tag{13}
$$

In the study of NF cycles, we are especially interested in searching for the condition for non-existence of the cycles; in fact, since these cycles are not symmetrical about the vertical axis, we would like to eliminate them. The sufficient condition for this is that the point N reaches at least the parabola, since at this point a natural switching will be produced; the final limit cycle will then be type NN. This condition may be written:

$$
P_1[X_m - 1 - \lambda_1 e^{-X_m}] + P_2[1 + \lambda_1 e^{-X_m}] - \Delta = 0 \tag{14}
$$

Resolving Eqs. (13) and (14) produces a condition (for the given values of P_1, P_2 and R):

$$
\frac{e^{W} - e^{-W} - 2(a-1)(e^{-W} - 1)e^{R}}{-(e^{W} - e^{-W}) - 2(a-1)(1 - e^{W})} = \frac{(R+1-a+\delta)(e^{W} - e^{-W}) + 2We^{R}(a-1)}{(1-a+\delta)(e^{W} - e^{-W}) + 2W(a-1)}
$$

$$
\text{with } a = \frac{P_2}{P_1} \qquad \delta = \frac{\Delta}{P_1} \tag{15}
$$

This relation implies a condition that must be satisfied by the a and δ variables for getting a NN limit cycle. This condition is quadratic.

VIII. NN CYCLES

With the notation of the previous paragraph, we get:

$$
\begin{aligned}
&2X_m = \lambda_1 e^{-X_m} - \lambda_0 e^{X_m} \\
&2X_M = \lambda_1 e^{-X_M} - \lambda_0 e^{X_M} \\
&-P_1[X + 1 + \lambda_0 e^{X_0}] + P_2[1 + \lambda_0 e^{X_0}] - \Delta = 0 \\
&P_1[X_1 - 1 - \lambda_1 e^{-X_1}] + P_2[1 + \lambda_1 e^{-X_1}] - \Delta = 0 \\
&X_0 - X_m = R \\
&X_M - X_1 = R
\end{aligned}
\tag{16}
$$

Forming the expression $X_M - X_m$, it can be shown that Eq. (16) has only one solution. The expression for $X_M + X_m$ shows that this solution is such that $X_M = -X_m$.

This result is important since it shows that if the limit cycle is formed from natural switching, it is symmetrical. The amplitude $X_M - X_m$ of the limit cycle is then given by the solution of the equation:

$$2(X_M - X_m)\,e^{R} = 2\,\frac{\Delta + RP_1}{P_2 - P_1} - 1 - \frac{P_1}{P_2 - P_1}\,(X_M - X_m)(1 - e^{X_M - X_m}) \qquad (17)$$

Eq. (17) can be written:

$$2(X_M - X_m)\,e^{R} = \left[\,2\left(\frac{\delta + R}{a-1} - 1\right) - \frac{1}{a-1}\,(X_M - X_m)\right](1 - e^{X_M - X_m}) \qquad (18)$$

For given values of R and $X_M - X_m$, this relation is linear with a and δ.

With the relations, Eqs. (15) and (18), we can get abaci that show the range of permitted values for δ and a, for given values of $X_M - X_m$ and R.

The results are presented on charts (Figs. 13, 14, 15). Each chart is related to a fixed value of R. The linear relation between a and δ (Eq. (18) is presented for different values of the amplitude $(X_M - X_m)$. The limit value of $X_M - X_m$ is equal to R. In these charts the dotted lines do not correspond to experimental cycles. The relation (Eq. (15)) gives also a limitation to the possible values of a and δ. It is shown for different values of W. These curves are hyperbolic. For the smallest value of W equal to R, the curve is reduced to a straight line; it is possible to show that this line is the same as the line corresponding to $X_M - X_m = R$.

These charts indicate the possibility of determining the values a, δ, W for a given system, and show some general properties of the *NN* cycles:

- When the delay R increases, the amplitude $X_M - X_m$ increases proportionally.
- When δ decreases, the amplitude $X_M - X_m$ decreases. So it is possible to compensate at least partially the effect of the delay. This is a specially interesting property.
- When a increases, the amplitude $X_M - X_m$ decreases.

These properties justify the choice of a infinite that has been made for a practical application. In this special case we use only the second time-derivative of H for the switching rule. Fig. 16 gives the amplitude of the cycles versus the delay R for a given a. It shows that for a delay R, a minimum value δ obtained on the line $X_M - X_m = R$ is necessary for getting *NN* cycles. Fig. 17 shows that for a fixed Δ, W must be included between two extreme values for getting *(NN)* cycles, whatever be the initial conditions for the cycle.

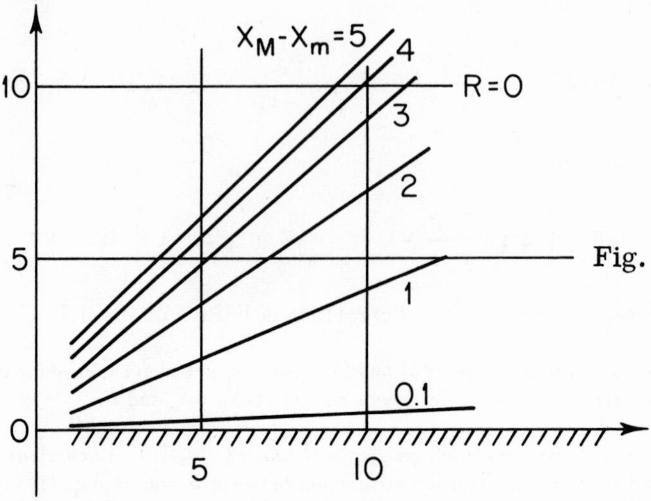
δ
$X_M - X_m = 5$
4
3
2
1
0.1
R=0
10
5
0
5
10
α

Fig. 13

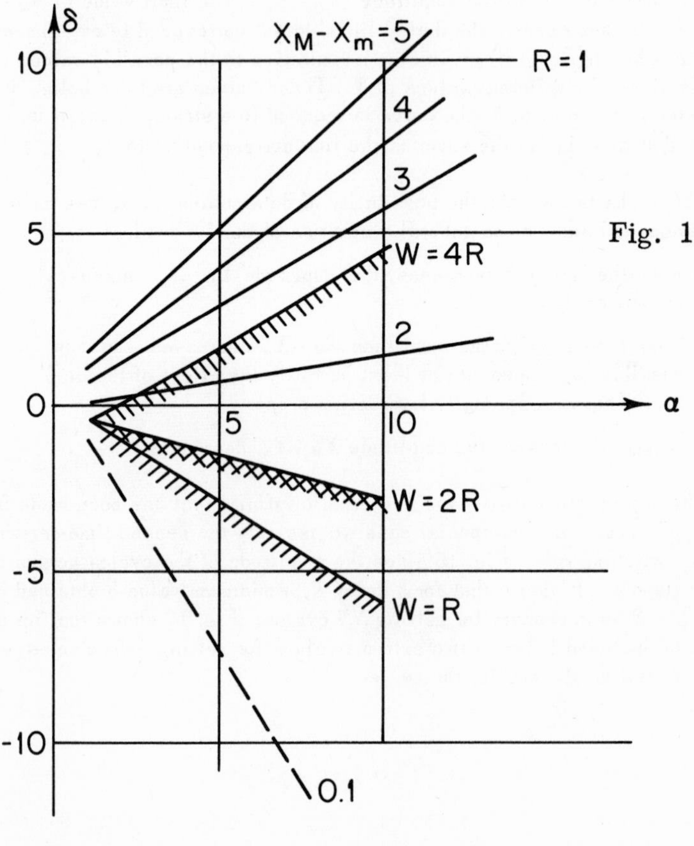
δ
$X_M - X_m = 5$
R = 1
4
3
W = 4R
2
W = 2R
W = R
0.1
10
5
0
-5
-10
5
10
α

Fig. 14

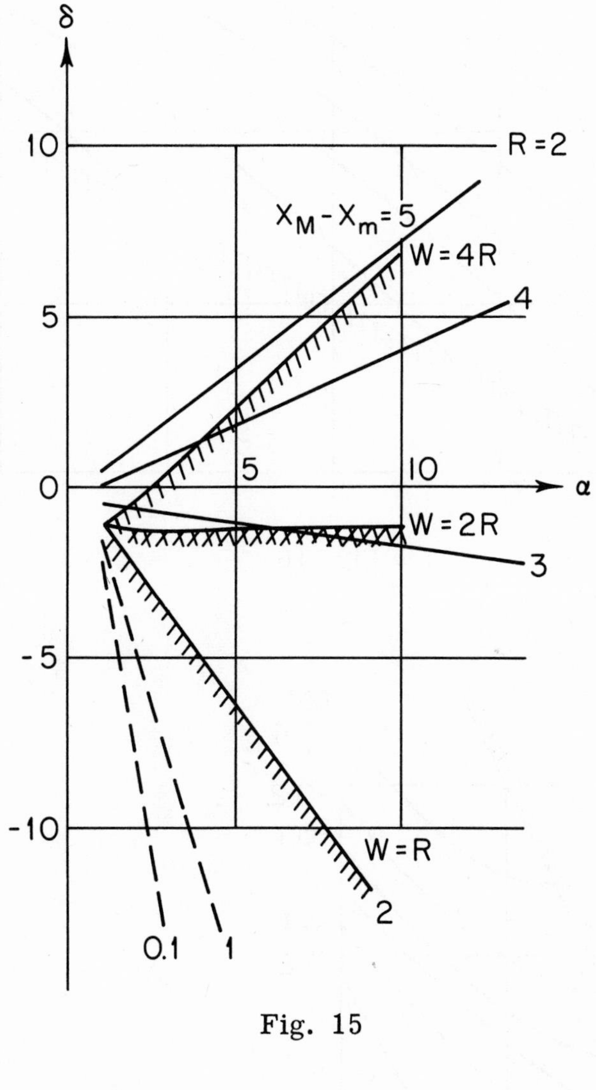

Fig. 15

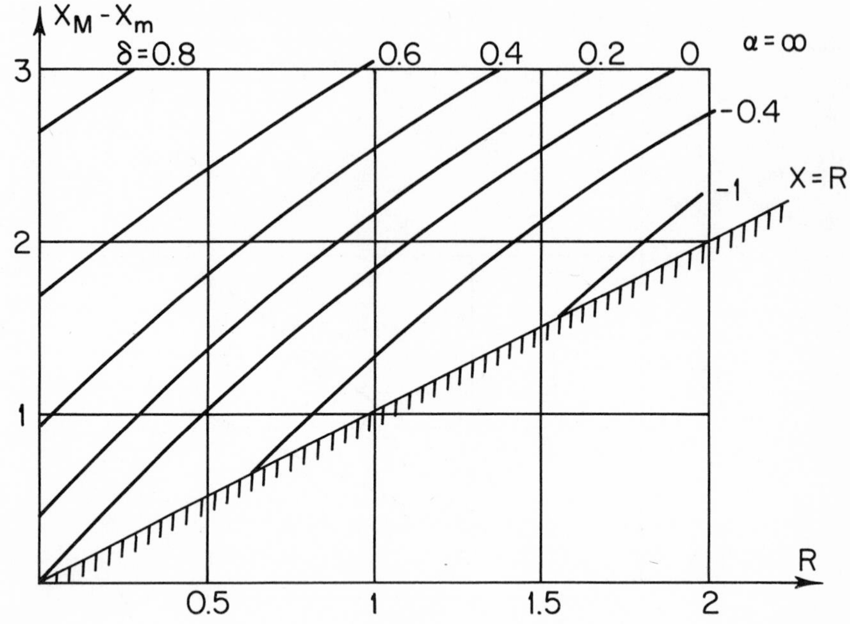
$X_M - X_m$
δ=0.8
0.6
0.4
0.2
0
α = ∞
-0.4
-1
X = R
3
2
1
R
0.5
1
1.5
2

Fig. 16

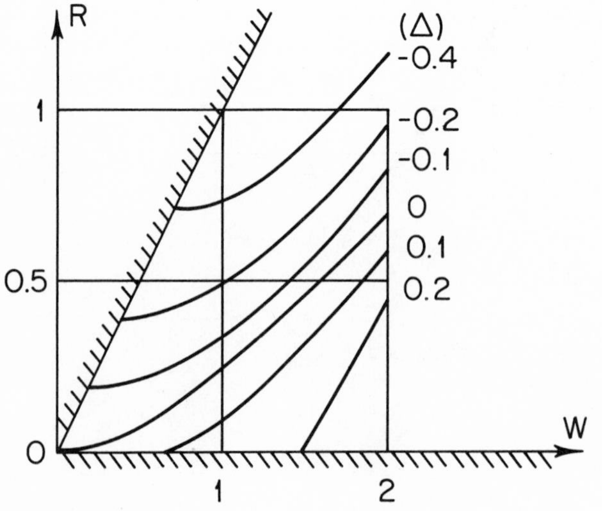
R
(Δ)
-0.4
-0.2
-0.1
0
0.1
0.2
1
0.5
0
W
1
2

Fig. 17

IX. FF CYCLES

When the parabola $H = X^2/2$ crosses zone (II), there is the possibility of production of FF cycles, i.e., forced switching only. They are produced if the threshold Δ is positive when $P_2/P_1 > 1$ or negative when $P_2/P_1 < 1$, and are given by the relationships:

$$
\begin{aligned}
2X_m &= \lambda_1 e^{-X_m} - \lambda e^{X_m} \\
2X_M &= \lambda_1 e^{-X_M} - \lambda_0 e^{X_M} \\
X_M - X_m &= W
\end{aligned}
\tag{19}
$$

This system has an infinite number of solutions, but only those for which

$$H(X_M) < \frac{X_M^2}{2} \qquad H(X_m) > \frac{X_m^2}{2}$$

are valid.

In practice, these oscillations are not stable. Any perturbation modifying their position, especially a dissymmetry in the period W, causes them to increase. They are thus not a great nuisance and, if they appear, they quickly disappear.

X. FORCED OSCILLATIONS

This study has only just been started. A periodic disturbing signal can be considered to be superimposed on the input $x(t)$. The study is simplified by supposing that this disturbing signal is a rectangular wave (Fig. 18). The corresponding trajectory $H(x)$ has a horizontal part AB which represents the edges of the rectangular wave, the length AB corresponding to the amplitude. The period T of the disturbance is indicated in the case where the system synchronizes to the disturbance when the switching parabola should cut the curve between A and B. If the parabola cuts the curve out of AB, a free oscillation is produced when the perturbation is superimposed on the free oscillation to produce a more complex cycle (Fig. 19).

The study of this interesting case involves a search for the possible existence of such cycles.

XI. CONCLUSIONS

An experimental computer has been built and tested. The switching rule uses the second derivative of the measured cost function. A more sophisticated strategy has been implemented in the computer. By using the symmetric property of the cycles with natural switching, it has been possible to fix periodically the system at its optimum. This on-line computer has a very simple hybrid structure, mixing

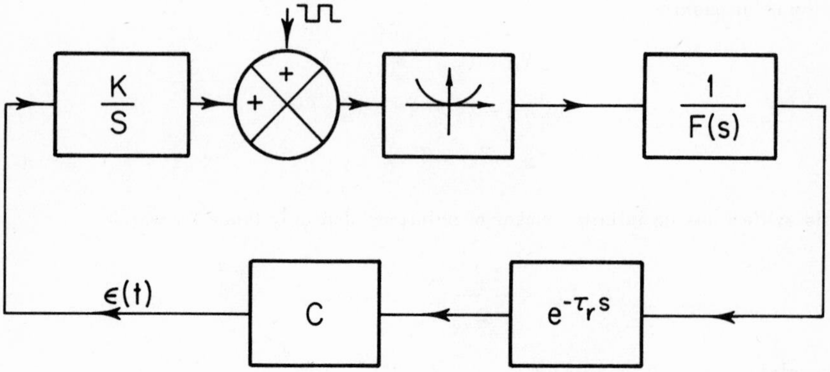

Fig. 18

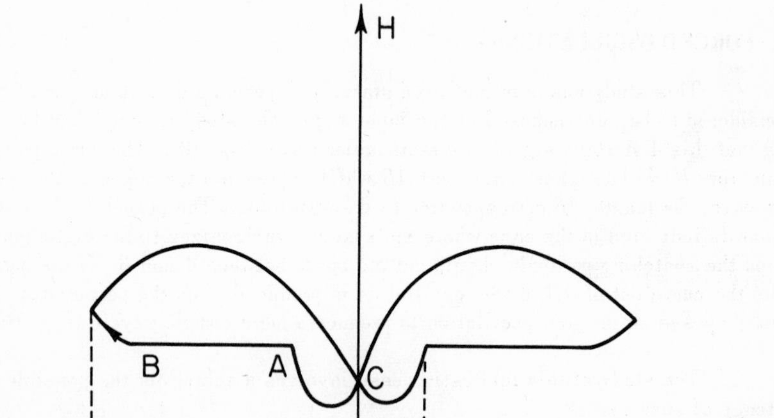

Fig. 19

analog apparatus and sequential switching circuitry. Experimental results have been given in a paper of the last I.F.A.C. Conference in Basel.[1]

ACKNOWLEDGMENTS

The support of the French Company Thomson – Houston is gratefully acknowledged.

[1] I.F.A.C. 1963: "Principle and Application of an Extremal Computer", *R. Perret and R. Rouxel*

THE APPLICATION OF HYBRID COMPUTERS TO THE ITERATIVE SOLUTION OF OPTIMAL CONTROL PROBLEMS

Elmer G. Gilbert
The University of Michigan
Instrumentation Engineering Program
Ann Arbor, Michigan

1. Introduction

In the past few years a number of iterative procedures have been developed for the solution of optimal control problems. Generally these procedures require repeated evaluation of rather complex integrals, leading to lengthy runs when digital computers are employed. This is not only expensive, but precludes the application of the iterative procedures to on-line control. High-speed analog computers are capable of much faster integration but are not adapted to the algebraic computations and decision making tasks which occur at each iteration. Thus it is appropriate to consider the utility of hybrid computers, which employ both digital and analog devices.

This paper explores certain programming aspects of hybrid computation as they pertain to the iterative solution of time optimal control problems. After reviewing the iterative procedures due to Eaton (1) and Neustadt (5, 6) related procedures are derived which are better suited to hybrid computation. Then the programming of these procedures is described, along with a brief discussion of the characteristics of hybrid computers. Finally, some computer results are presented.

Much of the material in sections 4. and 5. follows closely part of an earlier paper by the author (3).

2. Iterative Solution of the Time-Optimal Control Problem

It is assumed that the physical system to be controlled (hereafter called the plant) satisfies the following system of first order differential equations:

$$\dot{x}_i = \sum_{j=1}^{n} a_{ij}(t)x_j(t) + a_i(t) + b_i(t)u(t), \quad x_i(0) = x_{io}, \quad i=1, 2, \ldots n. \quad (1)$$

These equations are written more compactly in vector matrix notation as

$$\dot{x} = A(t)x + a(t) + b(t)u(t), \quad x(0) = x_0 \quad , \tag{2}$$

where x, a(t), and b(t) are n vectors and A(t) is an n x n matrix. It is assumed that a(t), A(t), and b(t) are continuous and that the initial state x_0 is prescribed. For simplicity the control u is taken to be a scalar, and must be admissible in the sense that it is piecewise continuous and

$$|u(t)| \leq 1 \ . \tag{3}$$

The time-optimal control problem is stated as follows: Given the plant Eq. (2) with initial state $x(0) = x_0$ and a desired terminal state or target function r(t) which is continuous, find an admissible control which makes x(t) = r(t) in the smallest possible t. If such an optimal control exists it will be called u*(t). The minimum time and optimal motion associated with u*(t) will be denoted by t* and x*(t), i.e., x*(t*) = r(t*). In what follows it is assumed that u*(t) exists.

One way to approach the theory of the time-optimal control problem is to consider the solution of a related problem. This problem is obtained by writing the solution of Eq. (2) as

$$x(t) = X(t)[\, x_0 + \int_0^t X^{-1}(\sigma)a(\sigma)d\sigma + \int_0^t X^{-1}(\sigma)b(\sigma)u(\sigma)d\sigma] \quad , \tag{4}$$

where X(t) is the matrix solution of $\dot{X} = A(t)X$, $X(0) = I$. Setting x(t) = r(t) and rearranging Eq. (4) gives

$$s(t) = -\int_0^t X^{-1}(\sigma)b(\sigma)u(\sigma)d\sigma \quad , \tag{5}$$

where

$$s(t) = x_0 - X^{-1}(t)r(t) + \int_0^t X^{-1}(\sigma)a(\sigma)d\sigma \ . \tag{6}$$

Thus the problem is to seek an admissible control such that Eq. (5) is satisfied in the smallest possible t.

Eq. (5) can be satisfied with an admissible control if s(t) is in the set

$$C(t) = \{-\int_0^t X^{-1}(\sigma)b(\sigma)u(\sigma)d\sigma \,|\, u \text{ admissible}\} \ . \tag{7}$$

Thus this set plays an important role in the solution of the optimal control problem (4). In particular, the properties of

$C(t)$ imply that $s(t^*)$ is in the boundary of $C(t^*)$. Further, it is known that the boundary points of $C(t)$ are obtained by using (bang-bang) controls of the form

$$u(t, \eta) = - \operatorname{sgn} v(t, \eta) \quad , \tag{8}$$

where $v(t, \eta)$ is given by the vector inner product

$$v(t, \eta) = (b(t), \xi(t, \eta)) \tag{9}$$

with

$$\xi(t, \eta) = (X^{-1}(t))' \eta \tag{10}$$

(the ' denotes the transpose of the matrix). Thus $u^*(t)$ must have the form $u(t, \eta)$ for some $\eta = \eta^*$. In order to guarantee that $u(t, \eta)$ is defined for almost all t it is assumed that the system (2) is normal (4), i.e., $v(t, \eta)$, all $\eta \neq 0$, is zero only at isolated values of t. By differentiating $\xi(t, \eta)$ with respect to t it can be seen that it is the solution of the adjoint differential equation

$$\dot{\xi} = -A'(t)\xi \quad , \quad \xi(0, \eta) = \eta \quad . \tag{11}$$

Thus it is not necessary to compute the fundamental matrix $X(t)$ in order to determine $u(t, \eta)$.

From what has been said it is clear that a necessary condition for an optimal control is that it has the form $u(t, \eta)$ for some $\eta = \eta^*$ (this is also a consequence of the Pontryagin maximum principle (8)). In the case of the special problem ($a(t) = r(t) = 0$) this also is a sufficient condition; specifically, if $\eta = \bar{\eta}$ is such that $x(t, \eta)$, the motion of the plant (2) with $u = u(t, \eta)$, is zero for some time $t = \bar{t}$, then $\bar{t} = t^*$ and $\bar{\eta} = \eta^*$ giving $x(t, \bar{\eta}) = x^*(t)$ and $u(t, \bar{\eta}) = u^*(t)$. For the general problem no such condition exists and it is more difficult to determine $u^*(t)$.

Even in the case of the special problem, the theory described above does not give an orderly procedure for determining η^*. Trial-and-error methods generally prove unsatisfactory, even for second order systems. By utilizing more fully the properties of $C(t)$, Neustadt (5, 6) has derived an iterative procedure for computing η^*, and consequently $u^*(t) = u(t, \eta^*)$. Recently, Eaton (1) has extended this procedure to the general problem. Similar procedures can also be derived for optimal control problems other than the time-optimal problem (6).

The iterative procedure for the general problem will now be described. Let

$$z(t, \eta) = -\int_0^t X^{-1}(\sigma)b(\sigma)u(\sigma, \eta)d\sigma \quad . \tag{12}$$

A sequence of vectors $\{\eta_0, \eta_1, \ldots\}$ converging to η^* is obtained as follows. Select η_0 such that $(\eta_0, s(0)) > 0$. Compute

$$\eta_{j+1} = \eta_j + k_j [s(t) - z(t, \eta_j)] \Big|_{t=T(\eta_j)} \quad , \quad k_j > 0 \quad , \tag{13}$$

where $T(\eta_j)$ is the first zero of

$$f(t, \eta_j) = (s(t) - z(t, \eta_j), \eta_j) \tag{14}$$

for $t > T(\eta_{j-1})$ (define $T(\eta_{-1}) = 0$). The scalar k_{j-1} must be sufficiently small so that $f(T(\eta_{j-1}), \eta_j) > 0$ (the inequality holds for $j=0$). If $\eta_{j-1} \neq \eta^*$, such a choice for k_{j-1} is always possible (1). If $\eta_j = \eta^*$ it is obvious from $s(t^*) = z(t^*, \eta^*)$ and Eq. (14) that $T(\eta_j) = t^*$ and $\eta_{j+1} = \eta_j$. For $\eta_j \neq \eta^*$ it is always true (1) that $t^* > T(\eta_j) > T(\eta_{j-1})$ and $s(T(\eta_j)) \neq z(T(\eta_j), \eta_j)$. If $\|\dot{r}(t)\|$ is bounded on $(0, t^*)$, Eaton also shows that it is possible to select the k_j so that $\lim_{j \to \infty} T(\eta_j) = t^*$ and $\lim_{j \to \infty} [s(T(\eta_j)) - z(T(\eta_j), \eta_j)] = 0$. Thus $\lim_{j \to \infty} \eta_j = \eta^*$.

Computer implementation of the above steps is complicated by the involved expressions for $z(t, \eta)$ and $s(t)$. Not only do these expressions require the computation of the n x n matrix $X^{-1}(t)$, but they must be completely re-evaluated every time an initial time different from $t = 0$ is prescribed. The modified formulation of the iterative procedure which follows avoids these difficulties and has other advantages.

3. Modified Formulation of the Iterative Procedure

Consider first the determination of $f(t, \eta)$. Define

$$d(t, \eta) = X(t)[s(t) - z(t, \eta)] \quad . \tag{15}$$

From Eqs. (4), (6), and (12) it can be seen that

$$d(t, \eta) = x(t, \eta) - r(t) \tag{16}$$

and therefore represents the difference between the plant

state and the target function $r(t)$ when the plant input is $u(t, \eta)$. Using Eq. (15) in Eq. (14) gives

$$f(t, \eta) = (X^{-1}(t)d(t, \eta), \eta) = (d(t, \eta), (X^{-1}(t))'\eta) = (d(t, \eta), \xi(t, \eta)), \quad (17)$$

where as before $\xi(t, \eta)$ is the solution of the adjoint differential Eq. (11).

Since $f(t, \eta)$ permits the computation of $T(\eta_j)$, $d(T(\eta_j), \eta_j)$ is readily obtained. But to evaluate the difference Eq. (13) for η_{j+1} requires

$$\gamma(\eta_j) = s(T(\eta_j)) - z(T(\eta_j), \eta_j) = X^{-1}(T(\eta_j))d(T(\eta_j), \eta_j) \quad . \quad (18)$$

It is possible to obtain the multiplication of the vector d by $X^{-1}(T)$ without first computing $X^{-1}(T)$. Note that the solution of the equation

$$\dot{w} = A(t)w \quad (19)$$

has the form $w(T) = X(T)w(0)$. Since $w(0) = X^{-1}(T)w(T)$, $\gamma(\eta_j)$ may be found by taking $w(T) = d(T(\eta_j), \eta_j)$ and solving Eq. (19) backwards in time from $t = T(\eta_j)$ to $t = 0$, i.e., $w(0) = \gamma(\eta_j)$.

By combining the above results with those of the previous section, the modified formulation of the iterative procedure is obtained. It entails the following steps:

1) Select k_0 and η_0 such that $k_0 > 0$ and $(\eta_0, x_0 - r(0)) > 0$. Define $T(\eta_{-1}) = 0$.
2) Assume for the calculation of η_{j+1} that η_j and $T(\eta_{j-1})$ are known.
3) Solve the adjoint differential Eq. (11) with $\eta = \eta_j$ and generate $u(t, \eta_j)$ from $\xi(t, \eta_j)$ by Eqs. (8) and (9).

   Simultaneously solve the plant Eq. (2) with $u = u(t, \eta_j)$, obtain $x(t, \eta_j)$, and compute $f(t, \eta_j)$ from Eq. (17).
4) Determine $f(T(\eta_{j-1}), \eta_j)$. If it is negative (k_{j-1} is too large), choose a k_j such that $0 < k_j < k_{j-1}$, set $\eta_j = \eta_{j-1}(\gamma(\eta_j) = \gamma(\eta_{j-1})$ and $T(\eta_j) = T(\eta_{j-1}))$, compute

$$\eta_{j+1} = \eta_j + k_j \gamma(\eta_j) \quad , \quad (20)$$

   return to step 2) with j replaced by j + 1. If

$f(T(\eta_{j-1}), \eta_j)$ is positive, find the first zero of $f(t, \eta_j)$ for $t > T(\eta_{j-1})$. This is $T(\eta_j)$.

5) Stop the solution of the plant Eq. (2) at $t = T(\eta_j)$. The terminal error at the jth iteration is $d(T(\eta_j), \eta_j) = x(T(\eta_j), \eta_j) - r(T(\eta_j))$. If it is not sufficiently small, set $w(T(\eta_j)) = d(T(\eta_j), \eta_j)$ and solve Eq. (19) backwards from $t = T(\eta_j)$ to $t = 0$ and obtain $\gamma(\eta_j) = w(0)$.

6) Select a $k_j > 0$ (a good choice is $k_j = k_{j-1}$) and compute η_{j+1} from Eq. (20). Return to step 2) with j replaced by j + 1.

For the special problem ($a(t) = r(t) = 0$) some simplification of the above procedure is possible. Since $a(t) = r(t) = 0$, $d(T(\eta_j), \eta_j) = w(T(\eta_j))$. Furthermore, Eq. (19) is identical to the plant Eq. (2) if u is set equal to zero. Thus in step 5) it is not necessary to solve Eq. (19), setting $u = 0$ and reversing time in the plant equations will do the same. An alternative procedure for computing $f(t, \eta)$ is also available. Since $s(t) = x_0$ Eqs. (14), (12), (10), (9), and (8) give

$$\begin{aligned} f(t, \eta) &= (\eta, x_0) + \int_0^t (\eta, X^{-1}(\sigma) b(\sigma) u(\sigma, \eta)) d\sigma \\ &= (\eta, x_0) + \int_0^t (\xi(\sigma, \eta), b(\sigma) u(\sigma, \eta)) d\sigma \\ &= (\eta, x_0) - \int_0^t |v(\sigma, \eta)| d\sigma . \end{aligned} \tag{21}$$

In practice this may be an easier expression to mechanize than (17) which involves n products of functions of t.

Before going on to the programming of the above procedure, the basic elements of the hybrid computer will be considered briefly.

4. The Hybrid Computer

The hybrid computer employs both analog and digital computing elements, which may conveniently be organized into three categories: analog, analog-digital, and digital, according to the class of signals with which they deal. Figure 1 gives symbols for the basic computer elements which will be required for the programming of the iterative procedure. To make signal designations clear, light-weight lines and lower-case letters are used for analog signals and heavyweight lines and upper-case letters are used for logic signals. $\bar{A}$ denotes the complement of A. Elements (a) - (e) are analog-digital and elements (f)-(j) are digital. Conventional analog elements are not shown.

Integrator (a). Each integrator is separately controlled through its operate (O) and hold (H) inputs.

$A = 0$: $e_0 = -e$, initial condition mode, B has no effect

$A = 1,\ B = 0$: $e_0 = -(RC)^{-1} \int_0^t e_1 \, d\sigma - e$, operate mode

$A = 1,\ B = 1$: e_0 = constant, hold mode

Switch (b) single throw, (c) double throw.

$A = 0$: $i = e_2$, $e_0 = -e_2$ (for (b), $e_2 = 0$)

$A = 1$: $i = e_1$, $e_0 = -e_1$

Comparitor (d).

$e_1 + e_2 > \epsilon$: $A = 1$

$e_1 + e_2 < \epsilon$: $A = 0$

When $|e_1 + e_2| < \epsilon$, $A = 0$ or 1 depending on the past history of $e_1 + e_2$: A has the value it last had when $|e_1 + e_2| > \epsilon$. This hysteresis dead zone of $\pm\,\epsilon$, which is small, assures uniformly fast and reliable transition of the comparitor output. $B = 1$ locks the comparitor output A at the level present when $B = 0 \rightarrow 1$ (the notation $B = 0 \rightarrow 1$ is used to indicate the transition of B from logic 0 to logic 1).

Analog Memory or Track-Transfer (e).

$B = 0$: $e_0 = e$, initial condition mode, A has no effect

$B = 1$, $A = 0 \rightarrow 1$: take $e_1 + e_2$ and transfer to e_0, hold e_0 constant until next $A = 0 \rightarrow 1$.

This memory element combines in a single unit the function of two track-hold memory units connected in cascade along with initial condition provisions.

AND Gate (f).

$D = A \cdot B \cdot C$: $D = 1$ only if $A = B = C = 1$

OR Gate (g).

$D = A + B + C$: $D = 0$ only if $A = B = C = 0$

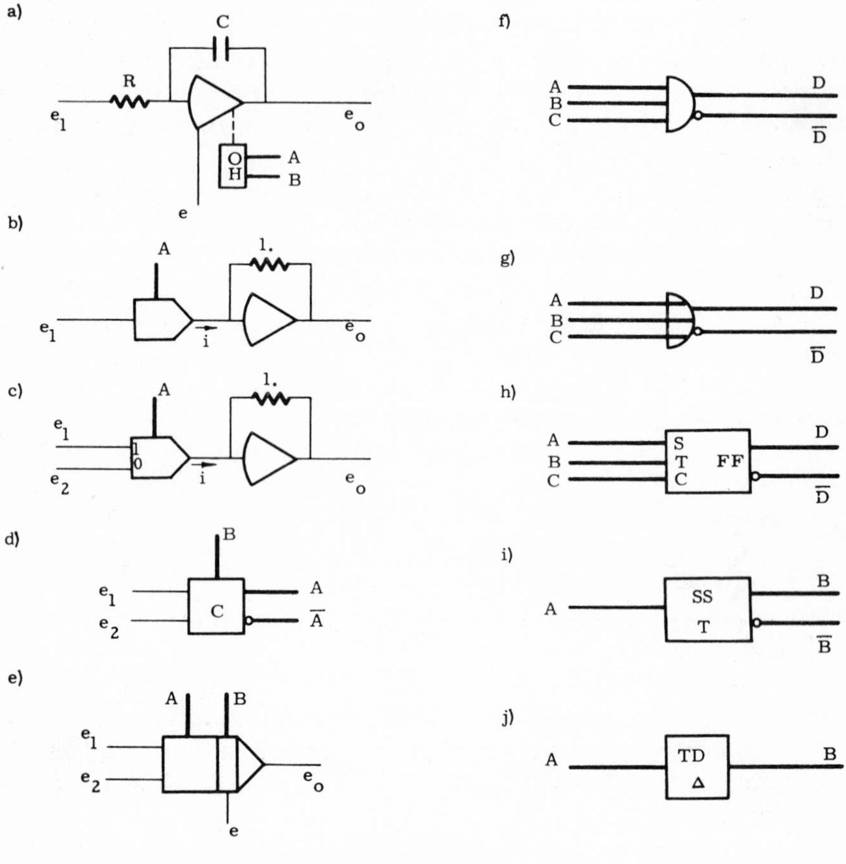

Figure 1. Computer Symbols

Flip-flop (h).

$A = 1 \quad C = 0$: $D = 1$, set flip-flop

$A = 0$, $C = 1$: $D = 0$, clear flip-flop

$A = C = 0$: $D = 1, 0$, store 1 or 0

$A = C = 0 \quad B = 0 \rightarrow 1$: complement D

The inputs A and C should not simultaneously equal 1.

Single-shot (i).

$A = 0 \rightarrow 1$: $D = 1$ for T seconds, otherwise $D = 0$

Time-delay (j).

$B = A$ delayed by Δ seconds

For ease of programming, each element with a logic output also has a complemented output. In some hybrid computers the elements with logic outputs are synchronous in the sense that their outputs may change level only at times specified by a master clock.

The above elements are sufficient when the main purpose of the digital elements is rather simple control of the analog-digital elements. For involved control and complicated numerical calculations a stored-program digital computer with flexible input-output features is also required.

5. The Programming of the Iterative Procedure

In this section the programming of the special problem ($a(t) = r(t) = 0$) is described. Extension of the results to the general problem is quite straightforward. Eq. (21) is used to determine $f(t, \eta)$ and the plant Eq. (2) also replaces (with $u = 0$) the Eq. (19) in w. First, the problem will be programmed for $k_j = k(k > 0$, small enough so that $T(\eta_{j+1}) > T(\eta_j)$ for all j) using the elements shown in Figure 1. Then it will be shown how a digital computer can be introduced to aid in both the numerical calculations and the control of the analog-digital elements.

The steps in the iterative procedure are sufficiently complex that it is wise to break the programming down into a series of subproblems: the solution of Eqs. (2), (8), (9), and (11), the control of these equations to produce $\gamma(\eta)$, the generation of $T(\eta)$, and the implementation of (20).

Figure 2 shows the programming of Eqs. (2), (8), (9), and (11). Block I generates $v(t, \eta)$. The operate input $F = 0 \rightarrow 1$ at $t = 0$ and $F = 1$ until $t = T(\eta)$. During the reverse time integration of Eq. (2), $v(t, \eta)$, is not required so during this period $F = 0$. Block II generates $u(t, \eta) = \text{sgn } v(t, \eta)$ for

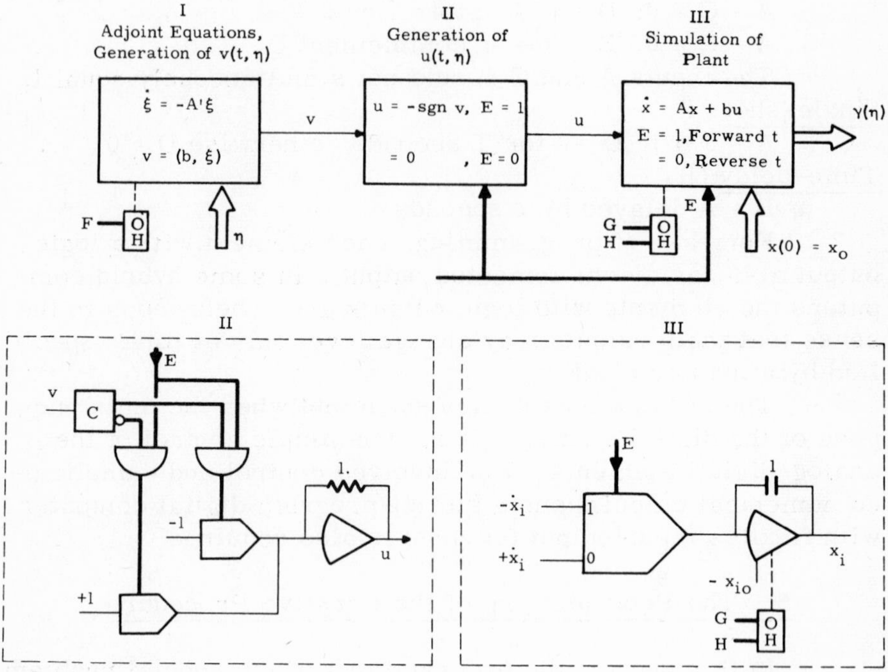

Figure 2. Computer Program for Generation of $\gamma(\eta)$

t increasing from t = 0 to t = $T(\eta)$ and u = 0 as t goes backwards from t = $T(\eta)$ to t = 0. The logic signal E, which is 1 for forward time and 0 for reverse time, exercises the desired control. When E = 0 both AND gates have 0 output causing both switches in block II to be open. On the other hand, when E = 1, either one switch or the other is closed depending on the sign of $v(t, \eta)$. Block III solves Eq. (2), a typical integrator being shown in the figure. When G = 0 → 1 simultaneously with F the integrators begin to operate. From t = 0 to t = $T(\eta)$, E = 1 producing forward time. At t = $T(\eta)$, E = 1 → 0 and the integrators begin to move backwards. When t = 0 again, the hold signal H = 0 → 1. Thus $\gamma(\eta)$ is held at the integrator outputs as long as G = H = 1.

The control program for generating F, E, G, and H is shown in Figure 3. From what has been said it is clear that E = F. The desired sequencing of E, G, and H is shown in the timing diagram. The signals E and I(never 1 at the same time) are the inputs to the control program. When I = 1 the integrators in Figure 2 are reset in preparation for a run. The 0 stored in the flip-flop maintains this condition even after I = 1 → 0. To produce a run, E = 0 → 1 at t = 0 and remains at 1 until t = $T(\eta)$, when E = 1 → 0 and stays at 0 until the next run. When E = 0 → 1 the flip-flop is set and G = 1 until the flip-flop is cleared by I for the next run. The integrator, comparitor, and AND gate produce H. The integrator output is positive during forward time and reverse time until t = 0 is reached on reverse time, when the comparitor causes H = 0 → 1. The inputs $\overline{E}$ and G to the AND gate prevent the possibility of H = 1 during reset or the beginning of forward t when the comparitor input is within the comparitor dead space. The input to L on the comparitor locks H = 1 until I = 0 → 1 causes G = 1 → 0. This assures H = 1 even when the integrator is held so long that it drifts out of the comparitor dead space. H is an important logic output because it indicates when $\gamma(\eta)$ is available.

The determination of t = $T(\eta_j)$ is made by a comparitor with input $f(t, \eta_j)$ and output J. The programming is straightforward and is shown in Figure 4. A switch and comparitor connected to $v(t, \eta)$ generate $|v(t, \eta)|$. Since $v(t, \eta)$ is obtained only when the adjoint equations are being solved, the integrator for $f(t, \eta_j)$ is controlled by F. J is 0 until t = $T(\eta_j)$.

The rest of Figure 4 shows the master control of the

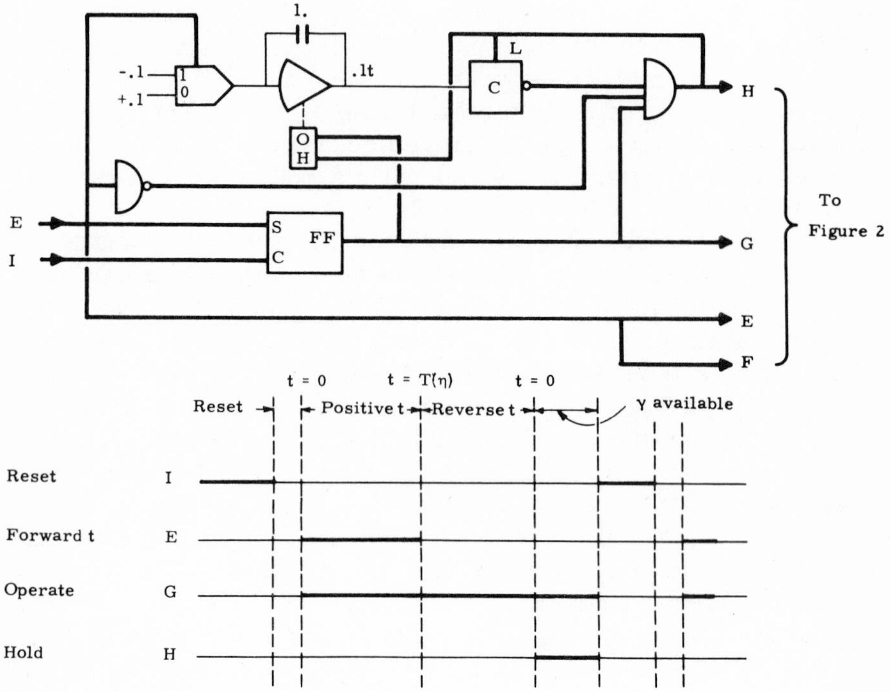

Figure 3. Control Program for Figure 2

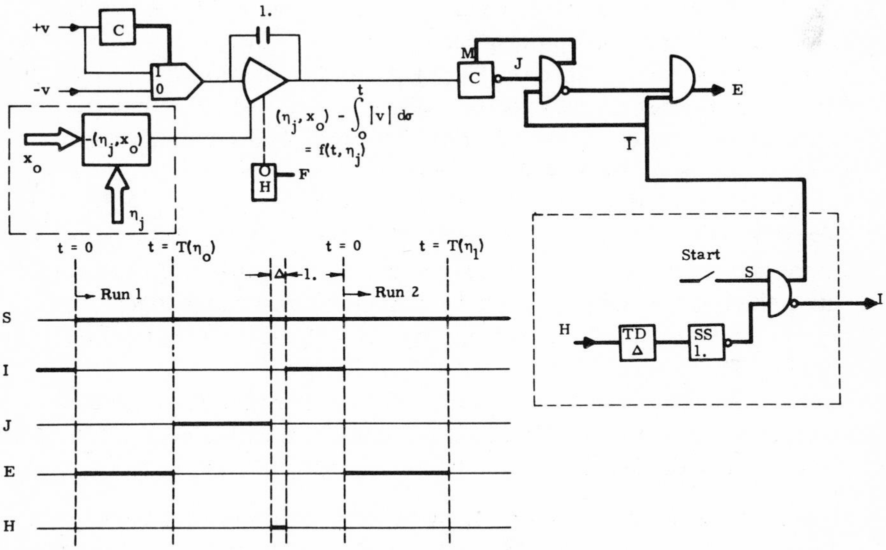

Figure 4. Computer Program for Master Control of Iterative Computations

iterative cycle. On the completion of a run η_j is updated. This computation is shown in Figure 5. Before the computer begins the first run S = 0. This established the initial condition on the memory units, η_0. The inputs E and I for Figure 3 are derived from the logic elements in Figure 4. When S = 0, I = 0 and the γ program is reset. When $S = 0 \rightarrow 1$ the first run begins. Since $f(0, \eta_0) > 0$, J = 0 and $E = 0 \rightarrow 1$. Thus the γ program begins. When $t = T(\eta_0)$; $E = 1 \rightarrow 0$. The M input on the comparitor holds E at 0 even though the f integrator is reset by F = E. When t returns to t = 0, $H = 0 \rightarrow 1$ ($\gamma(\eta_0)$ is available) triggering the memory units. After a delay of Δ the single shot causes $I = 0 \rightarrow 1$. This resets the γ program causing H and J to return to 0. The delay Δ makes sure that H = 1 long enough to trigger the single shot. After a reset period of duration 1, the single shot returns I to 0 beginning the second run.

As programmed the computer continues to produce runs indefinitely. Additional elements can be added (3) to indicate the condition $T(\eta_j) < T(\eta_{j-1})$, which would imply that k is too large (for the special problem this works as well as $f(T(\eta_{j-1}), \eta_j) < 0$, since $f(t, \eta_j) = 0$ for only one t). Also it is possible to provide an automatic stop when the terminal error vector $x(T(\eta_j), \eta_j)$ becomes sufficiently small.

The restriction that $k_j = k$ is constant is often an unreasonable one. Typically, k_j can be taken much larger for small j than for large j, reducing considerably the number of runs for a reasonable terminal error (2). One systematic scheme for changing k_j is the following (see Section 3 for details on how the changes are introduced into the steps of the iterative procedure):

$$\begin{aligned} T(\eta_j) > T(\eta_{j-1}) &: k_j = k_{j-1} \\ T(\eta_j) < T(\eta_{j-1}) &: k_j = 2^{-1}k_{j-1} \end{aligned} \qquad (22)$$

Still different methods have been proposed (2, 7) which avoid the decreasing k_j obtained from (22). Also, algorithms involving $\gamma(\eta)$ which are considerably more complex than Eq. (20) have been shown to be more rapidly convergent (2, 7).

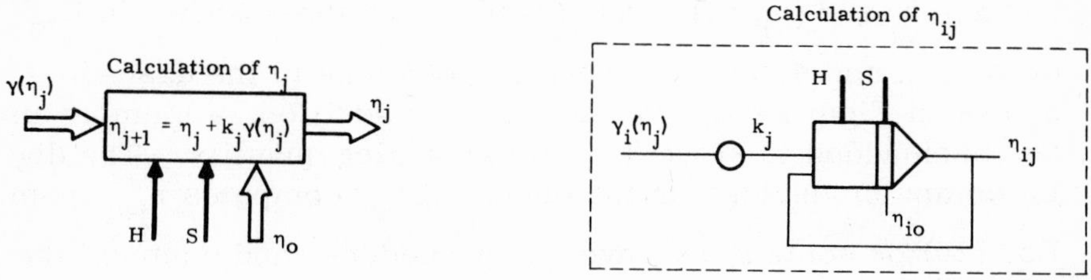

Figure 5. Computer Program for Updating η_j

In all of these situations the computer control and/or algebraic computations involving $\gamma(\eta)$ become more complex than those implemented in Figures 2, 3, 4, and 5. Although it is possible to extend the techniques described in these figures to the more complex situations, it may be simpler to introduce a digital computer.

Figure 6 shows in a general way what is required. The sole purpose of the analog computer is to generate $\gamma(\eta)$ and $T(\eta)$. Thus the necessary inputs to the analog computer for a run are η_j and (η_j, x_0). The circuits are those shown in Figures 2, 3, and 4, except that the operations in the dashed blocks in Figure 4 are not needed. In addition, a memory unit has been added to store $T(\eta_j)$ as an analog quantity. The digital computer decides on the choice of k_j, computes η_{j+1} from Eq. (20) or some more involved procedure, and controls the analog computer.

A run commences when the digital computer causes $I = 1 \rightarrow 0$. After a time period of $T(\eta_j)$, the memory unit samples $T(\eta_j)$ and holds it. After an additional period of $T(\eta_j)$, $H = 0 \rightarrow 1$ which holds $\gamma_i(\eta_j)$, $i = 1, 2, \ldots n$, at the integrator outputs and signals the digital computer that $\gamma(\eta_j)$ is available. The digital computer operating on its stored program, then activates the multiplexer and digital-to-analog converter so as to read $\gamma(\eta_j)$ and $T(\eta_j)$ into its memory. Since the analog computer outputs are then no longer needed, the digital computer sets $I = 1$, which resets the γ program in the analog computer. After computing the new η_j and (η_j, x_0), these quantities are set into the registers of the digital-to-analog converters and the analog computer is ready for the next run.

Although the hybrid system just described offers obvious advantages over the previous one, there are added complications. One of the more interesting of these is the quantizing of data by the converters. Since the fineness of quantizing is directly related to the speed and cost of the converters, it is important to know how the quantizing errors effect the convergence of the iterative procedure. The study of this and other problems will not be undertaken here. However, the example problems which follow demonstrate the feasibility of

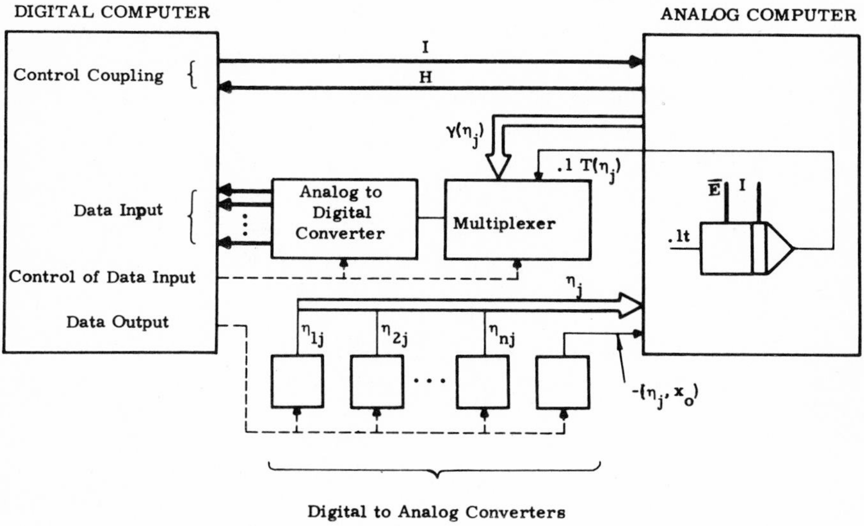

Figure 6. Hybrid System with Digital Computer

of hybrid computation.

6. Example Computations

Since a hybrid computer of the type described in Figure 6 was not available, the steps between runs of the analog computer were carried out manually. Analog computer inputs and outputs were read on a digital voltmeter having a maximum error of .0001 units, and then rounded to three places, simulating a quantizing level of .001 units. An additional source of inaccuracy was a timing uncertainty of about .001 units in the generation of E and H. The analog elements had a maximum gain error of .05%.

The plant equation for the first example problem is $\ddot{y} + \dot{y} + y = u$. By letting $x_1 = y$ and $x_2 = \dot{y}$ Eq. (2) is obtained with

$$A = \begin{bmatrix} 0 & 1 \\ -1 & -1 \end{bmatrix} , \qquad b = \begin{bmatrix} 0 \\ 1 \end{bmatrix}$$

The characteristic roots of A are complex and thus $u^*(t)$ may switch sign more than once.

Figure 7 shows the results for $x'_0 = [4 \ \ 0]$, $\eta'_0 = [1 \ \ 0]$, and $k_j = k = .1$. Plotted are the trajectories of the plant for $u = u(t, \eta_j)$. For every j, $T(\eta_j) > T(\eta_{j-1})$ and $u(t, \eta_j)$ switches sign once. The trajectories for runs 5 and 6 are not shown, but lie respectively, between those for runs 4 and 7 and 3 and 7 (the run number is j + 1). Run 7 yields negligible terminal error.

Figure 8 shows similar results for $x'_0 = [10 \ \ 0]$ and $\eta'_0 = [1 \ \ 0]$. For all runs $u(t, \eta_j)$ switches sign twice. For runs 2 and 3, $T(\eta_j)$ was smaller than for run 1. Thus $k_j = .1$ for run 1, $k_j = .05$ for run 2, and $k_j = .02$ for runs 3 through 6.

Several other second-order time-invariant problems have been solved with similar success. When the plant equations are stable, the adjoint Eq. (11) and the reverse-time plant equations are unstable. This causes some minor scaling problems, but does not appear to be a serious difficulty.

Systems of order greater than two are generally more troublesome. The accuracy in determining $T(\eta_j)$ is more critical, and the number of runs for reasonably small

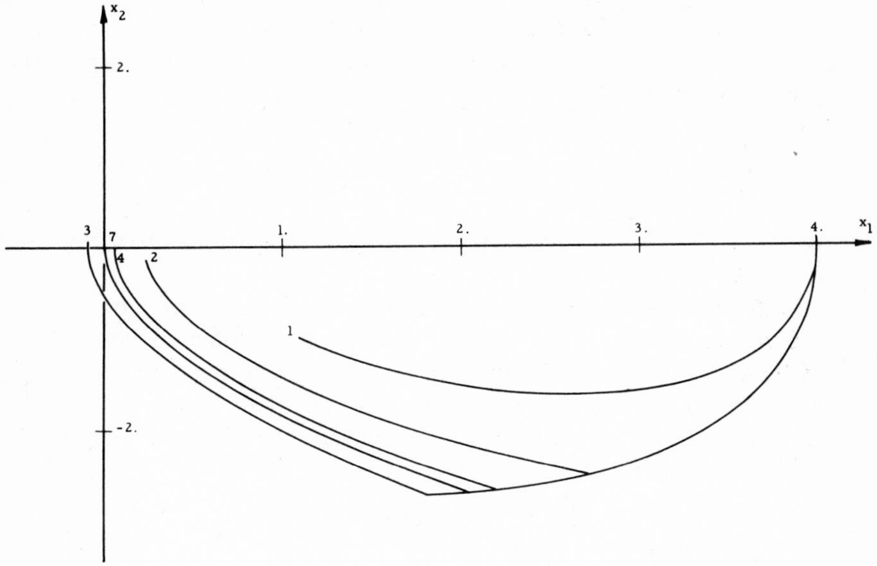

Figure 7. Trajectories for Second-Order Problem

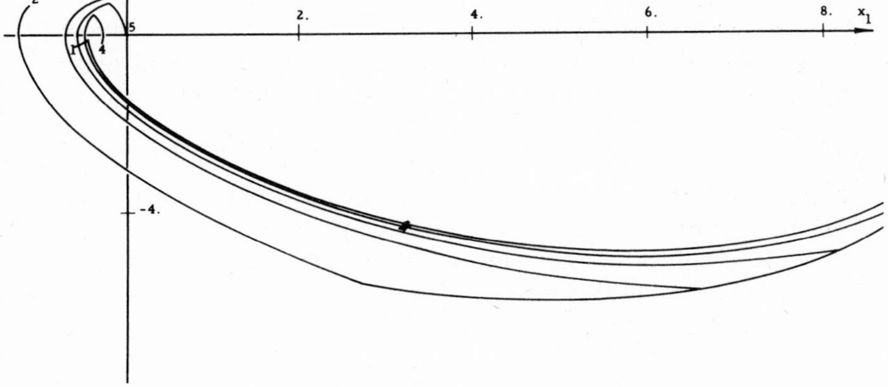

Figure 8. Trajectories for Second-Order Problem

terminal error may become very large (2). Since the system $\dddot{y} = u$ is known to lead to convergence difficulties and has been treated in detail elsewhere (2), it makes a good example problem. Letting $x_1 = y$, $x_2 = \dot{y}$, and $x_3 = \ddot{y}$ gives:

$$A = \begin{bmatrix} 0 & 1 & 0 \\ 0 & 0 & 1 \\ 0 & 0 & 0 \end{bmatrix} \quad , \qquad b = \begin{bmatrix} 0 \\ 0 \\ 1 \end{bmatrix} .$$

For the iterative computations to be described below $x'_0 = [2 \;\; 0 \;\; 0]$ and $t^* = 4$.

As a check on the accuracy of the computer, two runs were made with $\eta = \eta^*$. The results are shown in rows 1 and 2 of Table 1. The discrepances observed are typical of those encountered during the iterative computations.

The iterative computations were carried out under the following conditions:

1) $k_0 = .1$, $\eta'_0 = [1 \;\; 0 \;\; 0]$
2) $T(\eta_j) - T(\eta_{j-1}) < -.001$: take $\eta_j = \eta_{j-1}$ and k_j smaller than k_{j-1}. The values of k_j used were $k_j = .1, .05, .02, .01$.
3) $T(\eta_j) - T(\eta_{j-1}) > .001$: obtain η_{j+1} from Eq. (20) with $k_j = k_{j-1}$.
4) $|T(\eta_j) - T(\eta_{j-1})| \leq .001$: obtain η_{j+1} from $\eta_{j+1} = \eta_j + 2^{-1} k_j [\gamma(\eta_j) + \gamma(\eta_{j-1})]$, with $k_j = k_{j-1}$.

Condition 2) is consistent with the timing error of .001. Condition 4) was introduced to minimize oscillation about the "ridge" which the function $T(\eta)$ exhibits for $T(\eta)$ near t^* (2). Because of the quantization of η_j, the computational procedures cause $\eta_{j+1} = \eta_j$ when $k_j |\gamma_i^j(\eta_j)| < .0005$ for $i = 1, 2, 3$ (or $2^{-1} k_j |\gamma_i(\eta_j) + \gamma_i(\eta_{j-1})| < .0005$ for condition 4)) . Thus there is a natural stopping point. In the example, the computations terminated after 65 runs (at $j = 64$).

Highlights of the run are shown in Table 2. At $j = 9$, 11, 56, condition 2) occurs; while at $j = 36$, 58 through 64, condition 4) occurs. Several detailed results are shown in rows 3, 4, and 5 of Table 1. The general character of the computations is quite similar to that obtained under somewhat different conditions by a digital computer (2).

Table 1

η	η' $x'(T(\eta), \eta)$ $\gamma'(\eta)$			$T(\eta)$
η^*	+ .371 + .009 + .027	+ .743 + .001 - .019	+ .557 + .007 + .007	4.009
η^*	+ .371 + .004 + .018	+ .743 + .005 - .011	+ .557 + .003 + .004	4.009
η_{10} †	+ .504 +7.110 +1.540	+ .824 +4.301 -1.379	+ .264 +1.360 +1.370	3.741
η_{35} †	+ .406 +2.150 - .237	+ .768 +1.019 - .041	+ .494 + .262 + .265	3.989
η_{64} †	+ .378 + .220 - .076	+ .749 + .128 + .016	+ .550 + .028 + .030	4.006

† Computer values, but normalized to have unit Euclidean length ($\|\eta_j\| = 1$).

Table 2

j	$T(\eta_j)$	k_j	$\|\gamma(\eta_j)\|$
0	2.297	.1	3.46
8	3.721	.1	1.55
9	2.573	.05	1.55
10	3.741	.05	2.48
11	3.671	.02	2.48
12	3.782	.02	1.36
35	3.989	.02	.347
36	3.989	.02	.330
37	3.992	.02	.306
55	4.005	.02	.084

j	$T(\eta_j)$	k_j	$\|\gamma(\eta_j)\|$
56	4.003	.01	.084
57	4.005	.01	.412
58	4.005	.01	.189
59	4.006	.01	.118
60	4.005	.01	.240
61	4.006	.01	.131
62	4.006	.01	.191
63	4.006	.01	.160
64	4.006	.01	.083

7. Conclusions and Acknowledgements

It has been shown that hybrid computer techniques are appropriate to the iterative solution of time-optimal control problems. In order to make effective use of the analog elements the iterative procedures must be modified to obtain the required integrals through direct solution of differential equations. While example problems illustrate the feasibility of hybrid computation a number of questions remain unanswered, e.g., the effects of quantizing errors. It is encouraging to note that modified iterative procedures similar to those described above also exist for other types of optimal control problems.

The author wishes to thank E. O. Gilbert and E. J. Fadden for their helpful comments. This work was sponsored in part under Air Force Contract No. AF33(657-11501).

References

1. J. H. Eaton, An Iterative Solution to Time-Optimal Control, J. Math. Anal. and Appl., 5(1962), pp 329-344.

2. E. J. Fadden and E. G. Gilbert, Computational Aspects of the Time Optimal Control Problem, to appear

3. E. G. Gilbert, Hybrid Computer Solution of Time-Optimal Control Problems, AFIPS Conference Proceedings, 23 (1963), pp 197-204.

4. J. P. LaSalle, The Time-Optimal Control Problem, Contributions to Theory of Nonlinear Oscillations, 5, Princeton Univ. Press, 1960, p. 1-24.

5. L. W. Neustadt, Synthesizing Time Optimal Control Systems, J. Math. Anal. and Appl., 1 (1960), pp 484-493.

6. L. W. Neustadt, On Synthesizing Optimal Controls, Presented at Second Congress of the International Federation of Automatic Control in Basel, Switzerland, Sept., 1963.

7. B. Paiewonsky and P. J. Woodrow, The Synthesis of Optimal Controls for a Class of Rocket Steering Problems, AIAA Paper No. 63-244 (1963).

8. L. S. Pontryagin, V. G. Boltyanskii, R. V. Gamkrelidze, and E. F. Mischenko, The Mathematical Theory of Optimal Processes, Interscience (a division of John Wiley and Sons), New York, 1962 (a translation).

SYNTHESIS OF OPTIMAL CONTROLLERS USING HYBRID ANALOG-DIGITAL COMPUTERS

Bernard Paiewonsky . . . . . Aeronautical Research Associates
Peter Woodrow . . . . of Princeton,Inc.,Princeton,N.J.

Walter Brunner . . . . Electronic Associates,Inc.,
Peter Halbert . . . . Princeton,N.J.

I. Introduction

A class of minimum time and minimum effort controllers can be synthesized by the application of an algorithm based on theorems due to Neustadt (2,3). The general idea can be stated concisely using a time optimal controller as an illustrative example. Suppose we are given a linear system:

$$\dot{x} = A(t)\ x + B(t)\ u \qquad (1)$$

where x is an n-vector
u is an r vector restricted to a set, U, of allowable functions
A and B are nxn and nxr matrices respectively.

The initial conditions $x_i(0)$ are known. The object of the control is to bring the system state to zero in the least possible time using an allowable control. Suppose that the limits for the allowable controls form a unit cube, i.e., $|u_k| \leq 1$.

The bang-bang form of the control is obtained from the maximum principle, but there are n-1 independent parameters to be specified so that the boundary conditions are satisfied.

The Hamiltonian for this problem is

$$H = \psi_i\ \dot{x}_i\ + 1$$

and the optimal control $u_k^{o} = -\text{sgn}\ \psi_i\ B_{ik}$

$$((\psi_i\ B_{ik}) \not\equiv 0 \text{ on any finite interval}).$$

The adjoint variables, $\psi_i(t)$, satisfy the differential equations:

$$\dot{\psi}_i = -\ \frac{\partial H}{\partial x_i}$$

The switching times for the bang-bang control are determined by the zero crossings of the function $\psi_i B_{ik}$.

Let the initial conditions for the adjoint system be called $-\eta_i$.

Neustadt's method provides an iterative procedure for finding the initial state of the adjoint (η). The method depends on the generation of a function

$$Z_i(t,\eta) = - \int_o^t X_{ij}^{-1} (\tau) B_{jk}(\tau) u_k(\tau,\eta) d\tau \qquad (2)$$

where $X^{-1}(\tau)$ is the inverse of the fundamental matrix solution to (1). $Z(t,\eta)$ can be generated easily on an analog computer.

The iteration procedure requires a choice of a vector η and then the integration to generate $Z(t,\eta)$. The integration is stopped at the time when

$$Z(t,\eta) \equiv \eta \cdot (Z(t,\eta) - x(0)) = 0$$

This time is denoted by $F(\eta)$,
i.e., $\eta \cdot (Z(F(\eta),\eta) -x(0)) = 0$ The vector $Z(F(\eta),\eta) -x(0))$ is recorded and provides the basis for the corrections to η.

$$\eta^{i+1} = \eta^i - \frac{k\ [Z(F(\eta),\eta) - x(0)]}{||\ Z(F(\eta),\eta) - x(0)||}$$

The object of this calculation is to find the η that maximizes $F(\eta)$. The η vector that does this also causes the boundary conditions to be satisfied. The normalizations and re-initializations of the various quantities are best carried out on a digital computer. The entire calculation is well suited to hybrid analog-digital computers.

II. Computer Studies

The initial studies of the convergence of this iteration scheme were carried out on the ARAP analog-digital computer. A description of this computer is contained in Appendix A. Several different second order linear systems with constant coefficients were used as test objects for a time-optimal regulator program. One example is shown here. This example had been solved long ago by other means (1) and the solution was well known.

<u>Example</u>:

$$\dot{x}_1 = x_2$$

$$\dot{x}_2 = -\omega^2 x_1 + u \qquad |u| \leq 1$$

$$u^o = \text{sgn}\ [-\eta_1 \frac{\sin \omega t}{\omega} + \eta_2 \cos \omega t]$$

$$Z_1(t) = -\int_0^t \frac{1}{\omega} (\sin \omega\tau)\, u(\tau,\eta)\, d\tau$$

$$Z_2(t) = \int_0^t (\cos \omega\tau) u(\tau,\eta)\, d\tau$$

$$\eta_1 \, [Z_1(t,\eta) - x_1(0))] + \eta_2 [Z_2(t) - x_2(0)] \le 0$$

The value of η for the first trial was taken as

$$\eta_i = \frac{-x_i(0)}{\|x(0)\|}$$

The analog computer integrates the equations for Z_1 and Z_2; it stops when $\eta \cdot [Z(t,\eta) - x(0)] = 0$. The analog computer is put into the "Hold" mode, Z_1 and Z_2 are sampled by the digital computer, and a new η vector is obtained from the iteration rule. These calculations are made in the digital computer.

In this case the convergence of the iterations was only mildly sensitive to the value of K. The value K = 1 proved satisfactory for the harmonic oscillator problem. Larger values of K resulted in oscillations about the correct solution; smaller values resulted in an increased number of cycles to converge. The tolerances on the end conditions during these tests were on the order of a large fraction of a volt. No attempts were made to obtain high accuracy in the terminal conditions. Figure 1 shows the sequence of $Z(t,\eta)$ trajectories converging to the optimal one. A variable step size for η corrections was required for the solution of the synthesis problem for $\dot{x}_1 = x_2$, $\dot{x}_2 = u$, $|u| \le 1$. This example gave a hint of the problems that were to come. The isochrones are fairly flat in some regions of the phase space. The hyperplane normal to η^o is nearly parallel to the Z trajectories in the vicinity of the solution. Consequently a small change in the slope of the trial hyperplane (η) produces a large change in $Z(F(\eta),\eta)$ and an infinitesimal change in time $(F(\eta))$. One of the advantages of the analog-digital computer is its ability to show the human operator what is happening via an on-line data output. In the present instance the operator could see the Z trajectories on the x-y plotter. The iterations were watched step-by-step and the source of the trouble was evident at once. The studies with second order systems were brought to a close after making some tests with simple input signals. No difficulty was encountered in steering to specified reachable points in phase space or in following step and ramp inputs.

The next problem to be studied was based on a simplified rocket steering model. Equipment limitations on the

ARAP Analog-Digital forced us to use a constant mass model for the initial studies.

$$\dot{x}_1 = A \operatorname{Cos} \alpha$$
$$\dot{x}_2 = x_3$$
$$x_3 = A \operatorname{Sin} \alpha$$

We were unable to obtain convergence of the Z sequence. This failure to converge was due to errors in establishing the time when $\eta \cdot (Z(t,\eta) - x(0)) = 0$, and to the lack of a good gain changing scheme for the steepest ascent problem. There are a number of ways to fix the first difficulty. We chose to use an interpolation scheme based on digitally sampled values of $\eta \cdot (Z(t,\eta) - x(0))$. A change in time scales or the use of a good comparator would probably have done the job just as well. The second problem, i.e., a gain changing scheme or step size selection method for the steepest ascent was more difficult to handle. The digital computer was programmed to find η^o by stepping along the vector $Z(F(\eta),\eta) = x(0)$ (recall that $F(\eta)$ is the solution of the equation $f(F(\eta),\eta) = 0$). The original procedure for finding the step size during the steepest ascent was very simple. It consisted of a trial and error search for a constant, K, such that the sequence $\eta^{i+1} = \eta^i - K\,[Z(F(\eta),\eta) - x(0)]$ converged. By convergence we mean that for some $\hat{\eta}$, the quantity $||Z(F(\hat{\eta}), \hat{\eta}) - x(0)|| \leq M$ where M is a preassigned number. The process was then modified; K was initially chosen to be large, and if for any i : $F(\eta^{i+1}) \leq F(\eta^i)$ the gain K was halved. It was at this point in the program that the main problem appeared. The maximum of $F(\eta)$ is very flat with respect to η. The maximization of $F(\eta)$ is only a means toward the end of solving the two-point boundary problem. During the steepest ascent a point was inevitably reached where $F(\eta^{i+1}) \leq F(\eta^i)$ for all step sizes within the capability of the computer. We were able to find the maximum of $F(\eta)$ but the boundary conditions were not satisfied. At this point the entire computational problem was transferred to the digital computer. The digital computer studies employed time varying equations for the rocket steering problem.

$$\dot{x}_1 = \frac{\beta\,Co}{M-\beta t} \operatorname{Cos} \alpha$$
$$\dot{x}_2 = x_3$$
$$\dot{x}_3 = \frac{\beta\,Co}{M-\beta t} \sin \alpha - g$$

where: x_1 = horizontal velocity

$\dot{x}_2$ = altitude
$\dot{x}_3$ = vertical velocity
F = thrust = $\beta \ C_o$
β = propellant mass flow rate
C_o = characteristic exhaust velocity
g = local gravitational acceleration
M = initial mass

$$A(t) = \begin{bmatrix} 0 & 0 & 0 \\ 0 & 0 & 1 \\ 0 & 0 & 0 \end{bmatrix} \qquad g(t) = \begin{bmatrix} 0 \\ 0 \\ -g \end{bmatrix}$$

$$B(t) = \begin{bmatrix} \frac{Co}{M/\beta - t} & 0 \\ 0 & 0 \\ 0 & \frac{Co}{M/\beta - t} \end{bmatrix} \qquad \beta \neq 0$$

The initial conditions and terminal conditions were selected to be representative of a class of nuclear rocket satellite injection paths. In order to determine the form $u^o(t)$, we construct the Hamiltonian.

$$H = \psi_o + -\psi_i(t) \left[A_{ij}(t) \ x_j(t) + B_{ik} \ u_k + g_i \right]$$

and apply the maximum principle. In the Hamiltonian $\psi(t)$ is the adjoint vector. Maximizing H setting $\frac{\partial H}{\partial \alpha} = 0$ we find that

$$\alpha^o = \mathrm{Tan}^{-1} \left[\psi_3(t) / \psi_1(t) \right]$$

The ψ vector is governed by the following differential equation.

$$\dot{\psi}_i = - \frac{\partial H}{\partial x_i}$$

A detailed account of these studies is contained in reference (4). There are several aspects of this work that should be mentioned here. The initial studies used numerical integration to evaluate $Z(t,\eta)$. It soon became apparent that this was impractical. It was possible to speed up the computation by integrating the $Z(t,\eta)$ equations in advance. In general it is not possible to evaluate the integrals explicitly and the problem of restricting the numerical growth of integration errors must be considered. Studies of seventh order systems have been made using numerical integration for $Z(t,\eta)$. The computation in these studies used double precision for the summations and employed a special test to detect multiple switches in a single integration interval.

The method of steepest descent requires great care in choosing the step size. The method is bound to work if the step taken is the optimum step. The function $F(\eta)$ however is an extremely flat function of η; the optimum step could not be found by examining values of $F(\eta)$.

Table 1. Typical Values of $F(\eta)$ and $\|Z(F(\eta), \eta) - x(0)\|$

Components of η			$F(\eta)$	Error Norm
η_1	η_2	η_3		
.54580027	.01316405	1.0729829	148.56863	22,700
.54580027	.01316405	1.0729839	148.56906	52,705
.54580027	.01316405	1.0734830	148.56824	7,410
.54580027	.01314405	1.0734830	148.56763	121,610

There is a very sensitive criterion based on the condition that the gradient of the function $F(\eta^{i+1})$ at the trial point $\eta^i - k\,\Delta(F(\eta^i))$ be orthogonal to the original direction $\Delta(F(\eta^i))$. A series of tests using this criterion showed that the gain, K, oscillates wildly; in some cases by a factor of 20. This type of behaviour suggests the presence of a gully or ravine in the parameter space. A convergence acceleration scheme due to Powell (5) had worked well in similar situations (6) and we decided to try it here. This is a recursive procedure and will find the minimum of a quadratic function in one descent. The next table shows the first 10 optimum steps using Powell's method.

Table 2. Reduction of Terminal Error Using Powell's Method

Trial	$F(\eta)$	Error Norm
0	29.3374	285.2
1	29.3695	55.1
2	29.3902	188.7
3	29.4359	45.1
4	29.4366	51.9
5	29.4369	33.9
6	29.4374	4.0
7	29.4377	14.7
8	29.4377	14.0
9	29.4377	14.4
10	29.4378	.12

Several other modifications and improvements were made to the program but the basic idea of a combined Powell's method-optimum step routine remained essentially unaltered.

The success with Powell's method encouraged us to study the synthesis of a controller for higher order system. The problem selected was the terminal phase of a space rendezvous maneuver. The object of the study was to obtain minimum time paths subject to a) restrictions on the maximum thrust levels and b) bounds on the propellant available for maneuvering. The problem was formulated in a state space of seven dimensions. The thrust acceleration levels were moderately low (1 ft/sec^2). The total propellant available for maneuvering was less than 5% of the total mass. The dynamical equations were simplified by neglecting the effect of the time varying total mass.

The set of linearized equations of relative motion of the space vehicle with respect to the target are given below.

Linearized Equations of Relative Motion

$$\dot{x}_1 = x_2$$

$$\dot{x}_2 = 2\omega x_4 + u_1$$

$$\dot{x}_3 = x_4$$

$$\dot{x}_4 = 2\omega x_2 + 3\omega^2 x_3 + u_2$$

$$\dot{x}_5 = x_6$$

$$\dot{x}_6 = -\omega^2 x_5 + u_3$$

$$\dot{x}_7 = A(t)$$

Constraints

$$|u_1^2 + u_2^2 + u_3^2| \leq A^2(t)$$

$$u_1 = A(t) \cos \theta \cos \Phi$$

$$u_2 = A(t) \cos \theta \sin \Phi$$

$$u_3 = A(t) \sin \theta$$

$$0 \leq A \leq A \text{ max.}$$

$$\int_o^T A(t)\, dt \leq M_p$$

$$A^o(t) = \begin{cases} 1, & \sqrt{\Psi_2^2 + \Psi_4^2 + \Psi_6^2} - \Psi_7 \geq 0 \\ 0, & \sqrt{\Psi_2^2 + \Psi_4^2 + \Psi_6^2} - \Psi_7 < 0 \end{cases}$$

$$\cos \theta^o = \frac{\sqrt{\Psi_2^2 + \Psi_4^2}}{\sqrt{\Psi_2^2 + \Psi_4^2 + \Psi_6^2}}$$

$$\sin \theta^o = \frac{x_6}{\sqrt{\Psi_2^2 + \Psi_4^2 + \Psi_6^2}}$$

$$\sin \Phi^o = \frac{\Psi_4}{\sqrt{\Psi_2^2 + \Psi_4^2}}$$

$$\cos \Phi^o = \frac{\Psi_2}{\sqrt{\Psi_2^2 + \Psi_4^2}}$$

The application of the maximum principle yields a set of equations for the optimal steering programs and the optimal thrusting program. The optimal paths consist of combinations of coasting and thrusting arcs. The computations were made on an IBM 7090.

Powell's method with the optimal step routine was successful in bringing the iterations to the point where the boundary conditions were satisfied. The test for the boundary conditions should be based on the x-trajectories and not on the Z trajectories, as it is the x-trajectories which represent the physical problem. The changes in X are related to the changes in Z via the matrix X(t). It is frequently convenient to work only with the Z's and compute the physical paths only after the optimal control has been found. In this case the tolerances on the Z's at the end are fairly tight as the matrix $X^{-1}(t)$ could be quite large. Specifically, in the problem at hand, we are seeking to reduce the initial position errors from 20 miles to less than 300 ft., and relative velocity errors from 300 ft/sec to less than 1 ft/sec.

Several other techniques were tried and some of the results are presented here. $F(\eta)$ and error vs. number of steps for Powell's method are shown in Figure 2. The optimal time is established early in the second cycle and the boundary conditions are satisfied in the third cycle; similar results for the method of steepest descent with optimal steps are shown in Figure 3. The bouncing character of the convergence in error norm is clearly seen. The optimal time is also established early.

Powell's method is recursive and does not make use of information gained during previous cycles. An iterative method that does use all available information was suggested by Fletcher and Powell (7). The Fletcher-Powell method was applied to the rendezvous problem and the convergence was extremely rapid. Figures 4 & 5 shows the convergence of the $\|Z\|$ and $F(\eta)$ to the optimal values.

The computational problems associated with the convergence of Neustadt's method have now been overcome. The next step is a return to a hybrid analog-digital computer to see if a simplified gain changing logic can be made to give convergence to reasonably accurate final conditions.

III. HYDAC Simulation

The HYDAC program was an extension of the work performed on the ARAP hybrid facility. Modifications included:

(1) A logic program, derived on the basis of the digital computer studies, to determine the iteration procedure and iteration gain.

(2) High-speed iteration of the analog solutions to reduce computation time.

The efficiency of the modified iteration logic in producing convergence and the magnitudes of errors at the boundary was of primary interest. The influence of computational speed was also examined. This is mainly a question of dynamic accuracy and reset time.

The EAI HYDAC 2000 is a hybrid computer consisting of two parts: a general purpose analog computer and the DOS-350, a digital operations system containing logic, storage, and interface components. The digital elements terminate on a patch panel and are inter-connected in a parallel fashion similar to analog computer usage. They can be programmed to automatically perform logical computations, implement direct control over analog operations, and make analog program changes on the basis of previous runs and external inputs. The nature and operation of these devices are described in Appendix B. Use of the parallel, high-speed digital components for control of analog computations permits exploitation of the high-speed iteration capabilities of the analog computer.

The equations implemented on the HYDAC computer are conveniently grouped as indicated below:

The "problem" equations describing vehicle motion and control are:

$$\dot{Z}_1 = \frac{C_o \cos \alpha}{\frac{M}{\beta} - t}$$

$$\dot{Z}_3 = \frac{C_o \sin \alpha}{\frac{M}{\beta} - t} - g^*$$

$$\dot{Z}_2 = - kt\dot{Z}_3$$

$$\cos \alpha = \frac{\eta_1}{\sqrt{\eta_1^2 + P_3^2}}$$

$$\sin \alpha = \frac{P_3}{\sqrt{\eta_1^2 + P_3^2}}$$

$$P_3 = \eta_3 - k\,\eta_2\, t$$

where C_o, $\frac{M}{\beta}$, g^*, and k are parameters and the η's are determined by iteration.

Errors are defined by

$$g_j = Z_j + \Delta x_j \; ; \; j = 1,2,3$$

where the Δx_j are constants specifying the boundary conditions.

Iteration equations are:

$$\lambda_j = \frac{g_j}{\| g \|}$$

$$\eta_j^{i+1} = \eta_j^{i} - k^* \lambda_j^{i} ; \; j = 1,2,3$$

The λ_j equations could be defined alternatively without normalization as $\lambda_j = g_j$. The iteration gain k* was determined by the logic below.*

$$k^*/2 \rightarrow k^* \qquad ; \; g^{i+1} < 0$$

$$i+1 \rightarrow i \qquad ; \; 0 < g^i \cdot g^{i+1} < h \| g^i \|^2$$

$$i+1 \rightarrow i,\; 2k^* \rightarrow k^* \; ; \; g^i \cdot g^{i+1} > h \| g^i \|^2$$

where h is a constant less than unity. The three conditions above represent measures of the degree of error improvement for any trial run, i+1, with respect to a previous successful run, i. The resultant actions were taken to obtain a

*Note: b $\rightarrow$ a means b replaces a

near optimum gain and maintain rapid convergence. Certain logical control operations depend on E, an indication of the end of a trial run, and S, a stop condition for the entire program.

$$E = \begin{cases} +1 & ; \eta^{i+1} \cdot g^{i+1} \leq 0 \\ 0 & ; \eta^{i+1} \cdot g^{i+1} > 0 \end{cases}$$

$$S = \begin{cases} +1 & ; \|g^{i+1}\| - \|g^{i+1}\|_{LIM} \leq 0 \\ 0 & ; \|g^{i+1}\| - \|g^{i+1}\|_{LIM} > 0 \end{cases}$$

The constant $\|g^{i+1}\|$ LIM is chosen arbitrarily small.

The various sections of the HYDAC program are illustrated in Figure 6. The computational tasks are divided between the analog and DOS computers as shown in Figures 7 and 8. The analog section is straightforward. A possible exception might be the use of a polar resolution technique in generating the sin α and cos α terms, employed to achieve higher accuracy. A time scale of 320 times faster than real time was standardly used in integrating the problem equations. A factor of 3200 was also tried successfully. These led to typical run times of 500 ms. and 50 ms., respectively. These high speeds dictate the use of electronic mode control for analog integrators and storage units as well as electronic (as opposed to relay) switching for k* determination.

The information flow for the DOS computer is shown in Figure 9. Standard digital programming symbols are used wherever possible. This diagram has the unique feature of parallel digital information processing. It indicates some of the timing required for iterative operation.

Convergence to a region near the desired boundary conditions was obtained. The occurrence of convergent sequence was independent of the choice $\eta(0)$. The terminal region is defined by $\|g\| \leq 1/200$. Attempts to reduce the size of this region were made by scaling g_j, $g^{i+1} \cdot g^i$, and $\|g^i\|$ with high gains. This provided only minor improvement. The major difficulty lay in determining the logical conditions with sufficient accuracy. Computation of $(g^i \cdot g^{i+1}) - h\|g^i\|^2$ near the optimum requires analog subtraction of two quantities near zero. The resulting noise in this computation led to oscillations in k* and an inability to approach the boundaries more closely. Since $g^i \cdot g^{i+1}$ and $\|g^i\|$ can vary over a wide range, there is no single scale factor for these terms which is optimum over the entire iteration. Rescaling is a possible solution. It is felt that a better alternative would be to evaluate $g^i \cdot g^{i+1}$, $\|g^i\|$, and their differences by means of digital techniques.

In a typical case with $\eta(0)$ far from optimal, convergence was obtained in 19 trials, including 7 updatings $(i+1 \rightarrow i)$. Total time for convergence was 15 seconds. Faster operation provided essentially the same results in 1.5 seconds.

The tolerances on the boundary condition errors however are much less stringent than those used in the digital computer studies. This simulation is regarded as successful. In any case, the significant cause of errors has been determined, and steps can now be made to obtain improvement. A promising alternative is the use of HYDAC 2400 system, which adds a CCC DDP-24 digital computer to the HYDAC 2000 system. The various components of this integrated system would perform these tasks:

(1) Analog integration of problem equations
(2) Analog computation of
$$\eta_j^{i+1} = \eta_j^i - k^* g_j^i$$
(3) Digital computation for $g^i \cdot g^{i+1}$, $\eta \cdot g$, and $\|g\|$.
(4) DOS timing and control of analog and digital operations and A-D conversion
(5) DOS logic computation for the iteration process.

References

(1) Bushaw, D. Contributions to the Theory of Nonlinear Oscillations, Edited by S. Lefschetz, Princeton University Press.
(2) Neustadt, L. Journal of Mathematical Analysis and Applications, Vol. I, #3,4, December 1960.
(3) Neustadt, L. SIAM Journal on Control, Vol. I, #1, 1962.
(4) Paiewonsky, B. and Woodrow, P.J. AIAA Preprint 63-224, Los Angeles, June 1963.
(5) Powell, M.J.D. The Computer Journal, July 1962.
(6) Woodrow, P.J. Technical Report #4, Department of Electrical Engineering, Princeton University, Princeton, New Jersey, November 1962.
(7) Fletcher, R. and Powell, M.J.D. The Computer Journal, July 1963.

Appendix A

ARAP has been operating a hybrid analog-digital computer since 1960. The installation is composed of a Libratrol[1] 500 process control digital computer and a

[1] Trademark, Librascope Division, General Precision, Inc.

PACE[2] 221R general purpose analog computer. A considerable number of modifications have been made in these two computers to enable them to work together as a unit. The analog-digital conversion equipment lies wholly in the Libratrol 500; except for this the computer is basically an LGP-30.

The input equipment consists of a three-relay multiplexor to select one of eight analog input voltages and an Adage Voldicon[3] octal voltmeter to convert this to a series of digital pulses. Each of the two output modules is essentially a resistor matrix with associated relays which convert digital pulses into analog output voltages. Both the input and output equipment are under program control.

In the LGP-30 section of the Libratrol one track (64 memory locations) is set aside for communication with the analog computer. Eight words of this track are used to store the eight converted analog inputs. Another word is used to control the multiplexor and to set four relays used for mode control of the analog computer (e.g., operate, hold, and initial condition). The multiplexor can be reset to input Channel 0, put into an automatic stepping mode, or can be stopped to input only a specific channel. Each of the output modules remains at its preset value until a new word is stored in a memory location of the communication track. This word contains the address of the output module to be changed and the new digital version of the output. Also contained in the special track is a memory location reserved for a digital clock. A count of one is added to the word stored in this memory location every thirtieth of a second.

Unfortunately, the digital computer is slow. As a measure of its speed, one tenth of a second is required to sample eight analog voltages and a minimum of twenty milliseconds is required to change one output. Nevertheless the Libratrol 500 serves to considerably enlarge the small analog computer. The PACE 221R at ARAP contains only twenty amplifiers (eight integrators), twenty potentiometers, one servo multiplier, and one three channel quarter-square multiplier. The Libratrol 500 serves to greatly enlarge the complement of non-linear analog equipment as well as to provide a good means of analyzing the analog output data.

Appendix B

The EAI HYDAC 2000 computer represents one current form of hybrid computation: the association of a general purpose analog computer with a complement of digital logic, storage, and interface components. The digital elements are contained in the DOS-350 and terminate on its patch panel. They can be inter-connected by patch cords. The fundamental

DOS logic components are gates and clocked flip-flops. The gates allow solution of all problems of propositional logic (AND, OR, NOT and their combinations). The flip-flops introduce sequential logic. With these elements all types of automata can be assembled. For convenience, some frequently used combinations of flip-flops and gates are provided in packaged form. These include shift registers, counters, monostable timers, digital differentiators, etc. Outputs and inputs to DOS units are logic levels rather than pulses.

The storage of intermediate results between consecutive analog computations can be done by means of analog track-store units. These operate under control of the DOS logic components. Each unit can store a single analog value. When an analog function must be stored, serial memory units (magnetorestrictive delay lines) in the DOS are used to store the converted digital form of the analog data for later reconversion into analog circuits under control of the logical devices.

The DOS also provided the necessary interface between the analog and digital sections of HYDAC. Interface must be considered at two levels: logical data and numerical data. For the transmission of logical data from analog to digital patchboards comparators are used providing binary indications of the sign of analog inputs. In the opposite direction, logic signals can control analog integrator modes (IC and OP), electronic switches, and the modes of analog storage units. For numerical data conventional A-D and D-A converters with multiplexers are provided.

A central timing unit (clock) is part of the DOS. Basic clock frequency is 2 Mc. The clock determines the rate of sequential logic computation. A variable clock is also available, allowing selection of any speed (lower than 2 Mc) for sequential logic computation.

The DOS is capable of operating on binary numbers as well as individual bits. Separation of the two functions is maintained for greater efficiency of operation and a higher speed capability. The DOS arithmetic capability was not employed in the rocket steering example, however.

---

[2] Trademark, Electronic Associates, Inc.

[3] Trademark, Adage, Inc.

Acknowledgment

The research at ARAP on the synthesis problem was sponsored in part by U.S. Air Force, Flight Control Lab. A.S.D. under contracts #33(657)7781 and 33(657)11319.

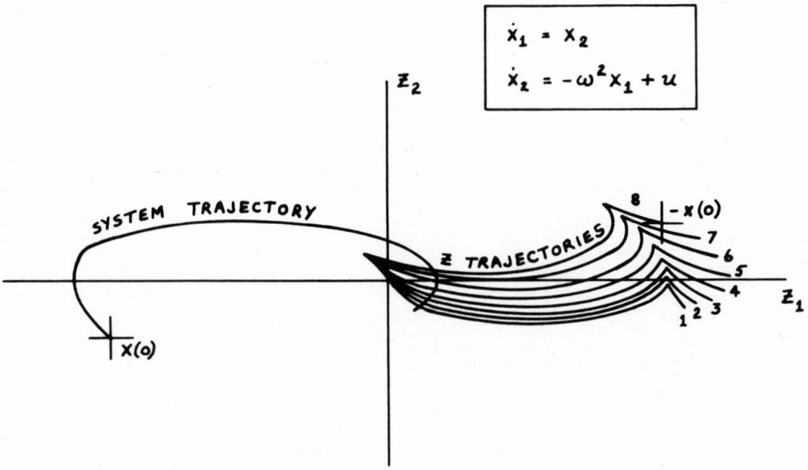

Figure 1. Sequence of Z Trajectories

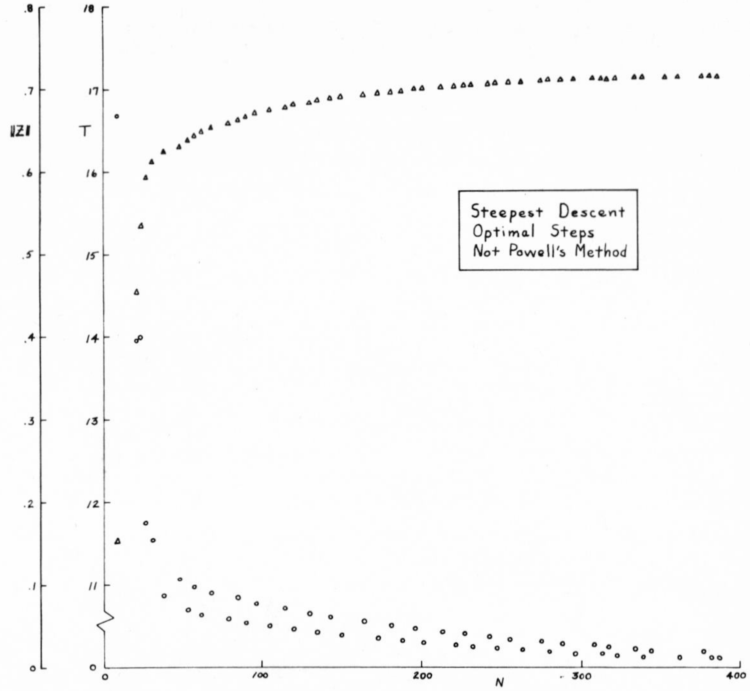

Figure 2. Convergence of Z(F(η),η) - x(0)
Using Optimal Steps

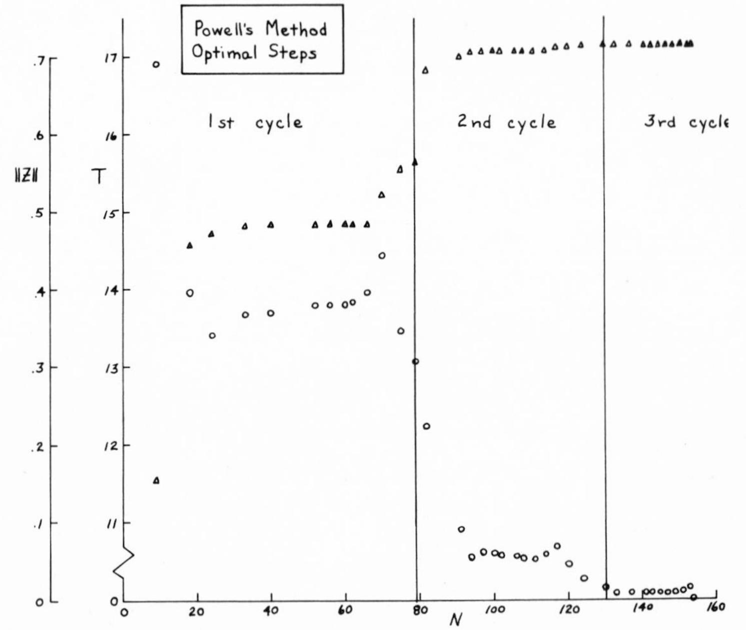

Figure 3. Convergence of Z(F(η), η) - x(0) and F(η)
Using Powell's Method for a Seventh Order System

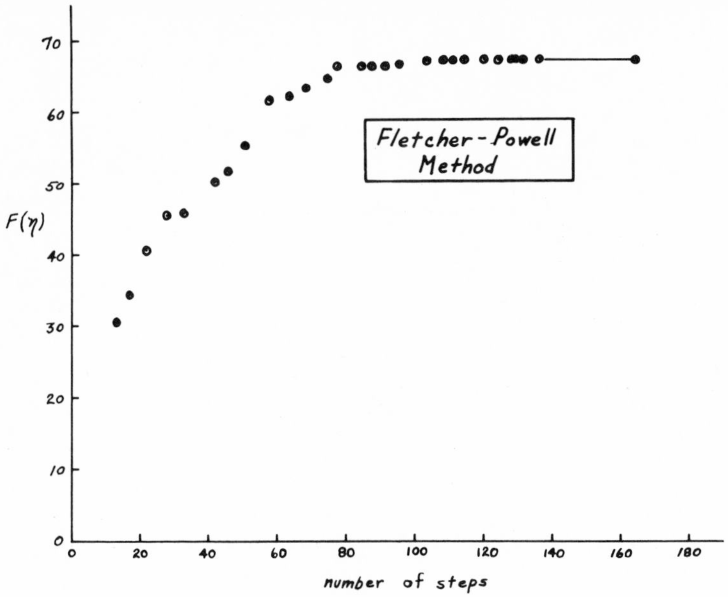

Figure 4. Convergence of F(η) to T^0 Using Fletcher-Powell Method for a Seventh Order System

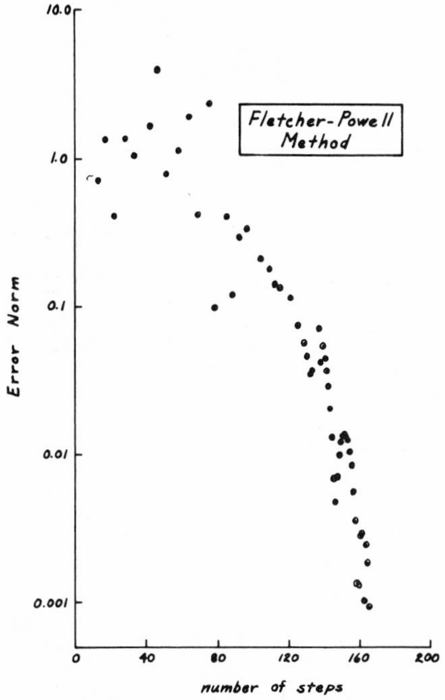

Figure 5. Convergence of Z(F(η), η - x(0) to Zero Using Fletcher-Powell Method for a Seventh Order System

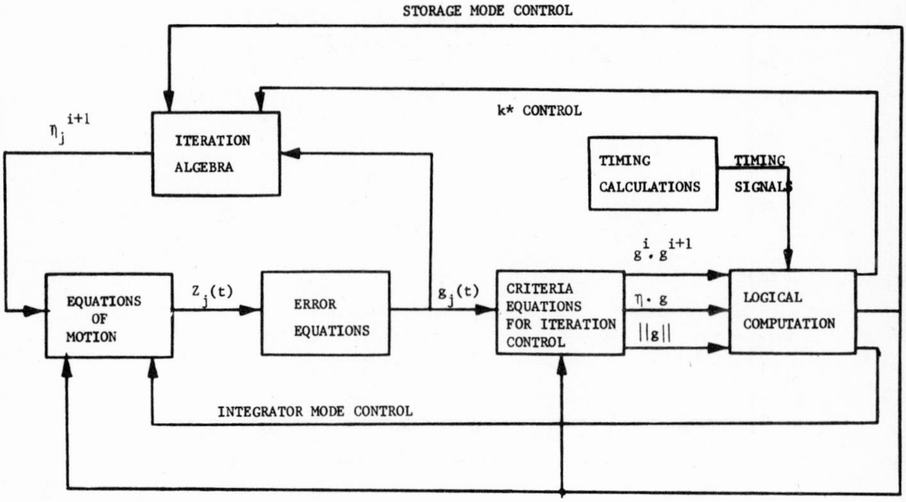

Figure 6. HYDAC Functional Block Diagram

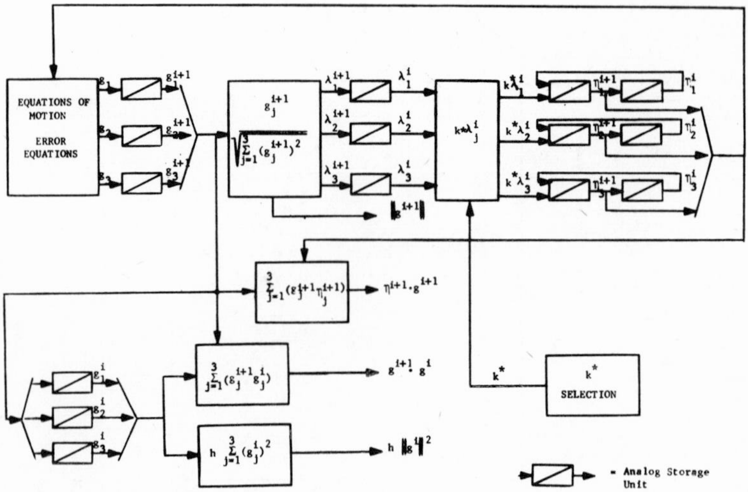

Figure 7. Analog Block Diagram

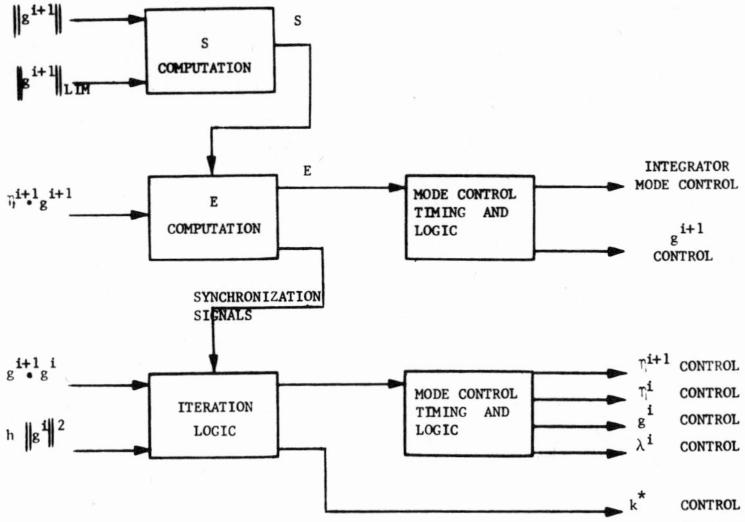

Figure 8. DOS 350 Block Diagram

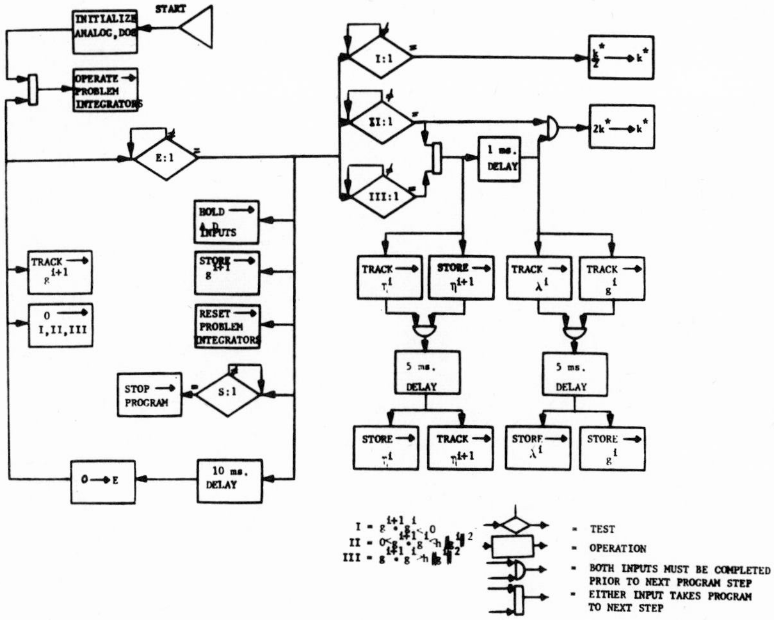

Figure 9. DOS 350 Information Flow (Simplified)

GRADIENT METHODS FOR THE OPTIMIZATION OF DYNAMIC* SYSTEM PARAMETERS BY HYBRID COMPUTATION

George A. Bekey and Robert B. McGhee

Electrical Engineering Department
University of Southern California
Los Angeles, California

I. INTRODUCTION

This paper is concerned with the computer implementation of both continuous and discrete gradient methods for adjusting the parameters of a dynamic system so as to match a specified response function as closely as possible. While the basic theory of parameter optimization by gradient descent has been known for some time, the limitations and convergence properties of particular methods of computer implementation are not yet well understood. This paper is intended to be a contribution toward obtaining a better understanding of these problems.

Continuous parameter optimization is an appealing concept and a number of "adaptive control" schemes have been based on it. The first part of this paper reviews the formulation of a continuous steepest descent algorithm and discusses its difficulties. Computer results relating to the nature of the gradient and the dependence of the path in parameter space on adjustment gain are given.

The second part of the paper reviews briefly several discrete gradient optimization techniques. An algorithm for automatic adjustment of step size for gradient descent is presented. The stability and convergence properties of first and second order iteration schemes are compared and some new results are presented in the form of a convergence theorem. The application of discrete parameter optimization methods to a nonlinear dynamic system is illustrated with an example.

---

* This research was supported in part at the University of Southern California under U. S. Air Force Office of Scientific Research Grant No. AF-AFOSR-75-63 and in part at Space Technology Laboratories, Inc., under National Aeronautics and Space Administration Contract NASℓ-2582.

The final section of the paper presents a formulation of a hybrid computational strategy for parameter optimization which includes the best features of both the analog and digital computer solutions.

2. CONTINUOUS PARAMETER OPTIMIZATION

We consider continuous dynamic systems described by

$$\dot{\bar{y}} = F(\bar{y},\ t;\ \bar{p}) \tag{1}$$

where $\bar{y}$ is an n-vector representing the state of the system and $\bar{p}$ is an m-vector representing the parameters to be optimized, including initial conditions. The parameter optimization problem under consideration is that of selecting $\bar{p}$ in such a way that the solution of Eq. (1) approximates a given function, $y_d(t)$, as closely as possible. The particular criterion function to be used as a basis for parameter adjustment in this paper is given by

$$\phi(\bar{p}) = \int_0^T [y(t;\bar{p}) - y_d(t)]^2\ dt \tag{2}$$

Gradient methods of optimization are based upon adjustment of parameters utilizing the local gradient vector. That is, a parameter change vector, $\bar{\Delta p}$, is computed according to the rule

$$\bar{\Delta p} = -\ K\ \bar{\nabla}\phi(\bar{p}) \tag{3}$$

where K is a positive definite matrix and $\bar{\nabla}\phi$ is the column vector

$$\bar{\nabla}\phi(\bar{p}) = \left[\frac{\partial\phi}{\partial p_1},\ \frac{\partial\phi}{\partial p_2},\ \cdots\ \frac{\partial\phi}{\partial p_m}\right]' \tag{4}$$

Following the i-th such calculation, the value of the parameter vector is given by

$$\bar{p}^{(i+1)} = \bar{p}^{(i)} + \bar{\Delta p}^{(i)} \tag{5}$$

The convergence properties of several iteration schemes of this type are discussed in Section 3 of this paper.

Consider now the case where continuous parameter adjustment is desired. It is clear that the criterion function defined by Eq. (2) cannot be used directly since it leads to an iterative adjustment algorithm. Let us therefore define an instantaneous performance criterion

$$f = \frac{d\phi}{dt} = [y(t;\bar{p}(t)) - y_d(t)]^2 \tag{6}$$

Unfortunately, f is a functional in $\bar{p}(t)$ rather than an ordinary function. Consequently, the gradient vector, $\bar{\nabla}f(\bar{p})$, does not exist unless $\bar{p}(t)$ is a constant. But this contradicts the original objective of the formulation, namely, to adjust $\bar{p}$ continuously as a function of time. Two different approaches to the resolution of this dilemma have been taken. If the desired output is a vector of derivatives, $\bar{y}_d(t)$, with dimension equal to the order of the system to be optimized, then Eq. (1) may be used to derive a criterion function which is a simple function of $\bar{p}$ even when $\bar{p}$ varies with time. Specifically, if

$$f_e(\bar{p}) = F^2(\bar{y}_d, t; \bar{p}) \tag{7}$$

then the gradient

$$\bar{\nabla}f_e(\bar{p}) = 2F \frac{\partial F}{\partial \bar{p}} \tag{8}$$

exists and may be used to find a minimizing value for $\bar{p}$ by making use of the adjustment algorithm

$$\dot{\bar{p}} = - k \, \bar{\nabla}f_e(\bar{p}) \tag{9}$$

This method, sometimes called the "equation error method" has been used by Graupe (1), Ornstein (2), and others in connection with identification problems.

While the equation error method avoids the difficulty associated with Eq. (6), computer implementation of the method requires that desired values for all of the system state variables be available. An alternate formulation, based on the work of Whitaker (3) and Margolis (4) does not require complete specification of the desired state, but leads only to an approximate gradient method. The degree of approximation is related to the rate of change of adjustment of the parameters as compared to the natural frequencies of both the system and the input process. The remainder of this paper is restricted to the latter formulation; i.e., to circumstances where y_d is a scalar function. While the basic technique to be described for continuous parameter adjustment is not new, the results pertaining to the dynamic properties of the parameter adjustment process have not been previously published.

2.1 The Approximate Gradient Method.

The performance criterion Eq. (7) requires complete knowledge of the desired state. Let us consider instead the criterion

$$f_c = (e_{c1} + q_1 e_{c2} + \cdots + q_{p-1} e_{cp})^2 \tag{10}$$

where $p < n$, n is the order of the system, and

$$e_{ci} = y_i - y_{di} = \frac{d^{(i-1)}y}{dt^{(i-1)}} - \frac{d^{(i-1)}yd}{dt^{(i-1)}} \tag{11}$$

When $y_d(t)$ is given as a scalar function, error derivatives must be obtained by analog computer differentiation. In many practical situations it is possible to choose all the $q_i = 0$, so that only the system output (or zero-state) is required. The quantity e_c represents "output error" and parameter optimization based on Eq. (10) may be called the "output error method".

Let us choose

$$f_c = (e_{c1} + q\, e_{c2})^2 \tag{12}$$

Then, if the parameters are constant, the components of the gradient are given by

$$\frac{\partial f_c}{\partial p_i} = 2(e_{c1} + q\, e_{c2}) \frac{\partial}{\partial p_i}(e_{c1} + q\, e_{c2}) \tag{13}$$

$$i = 1,2, \cdots m$$

Using the definition of e_{c1} and e_{c2} from Eq. (11) and since y_d is independent of the parameters, Eq. (13) can be written as

$$\frac{\partial f_c}{\partial p_i} = 2(e_{c1} + q\, e_{c2}) \frac{\partial}{\partial p_i} (y_1 + q\, y_2); \tag{14}$$

$$i = 1,2, \cdots m$$

where y_1 and y_2 represent the system output and its first derivative respectively. Let us denote the <u>influence coefficients</u> by the letter u so that

$$u_{ij} = \frac{\partial y_i}{\partial p_j} \tag{15}$$

The influence coefficients can be obtained by differentiation of the system Eq. (1) with respect to the approiate parameters and solving the resulting differential equation in u_{ij} (the "sensitivity equation") (5). Analog computer circuits can be used for the simultaneous evaluation of the u_{ij} and the y_i .

Now, if the parameters are adjusted, y_i becomes a

functional and the $\partial y_i/\partial p_j$ do not exist in the ordinary sense. Let us assume, however, that in a given solution interval, the variation is sufficiently slow so that p_j can be assumed constant. Then, a continuous gradient method is based on

$$\dot{p}_i = - k \frac{\partial f_c(\bar{p})}{\partial p_i} \tag{16}$$

However, analog computer circuits based on Eq. (16) are in fact mechanizations of

$$\dot{p}_i = - k\, g_i(\bar{e}_c, \bar{y}, \bar{p}) \tag{17}$$

where the vector $\bar{G} = [g_1, g_2, \cdots g_n]'$ is an approximation to ∇f_c which approaches ∇f_c as $k \to 0$. The u_{ij} which enter into the calculation of the g_i can be considered subsidiary variables, which equal the desired sensitivity coefficients when $\dot{\bar{p}} = 0$.

An analog computer implementation of the approximate gradient method (the output error method) is shown in Fig. 1 for $q = 0$ in Eq. (12). This figure illustrates the application of the method to an identification problem. As long as the switch S is open, the parameters are constant and $\bar{G} = \nabla f_c$. Consequently, the nature of the gradient can be studied in the open-loop case. Then, the switch can be closed for examination of the actual parameter adjustment path.

2.2 The Nature of the Criterion Surface

Let

$$f_c = e_{c1}^2 = (y_1 - y_{d1})^2 \tag{18}$$

and define the parameter offsets δp_i by

$$\delta p_i = p_i^{(o)} - p_i^{(f)}, \quad i = 1,2,\cdots m \tag{19}$$

where $p_i^{(o)}$ represents the assumed initial values of the parameters and $p_i^{(f)}$ the values which minimize f_c. Then, if the loop is open, we can expand f_c as follows:

$$f_c(t) = \left[e_c(\bar{p}^{(o)}) + \sum_{i=1}^{m} \frac{\partial e_c}{\partial p_i} \delta p_i + O(\delta p^2) \right]^2 \tag{20}$$

If the δp_i are sufficiently small, second and higher order terms may be neglected and

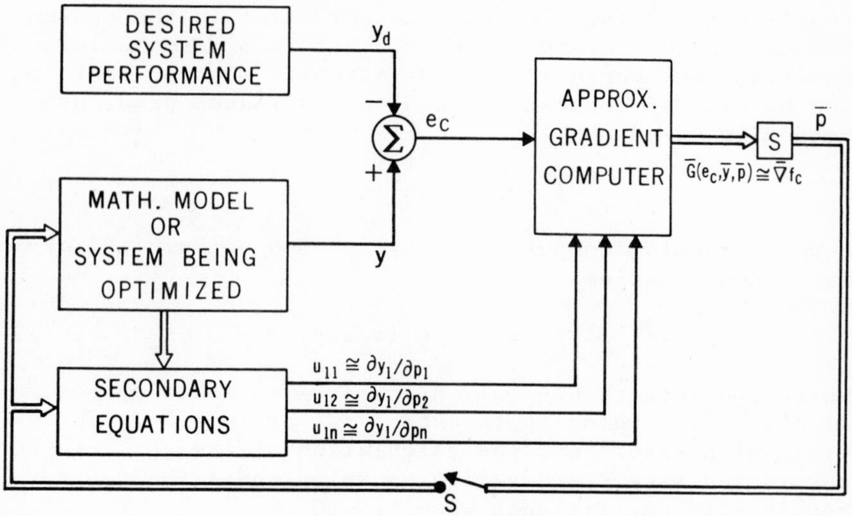

Fig. 1. Schematic of Continuous Parameter Optimization Method

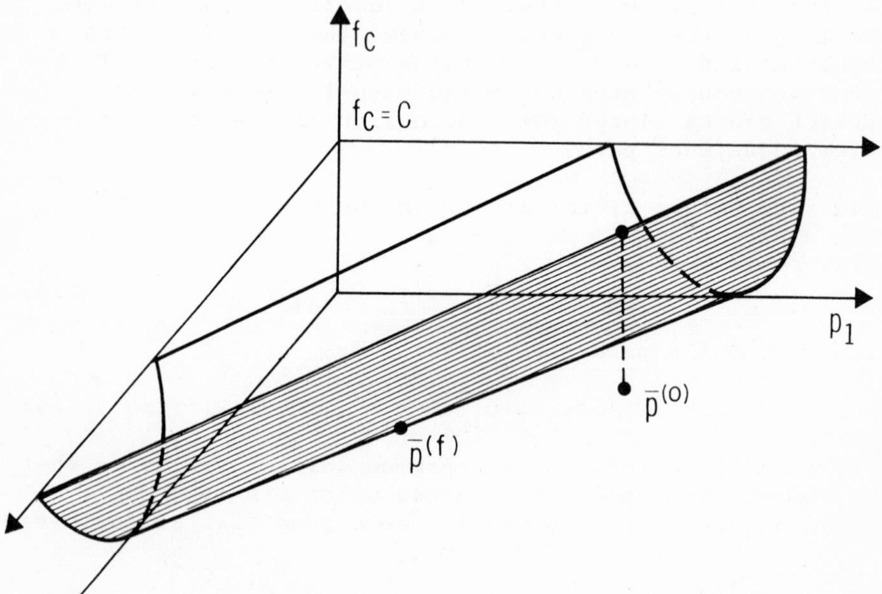

Fig. 2. Instantaneous Criterion Surface

$$f_c(t) = \left[e_c(\bar{p}^{(o)}) + \sum_{i=1}^{m} u_{1i} \ \delta p_i \right]^2 \tag{21}$$

Consequently, contours of constant $f_c(t) = C$, at any time t_j, can be found from

$$\sum_{i=1}^{m} u_{1i}(t_j) \ \delta p_i = \pm C^{\frac{1}{2}} - e_c(\bar{p}^{(o)}, t_j) \tag{22}$$

This equation represents two parallel lines in the m+1 dimensional space of the parameters and criterion function. If only 2 parameters p_1 and p_2 are present, it is possible to obtain a simple geometrical interpretation of this equation as shown in Fig. 2. It can be seen that the instantaneous criterion function surface is a parabolic trough, where the initial and final parameter values are indicated. The contour lines in the $p_1 - p_2$ plane are straight lines, while the intersection of the trough with the $f_c - p_i$ planes results in the familiar quadratic shape. It should be noted that Fig. 2 represents an instantaneous situation. As the u_{1j} and e_c change with time, the trough moves in such a way that its minimum still crosses the desired final point (6).

2.3 The Gradient Vector

Considerable insight into the nature of the adjustment process is gained if the gradient (with S open, of course) is evaluated with a sinusoidal input. The gradient is given by

$$\bar{\nabla} f_c = 2\left[e_c \ u_{11}, \ e_c \ u_{12}, \ \cdots \ e_c \ u_{1m} \right]' \tag{23}$$

Consider, for example, a desired response function obtained from a second order system described by the relation

$$\dot{\bar{y}}_d = A_d \bar{y}_d + B_d \bar{x} \qquad \bar{y}_d(0) = \bar{y}_{do} \tag{24}$$

where

$$A_d = \begin{bmatrix} 0 & 1 \\ -a_2 & -a_1 \end{bmatrix}, \quad B_d = \begin{bmatrix} 0 & 0 \\ a_3 & a_4 \end{bmatrix}, \quad \bar{x} = \begin{bmatrix} x \\ \dot{x} \end{bmatrix}$$

and the coefficients a_1, a_2, a_3, a_4 are constants. The signal $x(t)$ is the input to the process. It is desired to optimize the parameters α_1 to α_4 of a model described by

$$\dot{\bar{y}} = A\bar{y} + Bx \ , \qquad \bar{y}(0) = \bar{y}_o \tag{25}$$

where

$$A = \begin{bmatrix} 0 & 1 \\ -\alpha_2 & -\alpha_1 \end{bmatrix}, \qquad B = \begin{bmatrix} 0 & 0 \\ \alpha_3 & \alpha_4 \end{bmatrix}$$

using the criterion function of Eq. (18). The locus of the gradient vector can be plotted using the computer in the parameter plane defined by any two of the parameters. To further simplify the visualization of the results, let $\bar{y}_{do} = \bar{y}_o$ and $A_d = A$ so that the differences between y_d and y are due entirely to differences between B_d and B. To compute the gradient (as defined by Eq. (23) the sensitivity coefficients $u_3 = \partial y/\partial\alpha_3$ and $u_4 = \partial y/\partial\alpha_4$ will be required. These coefficients are obtained from computer solution of two subsidiary equations, derived from differentiation of Eq. (25) with respect to α_3 and α_4 respectively. The sensitivity equations for this case are

$$\begin{aligned} \dot{\bar{u}}_3 &= A\bar{u}_3 + C_3\bar{x} \\ \dot{\bar{u}}_4 &= A\bar{u}_3 + C_4\bar{x} \end{aligned} \tag{26}$$

where

$$C_3 = \begin{bmatrix} 0 & 0 \\ 1 & 0 \end{bmatrix}, \qquad C_4 = \begin{bmatrix} 0 & 0 \\ 0 & 1 \end{bmatrix}$$

$$\bar{u}_3 = \begin{bmatrix} u_3 \\ \dot{u}_3 \end{bmatrix}, \qquad \bar{u}_4 = \begin{bmatrix} u_4 \\ \dot{u}_4 \end{bmatrix}$$

Substitution of the solution of Eq. (26) into Eq. (23) yields the instantaneous values of the gradient vector. Typical results are shown in Fig. 3, where $x(t)$ is a sinusoid with a frequency of 1 rad/sec. Since the adjustment loop is open, the parameters remain constant, but the sensitivity coefficients and the matching error e_c vary with time, resulting in the Lissajous-like contours in the figure. Since for sinusoidal inputs and linear systems both y_d and y are sinusoidal, the error e_c is also sinusoidal and becomes zero every half-cycle. From an examination of this figure, it is clear that if it is attempted to adjust parameters with a velocity proportional to the gradient, the motion will be oscillatory and may instantaneously point in an erroneous direction.

2.4 Paths of Parameter Adjustment

The dependence of the parameter adjustment path on

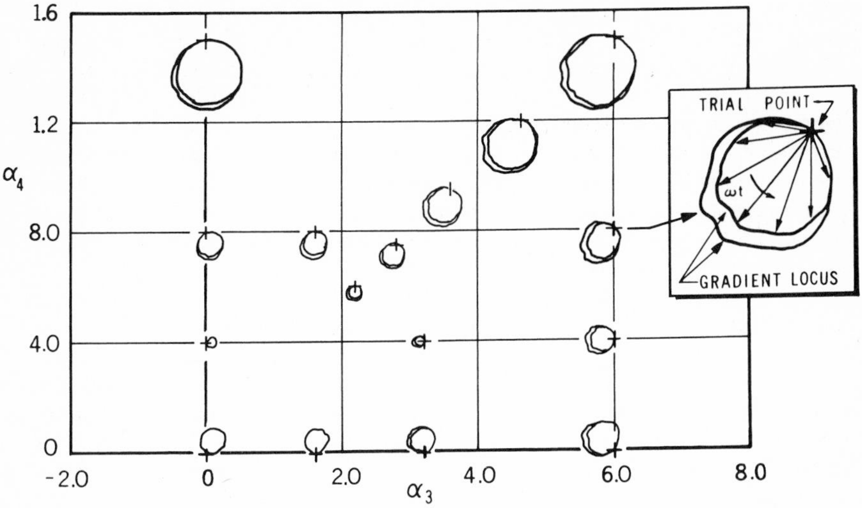

Fig. 3. Open Loop Gradient Loci in the α_3, α_4 Plane

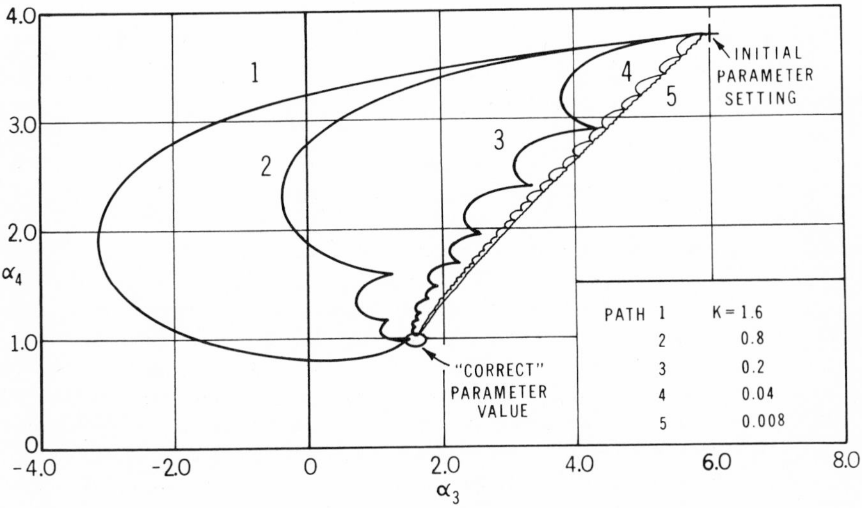

Fig. 4. Descent Trajectories in α_3, α_4 Plane-Sinusoidal Excitation

the parameter k in Eq. (17) is indicated in Fig. 4 for the example discussed previously. When k is very small, the path closely approximates a gradient trajectory. When k is large, the functions g_i are not equal to the respective coefficients of the gradient, but approach a gradient path as the $\delta p_i \rightarrow 0$. The "scallops" on the trajectories are due to the oscillatory nature of the approximate gradient vector. Values of k larger than those indicated in this figure may cause instability in the parameter optimization loops.

2.5 Stability of the Parameter Adjustment Loops

General analytical results on stability are not available at the present time. Stability in the small has been demonstrated by Margolis (4) for first and second-order systems with step inputs. Experiments using analog computers show that it is generally possible to find a value of k for which stability and convergence of two or three parameters is possible. However, attempts to improve convergence by increasing k or attempts to adjust more than three parameters simultaneously generally result either in instability or in lack of convergence (6).

At the present time a general existence theorem insuring local stability of the parameter optimization technique for sufficiently small gain is lacking. Such a theorem would prove that a value of k can be found in any particular case such that, for specified classes of inputs and initial conditions, both stability and convergence can be assured.

3. DISCRETE PARAMETER OPTIMIZATION

3.1 Discrete Gradient Descent

The convergence problems encountered in continuous parameter variation schemes may be largely circumvented by making use of a discrete iterative adjustment algorithm. When this is done it becomes possible to determine the true gradient of a given criterion function since parameter changes are made only at discrete points in time. For example, the criterion function given by Eq. (2) may be differentiated to produce

$$\nabla\phi(\bar{p}) = \int_0^T 2\left[y(t;\bar{p}) - y_d(t)\right] \nabla y(t;\bar{p})\, dt \tag{27}$$

Since $\bar{p}$ is a constant over the interval of integration, the partial derivatives of y appearing in this expression may be obtained by solving the parameter influence differential equations associated with the assumed equation for y.

The gradient vector computed from Eq. (27) may be used for discrete gradient descent employing Eq. (3). As in the continuous case, the convergence of this parameter adjustment procedure depends upon the values chosen for the elements of K. However, since the gradient used here is exact rather than approximate, discrete gradient descent may always be stabilized by multiplying every element of K by a sufficiently small scale factor. At the present time, an analogous statement cannot be made for continuous parameter adjustment procedures utilizing approximate gradients.

3.2 The Optimum Gradient Method

Since the criterion function, ϕ, is bounded from below by the value zero, it follows that in any region where ϕ is continuous there must exist at least one value for a scalar scale factor k, say $k = k^*$, such that whenever $|\bar{\nabla}\phi| \neq 0$,

$$\min_{k > 0} \phi\left[\bar{p}^{(i)} - k\, \bar{\nabla}\phi^{(i)}\right] = \phi\left[\bar{p}^{(i)} - k_i^*\, \bar{\nabla}\phi(\bar{p}^{(i)})\right] \qquad (28)$$

The "optimum gradient method" (7) utilizes k^* in Eq. (3) i.e., the matrix K is computed anew at every cycle of iteration as

$$K_i = k_i^* \, I \qquad (29)$$

This choice for K not only guarantees that the sequence of values for ϕ converges, but also assures that the steps taken in parameter space are large enough to make the convergence reasonably rapid.

With the restriction that only a finite number of values for k may be considered, the search for k^* may be carried out automatically by a digital computer. One method for accomplishing this can be based upon an initial value for k computed from the Newton-Raphson formula. If this gain value is called k^o, then at the i-th stage of iteration

$$k_i^o = \frac{\phi(\bar{p}^{(i)})}{|\bar{\nabla}\phi(\bar{p}^{(i)})|^2} \qquad (30)$$

and

$$\bar{\Delta p}^{(i)} = - k_i^o \bar{\nabla}\phi(\bar{p}^{(i)}) = - \frac{\phi(\bar{p}^{(i)})\bar{\nabla}\phi(\bar{p}^{(i)})}{\bar{\nabla}\phi(\bar{p}^{(i)})'\bar{\nabla}\phi(\bar{p}^{(i)})} \tag{31}$$

Starting with this gain, a binary scale factor search may be conducted by determining an integer $n \geq 0$ which at least locally minimizes the expression

$$\phi(\bar{p}^{(i)}, n) = \phi(\bar{p}^{(i)} - 2^{-n} k_i^o \bar{\nabla}\phi) \tag{32}$$

3.3 A Computational Algorithm for Scale Factor Adjustment

A program to implement scale factor adjustment using the approximate optimum gradient method described above has been written and tested (8). Fig. 5 is a flow-chart for this program *. This algorithm includes a quadratic interpolation formula to permit more accurate determination of an optimum scale factor.

In order to make efficient use of the binary search part of the algorithm illustrated by Fig. 5, it is important that the search begin at a good value for n. Whereas the full Newton-Raphson step $(n=0)$ obtained from Eq. (31) may produce good convergence in the early phases of iterative optimization, it has been found in numerical experiments that ever larger values of n are needed in the terminal stages unless ϕ attains the value zero at its minimum (8). This comes about because Newton-Raphson iteration is based upon linear extrapolation of ϕ to zero. When $\bar{\nabla}\phi$ approaches zero while ϕ remains positive, the computed parameter change vector grows without bound unless there is a corresponding increase in the value of n used in the binary scale factor of Eq. (32). Computational experience indicates that this difficulty may be resolved by beginning each scale factor search with the value for n which was found to be optimum during the previous search cycle (8).

3.4 Constrained Minimization

While application of the optimum gradient method to parameter optimization problems does indeed lead to a convergent sequence in ϕ, it cannot be assumed that the sequence in $\bar{p}$ also converges. This difficulty can be

---

* The numbers on the various blocks of this figure refer to FORTRAN statement numbers. In this diagram, the symbol $\vec{c}$ rather than $\bar{p}$ has been used to represent a parameter vector.

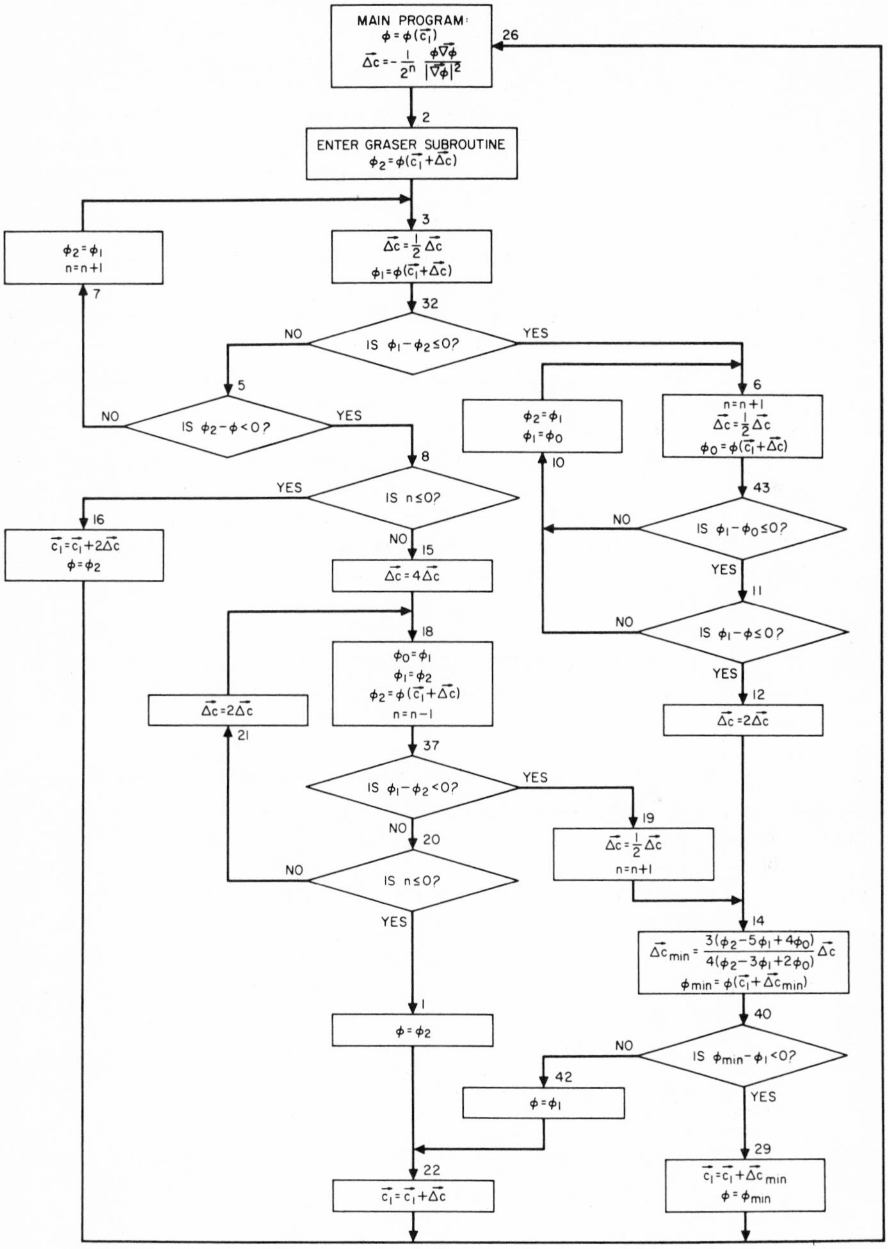

Fig. 5. An Algorithm for Determining the Optimum Scale Factor for Gradient Descent

avoided by specifying a bounded set from which $\bar{p}$ must be chosen. The "gradient projection" method devised by J.B. Rosen can be applied to closed convex constraint sets to obtain constrained minima by gradient searching (9,10). A very much simpler procedure has been developed to permit the use of the algorithm given in this paper in conjunction with independently constrained parameters (8); i.e. with constraints of the form

$$a_k \leq p_k \leq b_k \tag{33}$$

Application of such constraints often produces better convergence even in optimization problems not naturally constrained (8).

3.5 Second Order Methods

The convergence of iterative minimization procedures can be sharpened markedly in certain circumstances by making use of second derivative information. In particular, "Newton's" method, given by

$$\Delta\bar{p}^{(i)} = \left[\frac{\partial^2 \phi}{\partial p_i \partial p_j}\right]^{-1} \bar{\nabla}\phi(\bar{p}^{(i)}) \tag{34}$$

possesses quadratic convergence properties at a regular minimum of ϕ (11).

The matrix of second partials in Eq. (34) can be obtained by differentiating each row of Eq. (27) with the result

$$\left[\frac{\partial^2 \phi}{\partial p_j \, \partial p_k}\right] = \int_o^T 2\left(\bar{\nabla}y \; \bar{\nabla}y' + e\left[\frac{\partial^2 y}{\partial p_j \, \partial p_k}\right]\right) dt \tag{35}$$

$$= 2(S + D) \tag{36}$$

where

$$S = \int_o^T \bar{\nabla}y \; \bar{\nabla}y' \, dt \tag{37}$$

$$e(t;\bar{p}) = y(t;\bar{p}) - y_d(t) \tag{38}$$

$$D = \int_o^T e\left[\frac{\partial^2 y}{\partial p_j \, \partial p_k}\right] dt \tag{39}$$

The matrix S amounts to a regression matrix since it links the linear dependence of the response function, $y(t;\bar{p})$, to the integral squared error function, ϕ.

To avoid the computational difficulties associated with the determination of second derivatives, it has sometimes been suggested that Newton iteration be modified to include only the S matrix in Eq. (36) (12). If this is done, the basic iteration equation becomes

$$\Delta\bar{p} = -\frac{1}{2} S^{-1} \bar{\nabla}\phi(\bar{p}) \qquad (40)$$

This scheme has been called "Gauss-Newton" iteration (13). Depending upon the magnitude of D relative to S, it may not converge. More precisely, it is shown in the appendix to this paper that if ϕ possesses a regular minimum at $\bar{p} = \bar{p}_o$, then if S_o and D_o denote the values for S and D at $\bar{p}_o$, a region of convergence for Gauss-Newton iteration exists about $\bar{p}_o$ if and only if all of the eigenvalues of the matrix

$$Q = S_o^{-1} D_o \qquad (41)$$

are less than one in absolute value.

The residual error, e, existing at a minimizing value for $\bar{p}$, $\bar{p} = \bar{p}_o$, appears as a multiplicative factor in the expression for D. Consequently, the eigenvalues of Q will tend to be small when this error is small and large when it is large. When $y_d(t)$ represents a function which can be matched exactly by a solution of the assumed system equation, Eq. (1), then at $\bar{p} = \bar{p}_o$, e is identically zero and all of the eigenvalues of Q are likewise equal to zero. Gauss-Newton iteration reduces to Newton iteration in this circumstance and quadratic convergence is obtained utilizing only the first derivative information contained in S.

3.6 An Example of Discrete Parameter Optimization

The quadratic convergence predicted for Gauss-Newton iteration has been observed in numerical experiments (8). These experiments involved optimization of the four dimensional parameter vector associated with the nonlinear differential equation

$$c_2\ddot{y} + c_1\dot{y} + \sin y = 0$$

$$y(0) = c_3, \ \dot{y}(0) = c_4 \qquad (42)$$

The desired response, $y_d(t)$, was obtained from numerical solution of this equation with a given value for $\vec{c}$. An incorrect value was then taken as a starting point and the computer was permitted to adjust this value iteratively using both the optimum gradient and Gauss-Newton methods. Tables 1 and 2 summarize the results of this experiment. Table 2 shows that quadratic convergence is indeed obtainable through Gauss-Newton iteration even though only first derivative information is used.

4. HYBRID COMPUTER IMPLEMENTATION

4.1 Division of the Computation Load Between Analog and Digital Machines

In principle, any of the methods which have been described could be implemented on either a digital computer or an iterative analog computer. When realistic equipment limitations are taken into account however, continuous parameter adjustment is most naturally carried out by analog computation while iterative adjustment seems to be best suited to a digital computer. Both of these choices suffer from certain drawbacks, however. As has been noted, the stability of a continuous parameter adjustment algorithm is very difficult to ascertain a priori. Generally, manual intervention is required to achieve a loop gain producing reasonably rapid convergence without instability. On the other hand, when a completely digital solution to dynamic system parameter optimization problems is attempted, it is quite likely that an excessive amount of computer time will be required since digital machines are not naturally suited to high speed iterative solution of differential equations. For most optimization algorithms, the best features of both types of machines seem to be needed.

A combination of digital decision and branching capabilities and analog solution speed is available in a hybrid computer. With a hybrid computer possessing a sufficiently flexible control structure, analog computer potentiometers and initial conditions can be adjusted automatically under program control so that the analog machine effectively provides high speed subroutines to the digital computer whenever differential equation solution is required. Conversely, by monitoring the results of continuous parameter adjustment via analog to digital converters, the digital machine can assure stability in otherwise uncertain circumstances. Finally, an appropriate mixture of discrete and continuous parameter optimization algorithms can be used on the same problem under overall digital control. One might, for example, utilize discrete methods in large error conditions and continuous methods for "fine tuning" of parameters.

Table 1. Parameter Optimization by the Optimum Gradient Method

Iteration Number	c_1	c_2	c_3	c_4	ϕ
0	.5100	1.010	1.570	.01000	1.853×10^{-3}
1	.5053	1.005	1.567	.00589	4.662×10^{-4}
2	.5027	1.003	1.566	.00391	1.185×10^{-4}
3	.5012	1.002	1.565	.00295	3.109×10^{-5}
True Values	.5000	1.000	1.569	.0000	0

Table 2. Parameter Optimization by Gauss-Newton Iteration

Itera-tion Number	c_1	c_2	c_3	c_4	ϕ
0	.51000000	1.0100000	1.5700000	.01000000	1.853×10^{-3}
1	.50013945	.99966252	1.5690003	.00007233	4.428×10^{-7}
2	.50000021	1.0000002	1.5690004	.00000068	1.086×10^{-13}
True Values	.50000000	1.0000000	1.5690000	.0000000	0

4.2 An Algorithm for Parameter Optimization by Hybrid Computation

Figure 6 provides an example of an overall algorithm suitable for implementation on a hybrid computer. The REGRES subroutine appearing on this figure determines $\phi(\bar{c})$ and $\bar{\nabla}\phi(\bar{c})$ as well as the regression matrix, S , by analog solution of the assumed system equation and the associated parameter influence equations. The Gauss-Newton parameter change vector, designated $\bar{\beta}$, is then evaluated by digital inversion of the S matrix followed by matrix multiplication as in Eq. (40). GRASER is the Fortran Symbolic name attached to the scale factor adjustment routine illustrated by Fig. 5. The numerous evaluations of ϕ required in the execution of the GRASER subroutine are also intended to be accomplished by analog means. However, all of the decisions appearing at branch points of both Figs. 5 and 6 are realized by a digital program.

Both the Gauss-Newton and optimum gradient iteration techniques are incorporated into this algorithm. As Fig. 6 shows, the routine favors the Gauss-Newton parameter change vector, $\bar{\beta}$, and switches to the optimum gradient method during a given iteration cycle only when the Gauss-Newton vector fails to satisfy certain criteria. The algorithm provides for independent constraints on the values of each parameter; the region R refers to the n-dimensional box defined by these constraints.

Since the parameter adjustment procedures used here are all iterative, some means for stopping the iteration must be provided. Fig. 6 incorporates five different stopping rules operating in parallel. The d_ϕ and $d_{\vec{c}}$ criteria refer to the percentage change in ϕ and $\vec{c}$ in two successive iterations. When either of these variables falls below a value specified in advance, computation ceases.

4.3 Experimental Results

The algorithm proposed was tested using the system described by Eq. (42). The desired response function, $y_d(t)$, was obtained by numerical solution of this equation with a specified parameter vector. Since a hybrid computer was not available, digital subroutines were used to simulate the necessary analog computations.

Table 3 summarizes the results of this experiment. The column labeled "n" denotes the exponent of the optimum binary scale factor found by gradient searching (Eq. (32)). The entry G-N in this table indicates that

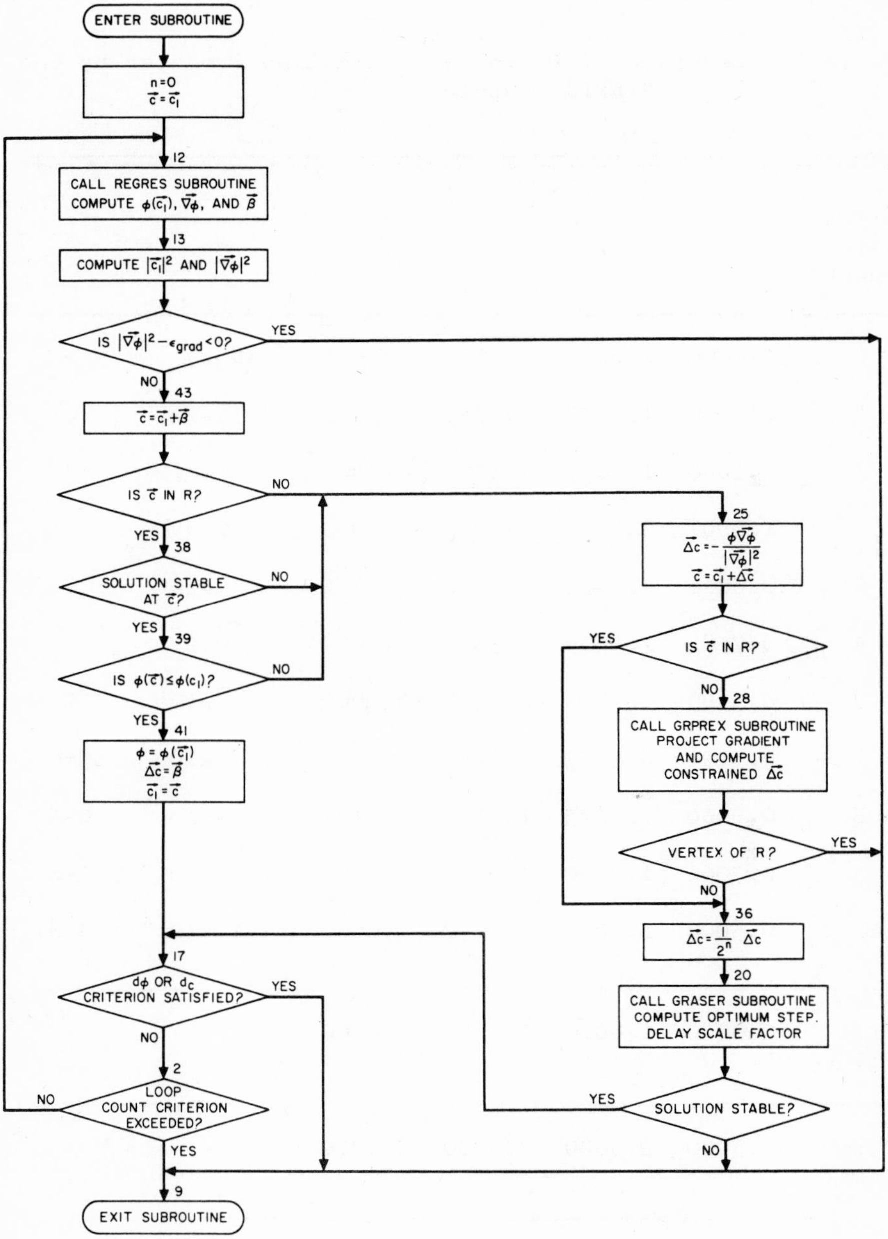

Fig. 6. A Hybrid Computer Parameter Optimization Algorithm

Table 3. Sequence of Parameter Estimation Produced by the Hybrid Computer Algorithm

Iteration Number	c_1	c_2	c_3	c_4	ϕ	n
0	1.0000	2.0000	3.0000	1.0000	360.3	-
1	1.5000	1.8176	2.5322	0.5201	34.12	0
2	1.5000	1.6091	1.6341	-0.2000	1.462	0
3	1.0907	1.4829	1.0000	-0.2000	0.690	0
4	0.8018	1.5123	1.3731	-0.1412	0.366	0
5	0.7581	1.4656	1.3567	-0.2000	0.270	1
6	0.5460	1.2693	1.3978	-0.2000	0.109	0
7	0.5494	0.9792	1.6642	-0.1253	8.48×10^{-3}	G-N
8	0.5000	1.0005	1.5619	-0.0111	2.49×10^{-4}	G-N
9	0.5001	1.0000	1.5691	-0.0001	1.78×10^{-8}	G-N
10	0.5000	1.0000	1.5690	0.0000	3.16×10^{-14}	G-N
True Value	0.5000	1.0000	1.5690	0.0000	0	-
Upper Limit	1.5000	2.5000	3.5000	1.5000	-	-
Lower Limit	0.0000	0.0000	1.0000	-0.2000	-	-

Gauss-Newton iteration rather than gradient searching was used at that step.

5. CONCLUSIONS

Continuous parameter optimization algorithms are conceptually simple but their convergence properties are difficult to determine. Global stability of optimizing algorithms can be obtained by making use of digital computer supervision and control. Since analog computers are naturally suited to the high speed iterative solution of differential equations, hybrid analog-digital computation seems to offer considerable promise as a practical means for system optimization.

APPENDIX

Necessary and Sufficient Conditions for the Existence of a Region of Convergence for Gauss-Newton Iteration

Theorem:

Let $\bar{p}_o$ represent a point in parameter space at which $\phi(\bar{p})$ attains minimum value and let S_o and D_o denote the values of the matrices S and D at this point. Assume that there exists an ϵ-neighborhood about $\bar{p}_o$ such that $\phi(\bar{p})$, $\bar{\nabla}\phi(\bar{p})$, $y(t;\bar{p})$, and $\bar{\nabla}y(t;\bar{p})$ all possess uniformly convergent Taylor series. Suppose further that the matrix S is non-singular everywhere in the same neighborhood. Then, provided that $S_o + D_o$ is a positive definite matrix, when $\bar{\Delta p}^{(i)}$ is computed by the Gauss-Newton formula and $\bar{p}^{(1)}$ is chosen so that

$$|\bar{p}^{(1)} - \bar{p}_o| < \epsilon_o \ , \ 0 < \epsilon_o < \epsilon \tag{43}$$

there exists an ϵ_o such that

$$\lim_{i \to \infty} \bar{p}^{(i)} = \bar{p}_o \tag{44}$$

if and only if all of the eigenvalues of the matrix $Q = S_o^{-1} D_o$ are less than one in absolute value.

Proof:

Let $\delta\bar{p}^{(i)}$ denote the difference between $\bar{p}^{(i)}$ and the desired minimizing value for $\bar{p}$; i.e.

$$\delta\bar{p}^{(i)} = \bar{p}^{(i)} - \bar{p}_o \tag{45}$$

Then from Eq. (35)

$$\phi(\bar{p}) = \phi(\bar{p}_o) + \delta\bar{p}' (S_o + D_o) \delta\bar{p} + O(\delta p^3) \quad (46)$$

and therefore

$$\nabla\phi(\bar{p}) = 2(S_o + D_o) \delta\bar{p} + O(\delta p^2) \quad (47)$$

Substituting this expression into the Gauss-Newton formula, Eq. (40), produces the result

$$\Delta\bar{p}^{(i)} = - S(\bar{p}^{(i)})^{-1} (S_o + D_o) \delta\bar{p}^{(i)} \quad (48)$$

However, under the assumptions regarding $y(t;\bar{p})$ and $\nabla y(t;\bar{p})$,

$$S(\bar{p}^{(i)}) = S_o + O(\delta\bar{p}^{(i)}) \quad (49)$$

so Eq. (48) reduces to

$$\Delta\bar{p}^{(i)} = (- I - S_o^{-1} D_o + R_i) \delta\bar{p}^{(i)} \quad (50)$$

where R_i is a remainder matrix which tends to zero as $\delta\bar{p}$ approaches zero. Now since

$$\delta\bar{p}^{(i+1)} = \delta\bar{p}^{(i)} + \Delta\bar{p}^{(i)} \quad (51)$$

Eq. (50) yields the recursion relation

$$\delta\bar{p}^{(i+1)} = (- S_o^{-1} D_o + R_i) \delta\bar{p}^{(i)} \quad (52)$$

By choosing ϵ_o sufficiently small, the remainder matrix, R, may be made as small as desired in comparison to Q. Therefore, for $|\delta\bar{p}^{(1)}| < \epsilon_o$, $\delta\bar{p}$ converges to zero if and only if all of the eigenvalues of Q are less than one in absolute value.

REFERENCES

1. Graupe, K. K., "Analog Solution of Some Functional Analysis Problems", AIEE Transactions, January 1961.

2. Potts, T. F., Ornstein, G. N., and Clymer, A. B., "The Automatic Determination of Human and Other System Parameters", Proceedings of the Western Joint Computer Conference, May 1961, pp. 645-660.

3. Whitaker, H. P., Yamron, J., and Kezer, H., Design of Model Reference Adaptive Control Systems for Aircraft, MIT Instrumentation Laboratory Report R-164, Sept., 1958.

4. Margolis, M., On the Theory of Process Adaptive Control Systems, the Learning Model Approach, Report No. 60-32, University of California, Department of Engineering, Los Angeles, California, (May 1960).

5. Meissinger, H. F., "The Use of Parameter Influence Coefficients in Computer Analysis of Dynamic Systems", Proceedings of the Western Joint Computer Conference, 1960, pp. 181-192 (May 1960).

6. Bekey, G. A., and Meissinger, H. F., and Rose, R. E., "Study of Model Matching Techniques for the Determination of Parameters in Human Pilot Models", Reports No. 8426-6002-RU-000, 8426-6003-RU-000, and 8426-6004-RU-000, Space Technology Laboratories, Redondo Beach, Calif. (1963).

7. Bromberg, N. S., "Maximization and Minimization of Complicated Multi-Variable Functions", AIEE Transactions, Vol. 58, Part 1, pp. 725-730, (January 1962).

8. McGhee, R. B., Identification of Nonlinear Dynamic Systems by Regression Analysis Methods, Ph.D. dissertation University of Southern California, Los Angeles, California (June 1963).

9. Rosen, J. B., "The Gradient Projection Method for Nonlinear Programming, Part 1, Linear Constraints", J. Soc. Indust. Appl. Math., Vol. 8, No. 1, pp. 181-217 (March 1960).

10. Rosen, J. B., "The Gradient Projection Method for Nonlinear Programming, Part II, Nonlinear Constraints", J. Soc. Indust. Appl. Math, Vol. 9, No. 4, pp. 514-532, (December 1961).

11. Chernoff, H., and Crockett, J. B., "Gradient Methods of Maximization", Pacific Journal of Mathematics, Vol. 5, pp. 33-50 (1955).

12. Williams, E. J., Regression Analysis, John Wiley and Sons, Inc., New York, N. Y., (1959).

13. Hartley, H. O., "The Modified Gauss-Newton Method for the Fitting of Nonlinear Regression Functions by Least Squares", Technometrics, Vol. 3, No. 2, pp. 269-280 (May 1961).